Choice, Control & Change

Using Science to Make Food & Activity Decisions

Pamela A. Koch
Isobel R. Contento
Angela Calabrese Barton

Published by Teachers College Columbia University

and the National Gardening Association
1100 Dorset St., South Burlington, VT 05403 • *www.garden.org* • *www.kidsgardening.org*

LINKING FOOD AND THE ENVIRONMENT

AN INQUIRY-BASED SCIENCE AND NUTRITION PROGRAM

Linking Food and the Environment (LiFE) is a collaboration of the Science Education and Nutrition Education programs at Teachers College Columbia University. It was established in 1996 with the vision of promoting scientific habits of mind through thoughtful, inquiry-based activities that integrate the study of food, food systems, and environmental and personal health. *Choice, Control & Change* is one module of the LiFE Curriculum Series. The mission of all the LiFE modules is to increase scientific conceptual understandings in life science, improve attitudes toward science, improve attitudes toward personal health and nature, and promote behavior changes in relation to personal and sustainable systems. For information about LiFE, please visit *www.tc.edu/life*. You can also find teacher professional development materials and student support materials on this web site.

TEACHERS COLLEGE
COLUMBIA UNIVERSITY

Teachers College Columbia University, Center for Food & Environment, 525 West 120th Street, Box 137, New York, NY 10027

The National Gardening Association (NGA) is a nonprofit organization established in 1972. Its mission is to promote home, school, and community gardening as a means to renew and sustain the essential connection between people, plants, and the environment. NGA's programs and initiatives are targeted to five areas: plant-based education, health and wellness, environmental stewardship, community development, and responsible home gardening. For more information on NGA and its programs, please visit *www.garden.org* and *www.kidsgardening.org* or call (800) 538-7476.

SCIENCE EDUCATION PARTNERSHIP AWARD

Supported by the National Center for Research Resources, a part of the National Institutes of Health

This publication was made possible by a Science Education Partnership Award (SEPA), grant number R25 RR20412, from the National Center for Research Resources (NCRR), a component of the National Institutes of Health (NIH). Its contents are solely the responsibility of the authors and do not necessarily represent the official views of the NCRR or NIH.

Additional funding for publication was provided by the W. K. Kellogg Foundation for Rethinking Food, Health, and the Environment: Making Learning Connections, a joint project of the Center for Ecoliteracy and Teachers College Columbia University.

ISBN 978-0-915873-55-5

Library of Congress Control Number: 2010921726

Printed in Canada.

Linking Food and the Environment Project Team

AUTHOR AND PROJECT DIRECTOR
Pamela A. Koch, EdD, RD, Executive Director, Center for Food & Environment, Teachers College Columbia University

PRINCIPAL INVESTIGATOR
Isobel R. Contento, PhD, Mary Swartz Rose Professor of Nutrition Education, Teachers College Columbia University

CO-PRINCIPAL INVESTIGATOR
Angela Calabrese Barton, PhD, Professor of Science Education, Michigan State University

Choice, Control & Change (C3) Team

Author
Pamela A. Koch, EdD, RD

Lesson Development and Observations
Jennie Brotman, PhD
Marcia Dadds, MS, RD
Aarti Mallya, PhD
Rabi Whitaker, PhD

Implementation and Evaluation
Rachel Bartlett, MS, RD
Heewon Lee, PhD, RD
Asako Miyashita, MS, RD
Wendy Sauberli, MS, RD
Edna Tan, PhD
Blakely K. Tsurusaki, PhD

Advisors
Madhabi Chatterji, PhD, Evaluation
Ronald DeMeersman, PhD, Human Physiology
Dympna Gallagher, EdD, Body Composition

Teacher Contributors
Yamel Alvarez
Aleta Marie Damm
C. Rajeshwari Menon

Field-Test Partners
Alameda County Office of Education Nutrition Learning Community Coalition, Hayward, CA; Christine Boynton, Director, 2007–2009
Center for Ecoliteracy, Berkeley, CA; Zenobia Barlow, Executive Director, 2006–2009
The Food Trust, Philadelphia, PA; Sandra Sherman, Director of Nutrition Education, 2008–2009
Michigan State University, East Lansing, MI; Angela Calabrese Barton, Professor of Science Education, 2007–2009
Middle School at Parkside, Jackson, MI; Aleta Marie Damm, Science Department Chair, 2007–2010
New York City Department of Education, New York, NY; Sheldon Young, Middle School Instructional Specialist, 2004–2010

Production Team

Editorial Director
Margo Crabtree

Editor/Writer
Rachel Bartlett

Copy Editor
Kate Norris

**Original Design for LiFE
Curriculum Series**
Lisa Cicchetti

Design, Art Direction, and Page Layout
Alison Watt, National Gardening Association

Illustrations
Anne Faust

Photography
Cover: Tyler/Barlow, Center for Ecoliteracy
Page 25: Winzworks/Dreamstime.com
Page 69: Ron ChappleStudios/Dreamstime.com
Page 101: Image Source
Page 143: Ernst Daniel Scheffler/Dreamstime.com
Page 163: Amy Myers/Dreamstime.com

To all youth learning to navigate the food-and-activity environment,
so they can fully achieve all their hopes and dreams.

Contents

UNIT 5: MAINTAINING COMPETENCE

Acknowledgments

The seed for LiFE was planted in the 1970s when Joan Gussow, EdD, the Mary Swartz Rose Professor Emeritus of Nutrition and Education, brought the perspective of food-system study to Teachers College Columbia University. LiFE began with the simple goal of developing an inquiry-based science curriculum that would educate children about food systems, food choice, and personal health. Because of the ideas, thoughts, and dedication of so many, the LiFE Curriculum Series has grown and expanded to include investigation of the interplay of biology and personal behavior with the present food system and technological environment, which encourage overconsumption and sedentary behavior. It is our hope that the LiFE Curriculum Series will enhance students' personal motivation and competence to use their science understandings to reflect upon and purposefully act upon their world with the aim of transforming themselves and the conditions of their lives.

Many people have been involved in the development of the *Choice, Control & Change* module of the LiFE Curriculum Series, and we are indebted to them all. To those who have reviewed our materials, offered suggestions and insights, and shared experiences and challenges, we thank you. To the many educators and students who tested lessons and offered feedback, we appreciate your enthusiasm for *Choice, Control & Change* and your valuable contributions. To the principals, teachers, and students at our field-test schools, we thank you for working with us to make *Choice, Control & Change* what it is today. We learned so much from you. The curriculum is better because of you and we had you on our shoulders as we wrote. To our families and friends who have lived with this project for many years, we are deeply grateful for your warm support and endless patience.

We thank the following schools for valuable feedback as we developed *Choice, Control & Change*:

New York City
Bronx Green, 2007–2010
IS 143, 2004–2005
IS 172, 2005–2007
Kappa IV, 2005–2007
MS 44, 2006–2008
MS 195–Mott Hall, 2005–2010
MS 246–Crossroads Middle School, 2007–2008
MS 247–Dual Language Middle School, 2007–2008
MS 256–Academic and Athletic Excellence, 2005–2007
MS 322, 2005–2008
MS 328–Manhattan Middle School for Scientific Inquiry, 2006–2008
MS 331–Bronx School of Science Inquiry and Investigation, 2005–2010
MS 448–Brooklyn Secondary School for Collaborative Studies, 2007–2008
MS 825–Isaac Newton School for Science, Mathematics, and Technology, 2005–2006
MS 860–Frederick Douglass Academy 2, 2005–2006

Michigan
Dwight Rich Middle School, Lansing, 2007–2010
Otto Middle School, Lansing, 2007–2010
Pattengill Middle School, Lansing, 2007–2010
Middle School at Parkside, Jackson, 2007–2010

California
Ochoa Middle School, Hayward, 2007–2010

Wisconsin
Bruce Guadalupe Middle School, Milwaukee, 2009–2010

Introduction

Welcome! You and your students are about to embark on an exciting adventure — learning how to use science to make food and activity decisions. The busy schedules of today's youth (and adults) make it challenging to make food and activity choices that enable people to sustain long-term health.

In the *Choice, Control & Change (C3)* module of the Linking Food and the Environment (LiFE) Curriculum Series, we bring together science education with nutrition education. This innovative curriculum engages students in inquiry-based classroom investigations that motivate them to apply their new science understandings and skills to their day-to-day lives. In *C3*, students think about their choices, take control, and make changes as they confront the array of foods available to them at fast-food places, restaurants, farmers' markets, corner stores, and elsewhere. They create personal plans for ways to balance video games and television, also called recreational screen time, with sports, dance, and other activities that get their bodies moving.

As we developed *C3* we worked with many urban youth across the country who responded enthusiastically to our approach and became empowered to change both their own lives and their food and activity environments. *C3* is vital for all of today's youth because of increasing rates of overweight and obesity, sedentary lifestyles, and high rates of chronic diseases related to lifestyle choices. These diseases contribute to decreased quality of life and to high health-care costs. *C3* targets middle-school students because they are gaining independence, spending more time with peers, developing a sense of who they are in the world, and beginning to develop their own habits. This makes them the perfect age for this reflective, thoughtful, and life-changing curriculum.

We hope your experiences with *Choice, Control & Change* bring learning and skills that your students will remember — and continue to use — years into the future.

Pamela Koch, EdD, RD
Isobel Contento, PhD
Angela Calabrese Barton, PhD

Goals of LiFE

Students who participate in LiFE will:

- **increase their knowledge and conceptual understandings** about how the biological world works and how it interacts with the world designed by humans.

- **develop skills in scientific inquiry** about the designed world — the use of evidence to justify statements; the use of both logical reasoning and imagination; and the ability to explain, predict, and identify and limit bias.

- **expand their ways of thinking or habits of mind** to include curiosity, flexibility, open-mindedness, informed skepticism, and creative and critical thinking.

- **improve their attitudes toward the processes of science** through enjoyable activities in a domain that is meaningful and familiar to them — food.

- **improve their attitudes toward their personal health** through an appreciation of the body's complexity, adaptability, and limitations; an understanding of the impact of food on health; and an appreciation of healthy eating habits.

- **understand the link between our choices and our health,** including the impact of the food environment on choice and our ability to affect our health through our everyday actions.

- **appreciate the connectedness** of science, technology, the natural environment, and everyday life in ways that are life-changing for the students and their interactions with society and the natural environment.

- **increase their confidence and commitment** to applying the above conceptual understandings, skills, attitudes, and habits of mind to personal decisions and public debate of issues related to food systems, health, and the natural environment.

Applying Science for Why to and How to Make Healthful Food and Activity Decisions

This curriculum was developed out of a belief that childhood obesity and its long-term health implications are a critical societal concern and a key topic for science education. It is of paramount importance to all of us that we decrease the rates of Type 2 diabetes, heart disease, and other lifestyle-driven diseases so that today's youth can grow up to be productive and fulfilled citizens. Yet we live in a culture that includes supermarkets filled with more than 50,000 items, of which most are highly processed food products, often high in added fat, sugar, and sodium; heavily advertised; and relatively cheap — particularly when compared calorie for calorie with more healthful foods. Additionally, we fill our lives with sedentary activities. Modern conveniences make many of our daily chores easier and vehicles move us from place to place. The forceful combination of readily available and commonplace food with a lack of vigorous activity can compromise our health. For our youth, this is the only reality they have ever known.

With this situation as a backdrop, LiFE's team of science educators, nutrition educators, and teachers has worked in classrooms across the country for several years to develop and evaluate *Choice, Control & Change*. This innovative curriculum provides teachers and youth with hands-on investigations about what they can do to make healthy food and activity choices. Our partnership of science and nutrition education has been like most relationships, with disagreements and thoughtful conversations that allowed us to understand and learn from each other to create something better than any of us could have ever created alone. The result is a curriculum that is driven by a carefully crafted question that frames all of the students' experiences: *How can we use scientific evidence to help us maintain energy balance?*

Through the *C3* lessons, students learn about life science by investigating how the human body works; why a state of dynamic equilibrium — balancing energy in and energy out — is important for our bodies to be able to function well; how conditions such as high blood cholesterol and high blood sugar develop and what we can do to prevent them; and how to make food and exercise choices that

will promote health and decrease the risk of many lifestyle-related diseases, such as heart disease, Type 2 diabetes, and some cancers. As you will see in Lesson 5, we also include investigations of students' food environment and physical-activity environment. Our emphasis on the environment was designed to reduce guilt by taking a system-blaming approach instead of a victim-blaming approach. The curriculum empowers students to take action. After learning "why-to" knowledge, they use a guided goal-setting process to make action plans for how they will navigate their food and physical-activity environments.

Often nutrition education is thought of as teaching students about food groups. *C3* takes the stance that to change students' food and activity choices, we need to focus the curriculum on concrete behaviors that make sense in the context of their lives. In *C3*, students gain an understanding of why healthful food choices are personally relevant and the skills they need to make these choices in the context of their lives. The curriculum focuses on behaviors that can help students achieve energy balance and over which youth have a large degree of control. The six food and activity goals for *C3* are: 1) eat more fruits and vegetables; 2) drink more water; 3) increase activity, particularly through walking more and taking the stairs more often; 4) drink fewer sweetened beverages; 5) eat less frequently at fast-food places, choose healthier options, and ask for smaller portions; and 6) eat fewer processed snacks (candy, chips, and packaged baked goods). These goals are supported by the recommendations of the federal government's MyPyramid and by a panel of experts on childhood obesity from 15 professional organizations.[1]

Students confront the risks associated with current diets and learn the benefits of the *C3* behaviors in reducing those risks as well as how to reduce the barriers that can keep them from carrying out healthier behaviors. Once students are motivated, they use a process of guided goal-setting through which they analyze their data from personal food logs to choose one of the *C3* food goals. They create concrete action plans and collect data so they can track and analyze progress toward their goal. Through this approach youth learn the why-to and how-to of making healthful choices.

This curriculum emphasizes science agency: the "realized capacity of students to utilize their science understandings to purposefully and reflectively act upon their world with the aim of transforming themselves and the conditions of their lives."[2] When students develop this agency, also called personal agency,[3,4] they become intentional about making healthful choices, they think ahead about the consequences of their choices, they are self-directed at creating goals for themselves and making plans to achieve their goals, and they reflect on their actions in order to build confidence that they can make healthful choices.

While personal agency is an important goal for everyone, it is critical for disadvantaged youth who need empowerment. In our work with middle-school students, we found that they are responsive to an approach that helps them understand that they have *choices*, can exert *control*, and can make *changes* in their own eating and physical-activity behaviors as well as their personal food environments to enhance their health and help their bodies do what they want them to do. This is particularly relevant for youth who are becoming more involved in both in-school and out-of-school activities. In addition, at this age, students are gaining independence and spending more time with peers, which often includes buying and eating food together.

In our field tests, students spent considerable time analyzing their own eating and physical-activity patterns and comparing them to the *C3* food and activity goals. We encourage you to make certain that you schedule enough time for your students to have this same experience. Research has shown that conducting such self-assessments can be motivating because they increase a sense of concern. Through our work, we have found that with inquiry-based science investigations, students develop an in-depth understanding of the rationale for taking action.

Common Misconceptions

Using this curriculum, you will better understand what misconceptions in the *C3* topic area students might have and how you can work with them on expressing their current conceptions — correct or incorrect — and come up with new knowledge constructs that accurately reflect current scientific knowledge.

Students may believe that:
- *We can get accurate scientific knowledge based on one article.* It seems that we often hear a news report that conflicts with previously reported nutritional information. When trying to make sense of the flood of information coming at us, it is important to keep in mind that it takes more than one study to establish scientific fact. Scientists test different parameters in order to find enough of an effect for statistical significance and to learn more about such things as the correct time period for measuring the effect and the correct amount of treatment to pro-

duce the effect. They must also have reproducible results in order to permanently sway the knowledge base of the field.

- *We can be healthy if we eat well OR if we are active.* In truth, it takes more than one or the other to be as healthy as we can be. To keep our bodies healthy, we need exercise, and to fuel our bodies well for exercise as well as the basic activities of daily living, we need healthy food. Optimum health is best reached by a healthy approach to both diet and exercise.[5]

- *Someone who appears slender is healthy.* You can't judge a person's health by the way he or she looks. It is true that being overweight, particularly in the abdominal area, raises one's risk for several chronic diseases such as diabetes and heart disease. However, someone might not carry extra fat on her body, but could have high blood pressure or plaque buildup in her arteries. Another person could have more fat on his body but exercise daily, eat a diet based on fruit, vegetables, and whole grains,[6,7] and have no chronic disease risk factors.

- *Eating too much sugar causes diabetes.* It's an imbalance of overall energy intake that causes the pancreas to become exhausted and fail to produce enough insulin, leading to Type 2 diabetes. Risk factors for developing Type 2 diabetes include a high-fat diet, high blood pressure, high blood triglyceride (fat) levels, a sedentary lifestyle, obesity, a family history of the disease, and certain ethnicities.[8,9]

- *Avoiding a whole class of nutrients is an appropriate way to address health issues.* [10] Our bodies require each of the three macronutrients (carbohydrates, fat, and protein) in order to function best. Eliminating entirely or almost entirely either fat or carbohydrates may cause short-term weight loss, but often the intake of vital vitamins and minerals is reduced in the process. Furthermore, scientists have found that there is no difference in weight loss or ability to maintain weight loss after one year between people following low-fat or low-carbohydrate diets and people who lose weight following a more balanced

diet. The best approach to weight loss is one that changes habits to reduce energy intake while maintaining macronutrient balance and increases physical activity in a way that is sustainable over time for the individual.

- *Fad diets are a quick fix to weight loss.* [11] Scientific evidence tells us that although following a fad diet may cause weight loss in the short term, weight is usually regained once a person resumes previous eating behaviors. Changing behaviors for the long term to reduce energy intake and increase physical activity is a more appropriate approach to long-term health.

- *The recent increase in obesity rates is due to individual weaknesses.* Environmental changes in the United States over the last several decades have had a large bearing on the prevalence of obesity in our population. Portion sizes in restaurants have grown, the availability of energy-dense convenience foods has increased in markets and schools, and the number of dollars spent on advertising these foods has increased. Activity has declined due to a lack of physical education in school and increased time spent on technology-driven activities such as watching television and playing computer and video games.[12,13]

[1] Barlow, 2007

[2] Calabrese Barton & Vora, 2006

[3] Bandura, 1989

[4] Bandura, 2001

[5] Nemet, Barkan, Epstein, Friedland, Kowen, & Eliakim, 2005

[6] Mirat, 2007

[7] Miller, Balady, & Fletcher, 1997

[8] Reinehr, Wabitsch, Kleber, de Sousa, Denzer, & Toschke, 2008

[9] MedLine Plus, 2009

[10] Klein, 2004

[11] Katz, 2005

[12] Brantley, Myers, & Roy, 2005

[13] Anderson & Butcher, 2006

Getting Acquainted with *Choice, Control & Change*

The question you and your students will study throughout this module is *How can we use scientific evidence to help us maintain energy balance?* For students to develop a thorough and thoughtful answer to this question, the module is made up of five units that build on one another. In the first two units, students learn about human biology, explore our current food and physical-activity environments, and make connections between food and activity choices and achieving the energy balance that can lead to optimal health. With the why-to-take-action understandings in place, students move to the how-to-take-action units. In Unit 3, students begin to learn practical skills to make specific changes that can maintain energy balance and health. Unit 4 reinforces and adds to the scientific evidence for why to take action. Unit 5 brings it all together and challenges students both to teach others what they have learned and to make a personal commitment to continuing to make healthy choices for themselves through middle school and beyond.

Unit 1: Investigating Our Choices explores how many factors influence what we choose to eat and what kind of activities we choose to do. The question for this unit is *What influences our food and activity choices?* The world around us offers many choices. The irony of our "freedom of choice" is that the food and activities that are the most heavily promoted and most readily available — foods such as candy, chips, sweetened beverages, baked goods, and fast food, and sedentary activities such as watching television, using the computer, and playing video games — can lead us to take in excessive energy from added fat and sugar, and to decrease the amount of energy we use. As an added complication, our biology leads us to naturally like fat and sugar. Furthermore, when given the choice we would choose activities that require us to move less. At the same time, our biology cannot handle regularly taking in more energy than we use. This can lead to various health problems. With these understandings students come to realize that the environment in which we make our choices is mismatched with our biology. This leads them into Unit 2, in which they learn more about our biology and how we can keep our bodies in balance.

Unit 2: Dynamic Equilibrium introduces key concepts about the body and energy balance. It explores the question *How can we make sure that we get the right amount of energy to help our bodies do what we want them to do?* Students look at the body as a whole system and develop an understanding that keeping this complex system in balance — getting the right amount of energy — is about balancing the energy we take in through food with the energy we use to keep our body working during physical activities. Students review how the digestive system takes in food and breaks it down into its core components, which are absorbed into the blood to travel around the body, ending up in the cells that make up every part of the human body. Within the cells, the nutrients in food are used for energy and as building blocks to maintain the body and help it grow. When cells are getting the right amount and the right combination of nutrients from food, the body is in balance. Our bodies are able to perform their best at everything we want to do, from concentrating in school to playing sports to helping out at home to playing games with our friends. With this solid understanding of why energy balance is important, students move into Unit 3, in which they learn how to develop action plans to move toward more healthful choices.

Unit 3: From Data to Health Goals teaches students to examine their own eating and activity behaviors as they study the question *How can we use personal data to help us make healthy food and activity choices?* Students become scientists who collect, analyze, and monitor data on their own eating habits and physical activities. Through analyzing their personal data, students choose from one of the *C3* food goals: eat more fruits and vegetables; drink more water; drink fewer sweetened beverages; eat less frequently at fast-food places; and eat fewer processed snacks. All students try to achieve the goal of walking 10,000 steps per day as measured by pedometers. (If students do not have pedometers, there is an alternative goal of being physically active for at least 60 minutes per day.) Students learn skills that help them achieve these goals, and track their progress. They complete food and activity logs and analyze the data from these logs in order to modify their plans to help ensure sustained success at making changes. Class discussions about students' personal triumphs and challenges in implementing their food and activity goals in their own lives enable students to work with one another and to become one another's support system for overcoming any barriers they face. As students continue to implement their goals and monitor their progress, they move to Unit 4, in which they learn more about why energy balance is important, and that helps reinforce their motivation to make and sustain changes.

Unit 4: Effects of Our Choices gives students a deeper understanding of the science behind the *C3* goals as they investigate the question *Why are healthy food and activity choices important for our bodies?* Students learn how healthy food and exercise habits can keep our hearts and lungs strong and healthy, keep our blood vessels clear of plaque made from fat and cholesterol, and maintain the ability of the hormone insulin to effectively move blood glucose (sugar) into our cells. This decreases the risk of developing Type 2 diabetes, heart attacks, strokes, and other diseases. Students move into the final unit, in which they confirm their commitment to healthy food and activity choices.

Unit 5: Maintaining Competence provides students with the understandings and skills to maintain a healthy lifestyle as they explore the question *How can I maintain my skills as a competent eater and mover?* Students create a project that gives them a way to share with others the science and skills they have learned or to take action to make changes in their food and activity environment. They continue to evaluate their progress toward achieving their food and activity goals and develop their own personal pledges, making a realistic commitment to continue implementing an aspect of what they have learned in the *Choice, Control & Change* curriculum in their lives. Students then revisit the scientific evidence that supports the *C3* goals and answer the Module Question *How can we use scientific evidence to help us maintain energy balance?* The module ends with students celebrating what they have created and accomplished during *Choice, Control & Change* through displaying their projects and sharing healthy food with other members of their school or community.

Promoting Inquiry

Teaching science as a process of inquiry makes science a process of doing and thinking instead of learning a set of predetermined facts. This changes the approach for answering student questions. Instead of being a source of science facts, you are a partner with your students in seeking answers or explanations. It means turning students' questions back on them. If a student asks, *How does my body use energy from food?* respond with, *Well, how shall we find out?* This sends the powerful message that knowing how to find an answer is as important as knowing the answer.

Ask open-ended questions that promote reflection and further questions. *How* and *why* questions work well: *Why do you think that is?* or *How would we find out?* Ask questions that encourage critical thinking, like *What evidence or observation leads you to that conclusion?* Help your students develop theories and bring closure to their explorations and experiments by asking, *How would you explain your results?* and *What theories can you think of to explain this?*

Deepening Science Process through the QuESTA Learning Cycle

How students learn is as important as what they learn in the LiFE Curriculum Series. The questions that drive the modules and units in LiFE challenge students to question, explore, investigate, analyze, synthesize, and act. To frame this process of learning, LiFE uses a five-phase learning cycle called QuESTA.

 Questioning. Students explore their prior knowledge and experiences related to the area of study, and develop and refine meaningful questions to guide further inquiry. They also share their current conceptions about the topic so that any misconceptions can be addressed.

 Experimenting. Students plan and conduct experiments to answer the questions within the area of study. Thus, students identify problems, state hypotheses, select methods, display results, and draw conclusions from these experiments to further their knowledge.

 Searching. Students seek out other information already known about their topic through readings provided in the module, researching in the library or on the computer, and interviewing people.

 Theorizing. Through thoughtful reflection and synthesis of what they have learned in the previous phases, students develop their own theories and constructs about how the world works. Students develop skills that enable them to articulate theories, give evidence to support their arguments, and appropriately challenge the theories of others.

 Applying to Life. Students apply the new constructs and processes they learned through the unit to decisions and actions they make each day. Students develop new questions to continue their exploration in the area of study.

In the procedure section of each lesson and at the top of student activity sheets, you will see the QuESTA icons. Keep in mind which phase of QuESTA is emphasized for the various activities and experiences. As you move through the units in *Choice, Control & Change* there is a natural flow through the QuESTA Learning Cycle. In the first unit, students are engaged in many **questions** about the food and activity choices that are in the environment around them, and they explore what influences those choices. In Units 2 through 4, students are more actively engaged in **experimenting, searching,** and creating their own **theories.** They also begin to **apply** what they are learning through developing action plans for change and monitoring their progress. In the final unit, most of the activities are application. Students create a project through which they can teach others what they have learned. They also make a commitment to continue to apply their new knowledge to their daily food and activity choices.

Assessment Strategies

Authentic assessment tasks provide students with opportunities to construct meaning from what they have learned. The LiFE Curriculum Series offers different assessment strategies to help you track your students' progress.

Pre-assessment

In the first lesson of *Choice, Control & Change*, students discuss the Module Question, *How can we use scientific evidence to help us maintain energy balance?* Later in the lesson, students are given cards with various scenarios with information about healthy food and activity choices. Students discuss the information and determine whether or not the scenario is an example of scientific evidence. You can use this discussion as a pre-assessment of the students' ability to use scientific evidence to make healthful food and activity choices. Assess whether they recognize persuasive language, can rate the accuracy of various sources of information, and can list ideas for where to seek out more information.

Post-assessment

As a post-assessment for the module, you can use the **Scientific Evidence that Supports My Goals** and **Reflections** sections of *The C3 Journey* (pp. 273–274). This asks students to reflect on the scientific evidence they used to support healthful food and activity choices, to describe how their answer to the Module Question has changed based on what they have learned, and to discuss what information they would like to share with others.

Ongoing Assessment

Throughout the lessons, students have multiple opportunities to participate in full-class discussions, to work and discuss materials in small groups, and to present their work to the class. These opportunities offer the chance to assess how students are thinking about the topics being studied, their level of sophistication in what they are thinking and saying, and their ability to engage in discussions, debates, and scientific arguments with their peers. These types of assessments may be particularly useful for students who are challenged by writing and public-speaking skills. In each lesson, students are assigned homework questions to reflect on the *Calvin and Carol Take Charge* readings. During each lesson they write in their LiFE Logs, synthesizing what they have learned. These opportunities to write give students the freedom to express in their own words what they are learning in their homework and in class. Often the LiFE Log assignment will be an answer to an open-ended question, which will help you gauge how students have internalized what they learned in the lessons, how they made meaning of new concepts, and how they brought earlier ideas to bear on new understandings. Students also collect personal data on food intake and physical activity, giving them the opportunity to collect complete and accurate data. Additionally, once students create food and activity goals, they monitor their progress by recording data in food and activity logs, providing the opportunity for long-term data collection and analysis.

Choice, Control & Change Planner

Use this page to help you plan and as an overview of how the science concepts (why to take action) and behavioral nutrition concepts (how to take action) build from unit to unit.

Unit	Lesson	Materials to Order or Make	Projects	Science Concepts: Why to Take Action	Behavioral Nutrition: How to Take Action
Investigating Our Choices	**1.** Making the Case	Order pedometers for Lesson 11, p. 122		Students explore different factors that influence our food and activity choices.	
	2. As a Matter of Choice	Buy ascorbic acid (vitamin C), p. 42			
	3. Investigating a Taste for Sugar				
	4. Investigating What's in Food	Make play dough (recipe, p. 281)			
	5. Exploring Food and Activity Environments		Students conduct research projects.		
Dynamic Equilibrium	**6.** Exploring Dynamic Equilibrium			Students learn about energy balance, review digestion and metabolism, and think about why healthful choices are important.	
	7. Digesting Food				
	8. Burning Up	Set up calorimetry experiment, p. 91			
	9. Creating Self-Portraits	Gather art supplies, p. 94	Students make self-portraits.		
From Data to Health Goals	**10.** Collecting Food-Intake Data			Students learn more about the long-term health benefits of following the *C3* behavioral goals.	Students collect personal data on current food and activity choices. They create action plans for change and collect data to monitor their efforts to change. These activities help them learn how they can navigate their food and activity environments to make healthful choices.
	11. Investigating Physical Activity	Use pedometers, p. 129			
	12. Selecting Food Goals		Students develop personal food and activity goals and monitor progress.		
	13. Creating Daily Activity Goals				
Effects of Our Choices	**14.** Keeping It Pumping			Students participate in activities that synthesize why the *C3* behavioral goals reduce chronic disease risk.	
	15. Keeping the Flow	Buy PVC tubing, p. 150; make play dough, p. 281; make cornstarch "blood," p. 282			
	16. Fighting Type 2 Diabetes				
Maintaining Competence	**17.** Telling Others	Gather art supplies, p. 164	Students create projects to share what they have learned.	Students review the why-to evidence they have learned.	Students make personal pledges for sustaining healthful choices.
	18. Bringing It All Together	Plan for celebration, p. 182			
	19. Sharing the Health	Prepare food, pp. 173–178			

How to Use this Book

Each module of the LiFE Curriculum Series includes lesson plans, teacher materials, and student pages. In this way, everything you need to teach each lesson is all in one place. We recommend reviewing these materials as you prepare for the lesson.

Header: This indicates the type of page. For example, it might be a lesson plan, experiment sheet, teacher note, lesson resource, student reading, or activity sheet.

Footer: The lesson number, title, and page number are shown at the bottom of each page.

Units: The module's unit titles are listed in order down the side of the page. The name of the unit you are working with is shown in bold type.

LESSON FORMAT

Each lesson contains an activity and supplemental materials that support the activity. These materials will include any background information, teaching suggestions, illustrations, student readings, or student activity sheets that are needed to teach the lesson.

Overview: This section provides a description of the lesson and details what the students do and what they learn during the lesson.

Aim: This summarizes the main idea of the lesson.

Scientific Processes: These terms are related to specific phases of the QuESTA Learning Cycle. They indicate which QuESTA phases are emphasized in the lesson and the skills that students will be using as they complete the activity.

Objectives: These highlight what you can expect your students to know and be able to do at the end of the lesson.

Materials: This list includes materials that are commonly found in the classroom, such as chart paper, construction or drawing paper, markers, scissors, and rulers. It also contains other materials that can be purchased at a supermarket or hardware store. See p. 15 for materials to order or make ahead of time. The materials list also includes LiFE Logs (composition notebooks that each student uses to record observations and for reflective writing). Materials listed in ***bold italics*** are teacher and student pages provided in this book. The names of certain student readings are not italicized.

Before You Begin: Some activities require advance preparation. You may need to make copies of reproducibles, gather materials, post the Module and Unit questions, or review the teacher note, experiment sheet, or student pages.

Module Question: Each lesson lists the Module Question.

Unit Question: Each lesson lists the Unit Question.

Lesson Procedure: The lesson procedure provides step-by-step information on completing the lesson. QuESTA icons used throughout the procedure indicate which phase of the QuESTA Learning Cycle is being emphasized. Each lesson begins by engaging students in the concept, and presents an opportunity for you to check for student understanding, review the Module Question, and introduce or review the Unit Question.

SUPPLEMENTAL TEACHER MATERIAL

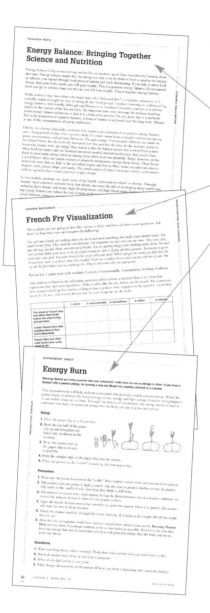

Teacher pages, such as the teacher note, experiment sheet, and lesson resource, follow the lesson procedure.

Teacher Notes include helpful background information. Look here for more in-depth discussion of the lesson topic that you can use for your own learning and to guide the lesson's activities.

Lesson Resources provide information that supports the activity. The pages include reference materials that you can use to guide the lesson's activities.

Experiment Sheets provide a detailed description of the setup, procedure, and questions to guide class discussion.

STUDENT PAGES

Each module in the LiFE Curriculum Series includes reproducible student pages. These include activity sheets that go with specific lessons and student booklets that are in the back of the book.

Activity Sheets. These pages help students focus their learning and organize data collection and analysis. Completed activity sheets can help you assess student learning as you progress through each unit.

Calvin and Carol Take Charge. This reading series is the story of two middle-school students whose doctors refer them to the LiFE Center so that they can get help in maintaining energy balance. Along the way, the two meet up with various health science professionals, including a dietitian, a systems scientist, a behavioral scientist, a cardiologist, an endocrinologist, an exercise physiologist, and an art therapist. This story combines learning science content with the realistic experiences of middle-school students. We recommend that you photocopy and bind the entire ***Calvin and Carol Take Charge*** reading series and give it to your students when you start implementing *Choice, Control & Change*.

The* C3 *Journey. The aim of *Choice, Control & Change (C3)* is for students to use science to make food and activity decisions. ***The* C3 *Journey*** is distributed in Lesson 12 and is used to guide the behavioral nutrition aspects of *C3*.

***Choice, Control & Change* Food and Activity Goals.** These food and activity goals are the foundation of the module. You may wish to enlarge the first page of this section and post it in your classroom for use throughout the module. The rest of this section devotes one page to each of the *C3* behavioral goals, with a bulleted list that summarizes the scientific evidence for why the goal is important and a list of how-to tips for achieving the goal. We recommend that you read through these pages before you begin the curriculum. From our experience, classes have discussions about the scientific evidence beginning with Lesson 1.

Analyze Food Data. This section uses a guided goals-setting process. Students analyze their personal data and set goals for how they are going to work toward making sustained healthful changes to their food and activity choices. Students choose one of the *C3* food goals and a physical-activity goal and create their own personalized plan for change.

Making the Most of *Choice, Control & Change*

Just about everyone deals with food every day. Help students connect what they are learning in *Choice, Control & Change* to what they eat as often as possible. This will not only make the lessons more meaningful, it will also help misconceptions come to light. When this happens, students can come to understand why their constructs were incorrect and ask the questions and have the discussions that will enable them to revise and build on their personal theories about how the world works.

Working in Small Groups

Group work provides an opportunity for hands-on learning and active participation for all. Group collaboration also promotes cooperation, teamwork, and shared responsibility — which mirrors how scientists actually work. Collaboration, teamwork, and drawing on different viewpoints and skills are essential for solving most scientific problems. Encourage groups to present their findings to other groups in the class. This enhances students' communication skills and their ability to defend their findings and answer questions from their peers. Have students work in the same groups each lesson or change around the makeup of the groups — whatever you think will promote a positive experience of doing, thinking, reflecting, and growing.

Personal Data Collection

In *Choice, Control & Change*, students don't gather just any data; they collect and analyze data on their own behaviors and the environment around them. This presents an opportunity for them to take a more objective look at their personal habits and environmental influences and how these affect the choices they make every day. It is also an opportunity to see how they are doing in relation to guidelines suggested for good health. In Lesson 5, students gather data about their food environment and physical-activity environment. In Lesson 9, students track their energy intake using the ***Bite and Write Food Log*** activity sheet. They use this data to fill out the ***24-Hour Food Intake*** activity sheet in Lesson 10. This personal data collection is a starting point from which students choose their food goal in Lesson

12. In a similar fashion, the ***Step and Write*** activity sheet helps students assess where they are when they begin using pedometers with the goal of taking 10,000 steps per day.

Setting Goals

After students learn about the environment around them and how their bodies use energy, gather data about their personal behaviors, and analyze the data, they are poised to use what they've learned to make real changes in their everyday lives. One way to encourage students to focus their energy and sustain change is to set food and activity goals. In Lesson 12, students use ***The C3 Journey*** to develop their personal action plans and monitor their progress. Behavioral nutrition research shows that when people set goals, they are more likely to follow through with the actions they intended to take. *Choice, Control & Change* teaches students why the goal is important and how it will affect their health. Having the opportunity to choose which goal to strive for empowers and motivates students to work on this goal.

Nutrition in the News

As you and your students begin your *Choice, Control & Change* studies, look in the media for articles that relate to what you are studying in class. Newspapers are a rich source of stories about new findings on food, exercise, and health. The lifestyle or health section of the paper often has stories about healthy living or healthy recipes. Be sure to look for any new developments in your community that pertain to the food and activity environments. For example, there may be a new bike path, a trend of grocery stores closing, or a fund-raising walk. If you miss a story appearing in print, your local paper may have a Web site with free access to stories. Google News or databases such as ProQuest or LexisNexis are easy ways to make keyword searches of online news. You may wish to consider tracking changes in your school's wellness policy; the availability of processed, packaged snacks; or the amount of time students spend in physical education.

Look for ways to connect informational materials, such as newspaper and magazine stories, to what students are learning in their language-arts classes. Engage students in a discussion of ways that the format, graphics, or illustrations help make the information accessible. Use these materials to help them gain experience in learning to distinguish fact from opinion in text.

Consider keeping a scrapbook of the news stories you find and reviewing them at the end of the module. You may find that your students have a different perspective on stories when they apply what they have learned.

Connecting what students are learning in the classroom to real-world stories that are covered by the media is a great way to help students realize that the science they are learning is relevant to public debate about important issues that involve science and technology.

Science Standards Matrices

BENCHMARKS FOR SCIENCE LITERACY to be met by the end of 8th grade*	CHOICE, CONTROL & CHANGE UNITS				
	UNIT 1 Investigating Our Choices	UNIT 2 Dynamic Equilibrium	UNIT 3 From Data to Health Goals	UNIT 4 Effects of Our Choices	UNIT 5 Maintaining Competence
1. THE NATURE OF SCIENCE					
A. The Scientific World	X	X	X	X	X
B. Scientific Inquiry	X	X	X	X	
C. The Scientific Enterprise	X	X	X	X	X
3. THE NATURE OF TECHNOLOGY					
A. Technology and Science					
B. Design and Systems		X			
C. Issues in Technology					
5. THE LIVING ENVIRONMENT					
A. Diversity of Life					
B. Heredity		X		X	
C. Cells		X		X	
D. Interdependence of Life					
E. Flow of Matter and Energy		X	X	X	X
F. Evolution of Life					
6. THE HUMAN ORGANISM					
A. Human Identity	X	X			
B. Human Development		X		X	
C. Basic Functions		X	X	X	X
D. Learning	X				X
E. Physical Health	X	X	X	X	X
F. Mental Health					
7. HUMAN SOCIETY					
A. Cultural Effects on Behavior	X	X	X	X	X
B. Group Behavior			X		X
C. Social Change	X				X
D. Social Trade-offs	X	X			X
E. Political and Economic Systems					
F. Social Conflict					
G. Global Interdependence					

BENCHMARKS FOR SCIENCE LITERACY to be met by the end of 8th grade*	CHOICE, CONTROL & CHANGE UNITS				
	UNIT 1 Investigating Our Choices	UNIT 2 Dynamic Equilibrium	UNIT 3 From Data to Health Goals	UNIT 4 Effects of Our Choices	UNIT 5 Maintaining Competence
8. THE DESIGNED WORLD					
A. Agriculture					
B. Materials and Manufacturing					
C. Energy Sources and Use		X	X		
D. Communication	X			X	X
E. Information Processing					X
F. Health Technology	X	X	X	X	X
11. COMMON THEMES					
A. Systems	X	X	X	X	
B. Models	X	X		X	
C. Constancy and Change				X	X
D. Scale					
12. HABITS OF MIND					
A. Values and Attitudes	X	X	X	X	X
B. Computation and Estimation	X		X	X	
C. Manipulation and Observation	X	X	X	X	
D. Communication Skills	X	X	X	X	X
E. Critical-response Skills	X	X	X	X	X

* Benchmarks for Science Literacy by the American Association for the Advancement of Science (AAAS), Project 2061. *www.project2061.org/publications/bsl/online/bolintro.htm* **KEY: X** Addresses Benchmark

NATIONAL SCIENCE EDUCATION STANDARDS

to be met by the end of 8th grade*

CHOICE, CONTROL & CHANGE UNITS

NATIONAL SCIENCE EDUCATION STANDARDS	UNIT 1 Investigating Our Choices	UNIT 2 Dynamic Equilibrium	UNIT 3 From Data to Health Goals	UNIT 4 Effects of Our Choices	UNIT 5 Maintaining Competence
A. SCIENCE AS INQUIRY					
1. Abilities Necessary to Do Scientific Inquiry	X	X	X	X	
2. Understandings about Scientific Inquiry	X	X	X	X	
C. LIFE SCIENCE					
1. Structure and Function in Living Systems		X	X	X	
2. Reproduction and Heredity	X	X		X	
3. Regulation and Behavior	X	X	X	X	X
4. Populations and Ecosystems					
E. SCIENCE AND TECHNOLOGY					
1. Abilities of Technological Design				X	
2. Understandings about Science and Technology	X		X	X	X
F. SCIENCE IN PERSONAL AND SOCIAL PERSPECTIVES	X	X	X	X	X
1. Personal Health					
2. Populations, Resources, and Environments	X				
3. Natural Hazards					
4. Risks and Benefits	X			X	
5. Science and Technology in Society	X	X		X	X
G. HISTORY AND NATURE OF SCIENCE					
1. Science as a Human Endeavor	X	X	X	X	X
2. Nature of Science	X	X	X	X	

*National Research Council, Center for Science, Mathematics, and Engineering Education, National Science Education Standards (1996). **KEY: X** Addresses Standard

Investigating Our Choices

Making the Case

OVERVIEW

In this lesson, students are introduced to the Module and Unit questions. Second, students discuss how they can use scientific evidence to help them make healthy food and activity choices. Next, students engage in a class discussion of what *choice*, *control*, and *change* mean. Through a brainstorming activity, the class shares what they already know about what influences our food choices. The teacher note offers background information on the science of food choice. A pre-assessment activity helps you uncover student understanding of scientific evidence by exploring various scenarios related to food and physical activity and discussing how to evaluate the credibility of both the source and the content. This lesson also introduces the module's student readings about Calvin and Carol, two adolescents who will serve as guides as your students investigate and learn about ways that dietary habits and personal behaviors can affect one's health. Finally, students are made aware of the communicative aspect of science through being introduced to LiFE Logs, science notebooks in which they will record questions, observations, data, and conclusions. Through periodically reviewing what they have written in their logs, students can track their own learning.

AIM

To begin to explore factors that influence health.

SCIENTIFIC PROCESSES

• question, contemplate, assess knowledge

OBJECTIVES

Students will be able to:

• appreciate how the Module and Unit questions will guide everything they learn in the module;

• describe relationships between eating, physical activity, and health;

• define choice, control, and change;

• evaluate the credibility of food and physical-activity information.

MATERIALS

For the teacher:
• Homework questions for Lesson 2 (p. 247)
• *The Science of Food Choice* teacher note
• *What Does It Mean?* lesson resource
• *Introducing Calvin and Carol* lesson resource
• (Optional) Chart paper
• (Optional) Markers

For the class:
• *Analyzing Health and Nutrition Information* lesson resource

For each student:
• **Becoming Researchers** student reading (p. 186)
• **Snack Foods Everywhere** student reading (p. 188)
• (Optional) *Homework Notes* activity sheet (p. 275)
• LiFE Log

PROCEDURE

Before You Begin:

- Read the *Science of Food Choice* teacher note and the *What Does It Mean?*, *Introducing Calvin and Carol,* and *Analyzing Health and Nutrition Information* lesson resources.

- Make one copy of the *Analyzing Health and Nutritional Information* lesson resource and cut apart the cards.

- Review the **Becoming Researchers** and the **Snack Foods Everywhere** student readings and homework questions. Make a copy of both readings for each student. If you plan to distribute copies of the *Homework Notes* activity sheet, make enough copies to distribute one page to each student. Alternatively, students can take notes in their LiFE Logs.

- If you have not already done so, post the Module Question and Unit 1 Question at the front of the classroom.

MODULE QUESTION

How can we use scientific evidence to help us maintain energy balance?

UNIT QUESTION

What influences our food and activity choices?

 QUESTIONING

1. Introduce the Module

Acquaint students with *Choice, Control & Change.* Point out the subtitle of the module, "Using Science to Make Food and Activity Decisions." Explain that in this lesson series students will explore topics in health science while also learning about themselves.

2. Review Module and Unit Questions

Review the Module Question. Engage students in a class discussion. Point out that the Module Question frames everything they will do through this module. Explain that they are going to learn why and how to make healthy food and activity choices. Tell students that as they move through the lessons, they will collect data and keep records of the scientific knowledge they are gaining that will help them make healthy food and activity choices. Emphasize the importance of collecting, recording, and interpreting scientific evidence.

Introduce students to the Unit Questions. To become familiar with factors that influence our food and activity choices, we will investigate the Unit 1 Question. To learn more about energy balance, we will investigate the Unit 2 Question: *How can we make sure that we get the right amount of energy to help our bodies do what we want them to do?* To better understand how we can use scientific evidence to help us maintain energy balance, we will investigate two more Unit Questions — Unit 3: *How can we use personal data to help us make healthy food and activity choices?* and Unit 4: *Why are healthy food and activity choices important for our bodies?* The last Unit Question helps us apply what we have learned: Unit 5: *How can I maintain my skills as a competent eater and mover?*

As a pre-assessment of the Module Question, elicit students' ideas about energy balance and how we can use scientific evidence to help us maintain energy balance. Record these ideas on chart paper or on the board. Accept all answers. Tell the students that in this first unit, they will explore factors in their biology and their environment that influence the food and activity choices they make every day.

3. Discuss the Meaning of Choice, Control, and Change

Engage students in a discussion of the meaning of choice, control, and change. Refer to the *What Does It Mean?* lesson resource to guide the discussion. You may wish to read some of the examples from the lesson resource to stimulate student thinking. *What do we mean by* choice? *What are some choices that you make every day?* Record students' answers on chart paper or on the board. *What do we mean by* control? *What are some things that you can control?* Accept all answers and record them. *What do we mean by* change? *What are some things that you can change? Why do you think this curriculum is called* Choice, Control & Change? Accept all answers and record them.

Explore choice a bit further by creating a food-choice concept map. Write "Food Choice" on the center of a sheet of chart paper or on the board. Ask students to share factors they think influence their food choices. Accept all answers and record them as a concept map around the words "food choice." Once students have exhausted their thoughts ask them if they can think of any other factors related to food itself (taste, texture, past experiences, etc.), then ask what other factors are related to the individual making the choice (attitudes, habits, values, beliefs, self-confidence, etc.), and, finally, ask for other factors related to the social and physical environment (friends, family, availability, culture, etc.) that influence food choices. Refer to the *Science of Food Choice* teacher note for more background information.

4. Assess Critical Thinking Skills

Divide the class into groups of two or three students. Give each group one of the *Analyzing Health and Nutrition Information* cards. Tell group members to discuss what they think about the information itself. *Does the information fit in with what they already know? Why or why not? Do they think the source of the information is reliable? Why or why not? Where might they find out more?*

Are the claims vague? Is the language vague? After students have had small-group discussions, have a whole-class discussion. Try to gauge students' critical thinking skills when evaluating the scientific reliability of information and the accuracy of various sources. Check to see if they understand when a message is using persuasive language. Assess the ideas they have for seeking out further information. Use students' current level of understanding of how to evaluate information to guide you as you teach the module lessons.

 SEARCHING

5. Introduce Calvin and Carol

Distribute the **Becoming Researchers** student reading. Invite students to take turns reading or have them role-play Calvin, Carol, and Ms. Lopez.

 THEORIZING

6. Discuss Calvin and Carol

Use the following questions to guide a class discussion about Calvin and Carol. *What signs of poor health did Ms. Lopez notice?* (Calvin and Carol are both gaining more weight than is healthy for their age and height.) *What does "energy balance" mean?* (It means keeping the amount of energy coming into our bodies equal to the amount going out.) *What hypothesis is the LiFE Center testing?* (If people know why and how to make healthy food and activity choices, they will be able to maintain their energy balance.) *What changes has Calvin noticed in his energy balance?* (He doesn't play as much basketball.) *What changes has Carol noticed in her energy balance?* (She gets tired.) Tell students that with each lesson, they will read more about Calvin's and Carol's experiences at the LiFE Center. Refer to the *Introducing Calvin and*

Carol lesson resource for more background information on this reading series.

7. Review Homework Questions

Post the homework questions for the **Snack Foods Everywhere** student reading on the board. Have students copy them onto the *Homework Notes* activity sheet or into their LiFE Logs. If students are not familiar with this type of note-taking, model it for them. Record a question, read through the student reading, and jot down notes based on what you read. Tell students they will refer to their notes during the next class, when you will discuss the **Snack Foods Everywhere** reading. Check for student understanding.

8. LiFE Logs

To assess student understanding of choice, control, and change, have them take out their LiFE Logs and reflect on a choice they have made that they may want to change in the future. Then have them reflect on how they could have taken control of that choice to make a positive change. For students who are happy with their current choices, have them explain, in writing, why they are satisfied with them.

If students are not accustomed to this type of reflective writing, they may find it challenging. Help students understand that it is fine to sit in front of a blank page for a few moments as they think about what they want to write.

The Science of Food Choice

Think about what goes through your mind when you are looking at food trying to decide what you are going to eat. There are lots of things that affect your decision. For example, you might ask yourself, What options are available right now? Does it look appealing? Have I have had this before? Will I like the taste? Is it healthy for my body? Do I have the time? Do I have the money? What will my friends and family think? These are questions that people of any age consciously or subconsciously ask themselves as they make food choices.

Despite everything that might run through your mind as you make a choice, if you ask people why they eat what they do, the most common response is, "I eat what tastes good to me." Our sensory responses to the taste, smell, sight, and texture of food are a major influence on food preferences and food choices. So the question is, What are we born with and what is learned?

Scientists who study food choice conduct research to determine the factors that influence choice and investigate how these factors relate to each other. They divide the influences on eating behavior into four categories: biology, experience with food, personal factors, and social/environmental factors. Within each of these categories, there are many factors that influence choice (see diagram, p. 31).

Biology. Human beings appear to be born with unlearned predispositions toward liking things that taste sweet and rejecting things that taste sour or bitter. The liking for salt seems to develop several months after birth. This biologically determined predisposition contributes to some degree to preference and to food intake, particularly in children.

Experience with food. Another area of research suggests that people's food preferences and food-acceptance patterns are largely learned. Learning in this case means physiological learning or conditioning that comes from the repeated positive or negative consequences that people experience with food and eating, leading them to like a food or learn what "being full" means. Social conditioning comes from the positive or negative experiences we have socially when we eat a food, leading us to like or dislike a food. Scientists who study food choice call this the *social affective context*. Parenting practices also influence our food likes and dislikes. This conditioning begins at birth and continues to be modified and refined throughout life.

Personal factors. Our biology and personal experiences with food are not the only influences on our food intake. We also develop personal perceptions and expectations about food: how food should taste and what impact it will have on our sense of well-being. Interpersonal factors also influence food choice. We participate in a network of social relationships including our families and peers. Food choices and eating patterns are also influenced by the need to negotiate with others in the family about what to buy or eat. Relationships with peers have an impact on our day-to-day choices as well. Our attitudes, motivations, and values influence our choices and, of course, nutrition knowledge and skills are also important.

Social/environmental factors. Finally, environmental factors are powerful influences on food choice. The external environment influences food choices and dietary behaviors through factors such as the availability (array of food options) and accessibility (readiness and convenience) of food. In short, what is available in a community influences what is purchased and eaten. The availability and accessibility of fruits and vegetables at home and school enable their consumption by children.

TEACHER NOTE

INVESTIGATING OUR CHOICES : DYNAMIC EQUILIBRIUM : FROM DATA TO HEALTH GOALS : EFFECTS OF OUR CHOICES : MAINTAINING COMPETENCE

Social structures and cultural environments also influence food choice. Cultural practices have an important impact on food choices and eating practices even in modern, multiethnic societies. The media, part of the information environment, are the main source of information about food and nutrition for many people. Advertising has a powerful capacity to persuade. The food industry spends billions per year on marketing and advertising, with much of this aimed at children. Most of these advertising dollars are spent by companies that produce high-fat and/or high-sugar products. These marketing activities clearly influence food choice.

It's important to remember that although food-related factors and environmental contexts have important independent influences on diet, they also influence the development of beliefs, attitudes, and feelings, which in turn influence behavior. It becomes clear, then, that beliefs, attitudes, and feelings play a central role in food-related behaviors. This is good news to educators because these beliefs, attitudes, and feelings are to some extent modifiable through education.

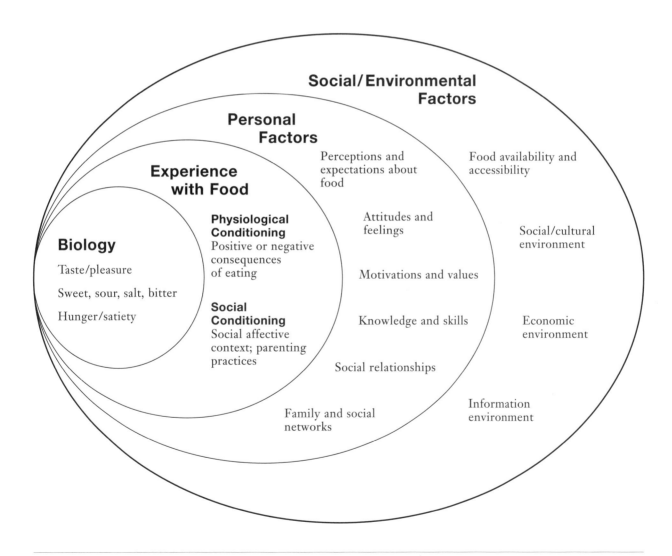

Diagram modified from I.R. Contento, 2010, p. 46

What Does It Mean?

Choice

A variety of things to select from

- **You have choices in what you wear to school each day.**
- **You have choices about who you want to be friends with.**
- **You have choices about what you eat and what type of physical activity you do.**

Control

The power to direct or command

- **You can take control of your time by doing your homework on Friday to have more time with your friends on Saturday and Sunday.**
- **You can take control of not feeling thirsty by bringing a water bottle when you go out.**
- **You can take control of how much activity you get by walking to school.**

Change

To make something different from the way it is

- **You can make a change in your activity level by playing soccer with your friends instead of playing video games.**
- **You can make a change in what you eat by choosing a piece of fruit for a snack instead of chips.**
- **You can make a change in how often you eat fast food by packing a sandwich in your bag instead of stopping for a burger.**

Introducing Calvin and Carol

In this module, students meet Calvin Green, Carol Cooper, and researchers at the Linking Food and the Environment (LiFE) Center. In each lesson, you and your students will learn about the challenges and triumphs that Calvin and Carol encounter as they work with the LiFE Center researchers to make choices, take control of the events in their daily lives, and make changes in their food and physical-activity choices. Each lesson includes a reading assignment to be done as homework, including questions to help guide the reading. In the next class period, the questions can be used to review the reading as a class.

Now, meet Calvin and Carol, two 13-year-old students who have been referred to the LiFE Center by their family physicians. Calvin attends school in a city and can walk to school and to his other activities. Carol lives in the suburbs and needs transportation to get to school and after-school activities. Sometimes her mother drives her and sometimes she takes the bus. Carol and Calvin say they are tired and don't have any energy. Their physicians are concerned that they both seem to be at risk for developing Type 2 diabetes and heart disease. Calvin's parents do not seem to be at risk for these diseases. However, his grandfather has had a heart attack. Carol's father seems to be at risk because of his eating patterns and weight gain over the past few years.

Most of Calvin's and Carol's risk of disease and feelings of tiredness can be resolved by making changes in their behavior; specifically, making some different food choices and being more active. They both love fast food, baked goods, candy, sweetened beverages, and watching television. Although they do like fruits and vegetables, they don't eat many.

Carol belongs to a dance club, but isn't dancing as much as she used to. Sometimes she doesn't have the time because she has to babysit her younger siblings. Because so much of her spare time has been spent dancing, she does not participate in any other physical activities. She is also having a hard time concentrating enough in the evening to finish her homework. Calvin has a very low activity level. He has never thought of walking as something important and wouldn't dream of taking the stairs if an elevator is available. He claims to hate exercise, but he does like to play basketball with his friends. Recently, he's stopped playing as much basketball and now plays video games.

Calvin and Carol don't realize the impact that eating so many foods that are high in fat and sugar can have on their bodies. They don't understand the concept of energy balance. The LiFE Center researchers help them learn that balancing the calories from food intake with the calories burned off in activity can help maintain weight at a healthy level. In the process, the two learn how important human body systems are to overall bodily function.

By the end of this module, Calvin and Carol learn how to successfully navigate their food and physical-activity environments so they can make healthy food and activity choices.

Analyzing Health and Nutrition Information

The media are the main source of information about food and nutrition for many people, which means they are a major source of informal nutrition education. Information about food and nutrition is widely covered in newspapers, magazines, and television programs. Many magazines focus on health and nutrition, and entire channels on TV are devoted to food-related shows. All of this media coverage means we are constantly bombarded by claims about health and nutrition. It's important to have the skills to distinguish between sense and nonsense.

You can turn this media coverage into an opportunity to reinforce habits of mind, particularly critical-response skills. Challenge students to use their knowledge to evaluate claims. Encourage them to think about who is making the claim. Is the person an expert or reporting what an expert has said? Does the claim use, or misuse, supporting evidence? Challenge students to listen closely to the language that is used and the logic of the argument. The American Association for the Advancement of Science's *Benchmarks for Science Literacy* states that by the end of eighth grade, students should:

- Question claims based on vague attributions (such as "Leading doctors say...") or on statements made by celebrities or others outside the area of their particular expertise;

- Be skeptical of arguments based on very small samples of data, biased samples, or samples for which there was no control sample;

- Be aware that there may be more than one good way to interpret a given set of findings;

- Notice and criticize the reasoning in arguments in which fact and opinion are intermingled or the conclusions do not follow logically from the evidence given.[1]

Use the cards on the following three pages to make an assessment of your students' critical thinking skills and what they consider to be scientific evidence. You may find it helpful to repeat this throughout the module to see how student thinking has changed. Remember, these are skills that are learned. Consider setting up a weekly discussion of health-and-nutrition media stories. Have students bring in ads, articles, food packaging, and so forth and, as a class, analyze the validity of the claims. By the end of this module, your students will be adept at distinguishing sense from nonsense.

---

[1] American Association for the Advancement of Science (AAAS), 1993, p. 299.

Card 1

On the Internet you go to your favorite game site. An ad pops up that reads, "Are you tired? Do you need more energy? Click here to find out more." Would you click on it to look for information about getting more energy? Why or why not?

Card 2

While you are watching the evening news with your parents, the news anchor reports on a new National Institutes of Health study that says one out of every five children is now obese. According to the anchor, the study suggests that this is directly related to kids spending too much time sitting in front of the computer. Do you think that sitting in front of computers is the cause of obesity? Why or why not? Where would you go to get more information?

Card 3

You walk into your favorite grocery store and hear an announcement over the loudspeaker: "Come on over to the produce section. People who eat at least five fruits and vegetables a day reduce their risk of getting cancer. Today we have on sale fresh local cherries and zucchini. Come and get them while they last." Would you believe what the announcer says about fruits and vegetables reducing the risk of cancer? Why or why not? Would you be persuaded to buy some produce? Why or why not?

Card 4

You hear an advertisement on the radio for a specific energy drink. The advertisement states, "Drink one can of this a day to get all the energy you need to live the life you want." Would you buy one of the energy drinks based on what you heard on the radio? Why or why not? Where might you look for more information to find out what is in this drink and if the ad's claim is accurate?

Card 5

At lunch your friends are talking about the latest fad diets. They have decided to try a few of them to see if they work. Do you join in? Why or why not?

Card 6

You overhear a discussion between your father and grandmother during which they disagree about the best way to maintain a healthy weight. Your grandmother thinks it is good for people to eat smaller portions of everything and keep all of the basic food groups as part of their diet. Your dad says he is going to cut out all carbohydrates (bread, pasta, rice, cereal, potatoes, etc.) from his diet to lose weight. Who do you believe? Where would you go to find the most accurate and trustworthy information?

Card 7

You see a pamphlet in the doctor's office discussing the increasing risk of heart disease among children your age. The pamphlet states that this is related to food and activity choices. You read the pamphlet and wonder if it is for real or if it is a joke. You don't understand how children your age could have such serious health problems. Do you ask your doctor whether it's accurate or not? Why or why not?

Card 8

An article in a popular teen magazine quotes a famous female hip-hop singer about her recent weight loss. She said she lost 10 pounds by eating only grapefruit and that now she can eat whatever she wants and does not gain back the weight. She said, "The grapefruit diet was hard for the first two days, then I felt the fat oozing away." She said she will do a grapefruit purge for a week every winter and summer. Would you follow her advice? Why or why not?

Card 9

You read an article in your local newspaper saying that a study shows that people who play video games that make them move around burn on average 350 calories an hour while playing the games. Would this make you want to play these games? Why or why not? Where might you look to get more information?

As a Matter of Choice

AIM

To reflect on personal experience with food and activity choices to create a foundation for future investigations.

SCIENTIFIC PROCESSES

- question, create research questions, construct new ideas

OBJECTIVES

Students will be able to:

- develop questions about food and activity choices;

- gather and organize interview data on food and activity;

- identify important factors that influence food and activity choices.

OVERVIEW

In this lesson, students start to develop skills that help them make the connection between food and physical-activity choices and health. First, students review the Lesson 1 homework questions and discuss what they have learned about energy balance. Next, in a classroom survey, students continue to explore their understanding of choice. Through a class discussion on the reasons why they chose the snacks they did, students build on their understanding about the factors that influence food choice. Next, they work in pairs to interview each other in order to learn more about their own personal food and exercise choices. As a class, they brainstorm ways to organize the class data. The lesson closes with a class discussion in which students begin to construct new ideas about factors that influence what they eat and what physical activities they do.

MATERIALS

For the teacher:
- Homework questions for Lessons 2 and 3 (p. 247)
- *Food and Exercise Interview Questions* lesson resource
- Chart paper
- Markers

For each student:
- **Sweet Tastes** student reading (p. 190)
- Notes from Lesson 1 homework
- (Optional) *Homework Notes* activity sheet (p. 275)
- LiFE Log

PROCEDURE

Before You Begin:

- Remind students to bring in their notes from their **Snack Foods Everywhere** homework assignment. Have the homework questions available for discussion.

- Review the *Food and Exercise Interview Questions* lesson resource. Copy the questions onto chart paper.

- Review the **Sweet Tastes** student reading and homework questions. Make a copy of the reading for each student. If you plan to distribute copies of the *Homework Notes* activity sheet, make enough copies to distribute one page to each student. Alternatively, students can take notes in their LiFE Logs.

- If you have not already done so, post the Module Question and Unit 1 Question at the front of the classroom.

MODULE QUESTION

How can we use scientific evidence to help us maintain energy balance?

UNIT QUESTION

What influences our food and activity choices?

 THEORIZING

1. Review Module and Unit Questions

Invite a student to read the Module and Unit questions out loud. Ask students to briefly summarize what they have learned thus far. Explain that in this lesson, students will further investigate choice, control, and change. They will also survey their classmates to find out about their food and physical-activity choices.

2. Discuss Homework

Have students take out their notes from their **Snack Foods Everywhere** homework reading. Engage students in a discussion of the reading. Use the homework questions to guide the discussion. Check for student understanding of energy balance. Have students take out their LiFE Logs and write a paragraph that explains energy balance.

 QUESTIONING

3. Discuss Food and Activity Choices

Write "candy bar," "apple," and "cereal bar" on the board or on chart paper. Tell students you are going to survey the class to find out which of these three items is the favorite snack. Point to each one and ask students to indicate, by raising their hands, which snack they would choose to eat. Encourage students to respond honestly. Ask them to indicate the snack they prefer, and not to be concerned about what their classmates are choosing or what they think is the "right" answer. You may wish to ask them to close their eyes during the selection process. Count the number of students who choose each snack and record the number beside each choice.

Circle the snack that most students chose. Invite student volunteers to give some reasons why they chose this snack. Accept all answers. Record them on the board or on chart paper. Next, if any students did not choose this snack, ask them to share why they did not choose it. Record the responses. Repeat for each snack. Explain that these lists of reasons represent some of the factors we consider when we make food choices. Point out that even if we don't stop to think about food choices, there are lots of factors that influence what we eat. Stress that each of us is unique and we all have our own reasons.

Make sure students do not feel they are being judged about choices they make. Emphasize that all answers are acceptable. Create a safe environment so students will speak honestly about what they would choose. This will help them develop the understanding that the factors aren't "good" or "bad," they are simply the reasons behind food or activity choices.

Tell students that the number one reason most people choose to eat something is that it tastes good to them. Point out that fresh fruits and vegetables, a healthy choice, can sometimes taste bad when they are not in season or when they are bruised, too ripe, or not ripe enough. One reason that many people, especially youth, choose processed, packaged foods is that they consistently taste the same.

Tell students that next they are going to conduct a survey about after-school activities with their friends. Write: "play sports," "watch TV," and "walk to the park to hang out" across the top of a sheet of chart paper or on the board. Survey the class and record the results. Circle the preferred activity. Discuss reasons for choosing or not choosing the activity, as you did with the snack. Point out that even if we don't think about it, there are many factors that determine our level of physical activity.

4. Interview Each Other

Have students work in pairs. Post the chart paper with the questions from the **Food and Exercise Interview Questions** lesson resource. Review the first three questions with the class. Remind students of the different factors affecting choice that they discussed earlier in this lesson and in the previous lesson.

Either record students' questions on the board or chart paper, or have the students write them in their LiFE Logs or on lined paper. Next, have the student pairs interview one another and discuss their own personal food and activity habits. Instruct them to take turns asking each other questions and writing down their

partner's responses. Encourage students to be honest in their answers, and to talk and write about any conversations they feel are interesting and relevant beyond the questions provided. Once students have interviewed each other, invite volunteers to share some of the interesting responses their partners gave. Identify any common experiences that other students might be able to relate to.

 THEORIZING

5. Analyze Responses

Challenge students to think of different ways to organize the class information. You may wish to guide the work by using one of the samples on the **Food and Exercise Interview Questions** lesson resource. Discuss the class data. *Do any of the results surprise you? What did you expect to find out? What was different?*

6. Review Homework Questions

Give each student a copy of the **Sweet Tastes** student reading. Post the homework questions for the reading on the board. Have students copy them onto the **Homework Notes** activity sheet or into their LiFE Logs.

7. LiFE Logs

Have students write at least two paragraphs describing factors that influence their own food and physical-activity choices.

Food and Exercise Interview Questions

Have the class use these interview questions to help them find out about food and exercise in their own lives. Post the questions on chart paper or on the board. Have student pairs interview each other and record the responses on a lined sheet of paper or in their LiFE Logs. Compile the responses. Challenge students to look for patterns and relationships.

1. *What kinds of foods do you usually eat at home with your family? Describe what a typical meal might be like.*

2. *Where does your family get the food and who gets it?*

3. *Who prepares the meals at your home?*

4. *What kinds of foods and drinks do you usually eat when you are hungry for a snack? If you think about where you snack, it may help you remember what kinds of snacks you eat.*

5. *Why do you choose these snacks?*

6. *Is there anything you wish you could eat or drink instead?*

7. *What kinds of activities do you usually do during your free time? For example, what do you do when you are not in class?*

8. *Why do you do these activities?*

9. *Is there anything you wish you could do instead?*

Sample Responses

	Fruits	Vegetables	Meat/Poultry	Fish	Take-out Pizza	Desserts
Foods We Eat at Home	√√√√	√√√√√	√√√	√	√√√√√√	√√√√√√√√√

	Supermarket	Farmers' Market	CSA	Bodega	We Have a Garden
Where My Family Buys Vegetables	√√√	√√√√√√	√√√√√	√√√√√	√√√√√√√√

	Cookies	Candy	Fast Food	Chips	Fresh Fruit	Energy Bars	Low-fat Yogurt
What I Eat for Snacks	√√√√√	√√√	√√√√ √√√√	√√√	√√√√√√	√√√	√√√

Investigating a Taste for Sugar

AIM

To examine biological taste preferences.

SCIENTIFIC PROCESSES

- experiment, observe, theorize, apply

OBJECTIVES

Students will be able to:

- explain that humans have an innate biological preference for sweet foods;

- describe the relationship between biology and food preferences.

OVERVIEW

In this lesson, students begin to investigate how taste influences our food choices. The lesson starts with a review of the homework reading from Lesson 2. Next, students participate in a tasting experiment in which they record their partner's responses to the taste of different powdered substances: sugar, salt, unsweetened cocoa powder, and ascorbic acid. They develop a table for recording their observations. Through the experiment, students learn that humans have a universal liking of sweet tastes, whereas salty, bitter, and sour tastes get more mixed responses. Finally, students apply what they have learned by analyzing their favorite foods and discussing how biological preferences may influence their own food choices.

MATERIALS

For the teacher:
- Homework questions for Lessons 3 and 4 (p. 247)
- *Building Theories about Taste* lesson resource
- *Taste* experiment sheet
- (Optional) chart paper
- (Optional) markers

For each student:
- 1/8 teaspoon sugar
- 1/8 teaspoon salt
- 1/8 teaspoon unsweetened cocoa powder

- 1/8 teaspoon crushed ascorbic acid (Vitamin C)
- 1 small paper plate
- Notes from Lesson 2 homework
- *How Does It Taste?* activity sheet
- **Fat Tastes Good** student reading (p. 192)
- (Optional) *Homework Notes* activity sheet (p. 275)
- LiFE Log

PROCEDURE

Before You Begin:

- Review the **Building Theories about Taste** lesson resource and the **Taste** experiment sheet. Gather the materials for the experiment. To set it up, follow the instructions on the experiment sheet. Check for food allergies to make sure students will be safe working with these materials. Review the **How Does It Taste?** activity sheet. Make enough copies to distribute one to each student.

- Remind students to bring in their notes from their **Sweet Tastes** homework reading assignment. Have the homework questions available for discussion.

- Review the **Fat Tastes Good** student reading and homework questions. Make a copy of the reading for each student. If you plan to distribute copies of the **Homework Notes** activity sheet, make enough copies to distribute one copy to each student. Alternatively, students can take notes in their LiFE Logs.

- Have students wash their hands before beginning the taste experiment.

- If you have not done so already, post the Module Question and Unit 1 Question at the front of the classroom.

MODULE QUESTION

How can we use scientific evidence to help us maintain energy balance?

UNIT QUESTION

What influences our food and activity choices?

 THEORIZING

1. Review Module and Unit Questions

Remind students of the Module and Unit questions. Tell them that in this lesson they will be investigating the ways in which our biology — specifically our biological preference for certain tastes — influences our food choices.

2. Discuss Homework

Have students take out their notes from their **Sweet Tastes** homework assignment. Engage students in a discussion of the reading. Use the homework questions to guide the discussion. Check for student understanding of energy balance.

 EXPERIMENTING

3. Investigate Taste

Prepare the classroom for the **Taste** experiment. In this experiment, student pairs taste four different powders. Through observation, students discover that humans have a predisposition toward liking sweet tastes and rejecting salty, bitter, and sour tastes. Pass out the **How Does It Taste?** activity sheet.

4. Record Observation

Using the **Taste** experiment sheet as a guide, ask students to conduct the experiment. Remind them to record everything their partner says or does during and after tasting each powder, including facial gestures and sounds, on the **How Does It Taste?** activity sheet. After the students have tasted and recorded their reactions to each substance, you can tell them what each powder is.

THEORIZING

 THEORIZING

5. Build Theories

Now that the students know what each of the substances is, have them compare their reaction with their partner's reaction and then come up with ideas about why they reacted the way they did. Use the questions on the *Building Theories about Taste* lesson resource to guide the class discussion. Students should begin to realize that humans have an innate preference for sweet things, by noting that just about everyone likes the taste of the sugar, whereas liking for the other basic tastes — especially bitter and sour — is more mixed.

6. Analyze Favorite Foods

Tell students that now that they understand some of the scientific evidence explaining taste, they are going to begin to analyze their own food choices. Make a list of students' favorite foods on the board or on chart paper. Encourage thoughtful, honest answers. Have students identify any patterns in their responses; for example, are most of the foods high in fat content or sugar? *Why are these your favorite foods?* You can expect the overriding response to be "Because they taste good." Encourage students to expand their responses to include convenience, cost, habit, availability, and so forth.

8. Review Homework Questions

Give each student a copy of the **Fat Tastes Good** student reading. Post the homework questions for the reading on the board. Have students copy them onto the *Homework Notes* activity sheet or into their LiFE Logs.

9. LiFE Logs

Have students reflect on taste and their personal preferences by writing at least two paragraphs about what they ate for lunch, focusing on how it tasted — for example, sweet, salty, bitter, or sour. Have them include whether or not they liked the foods, and why they did or didn't like what they ate.

 **APPLYING TO LIFE**

7. Draw Conclusions

To summarize today's lesson, ask students to apply what they have learned to their own lives. *Can you make a connection between your preferences and what you discovered in the experiment we just did? What ways can you think of to apply what you have learned to making food choices in the future?* (Eat fruit if I want something sweet. Limit the number of sweet foods that I eat.)

Building Theories about Taste

Have students review the observations they made during the experiment. Use these questions to guide their thinking.

Questions

1. *What was similar or different about your reactions and your partner's reactions to substance A (sugar, sweet taste)?*

2. *Why do you think you and your partner reacted the way you did to substance A?*

3. *What was similar or different about your reactions and your partner's reactions to substance B (salt, salty taste)?*

4. *Why do you think you and your partner reacted the way you did to substance B?*

5. *What was similar or different about your reactions and your partner's reactions to substance C (cocoa powder, bitter taste)?*

6. *Why do you think you and your partner reacted the way you did to substance C?*

7. *What was similar or different about your reactions and your partner's reactions to substance D (ascorbic acid, sour taste)?*

8. *Why do you think you and your partner reacted the way you did to substance D?*

Discussion

Hold a class discussion. Encourage students to look for reactions that seemed to be common among most people in the class and any unique reactions. Close the discussion by having students respond to the following questions in their LiFE Logs: *Do you think our reactions to these basic tastes influence our food choices? What types of foods are we most likely to enjoy eating?* Remind students to use observations from the experiment to support their conclusions.

Taste

In this experiment, student pairs taste four different powders. While one student tastes the powders, the other records the taster's reactions to each powder. Then students switch roles. Finally, students analyze their reactions to the four tastes and discuss how taste might influence food choices.

Setup

1. Prepare one tasting plate for each student. Use a marker to divide the plate into four sections. Label the sections: A, B, C, D.

2. Put approximately 1/8 teaspoon of each powder onto each plate.

A: sugar (represents sweet taste)

B: salt (represents salty taste)

C: unsweetened cocoa powder (represents bitter taste)

D: ascorbic-acid powder (represents sour taste)

Tasting Plate

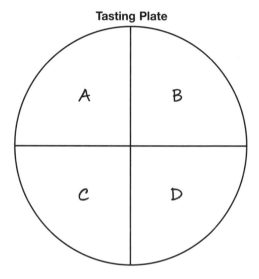

Procedure

1. Ask students to wash their hands before they begin this experiment.

2. Have students work in pairs. Distribute one prepared tasting plate to each student.

3. Have students use the ***How Does It Taste?*** activity sheet to record their partner's reactions to the various tastes.

4. Have one member of the pair taste each powder. Tell students to lick their pinkie and put it in the powder, and lick the powder off their pinkie. Have the partner record the taster's responses to each powder and then switch roles. Instruct students to record both what their partners say and what they do (such as faces or sounds they make) on the activity sheet.

5. After all students have completed the tasting, tell the class what the substances are.

Questions

1. *What was your partner's reaction to the sugar? Why do you think he or she reacted that way?*

2. *What was your partner's reaction to the salt? Why do you think he or she reacted that way?*

3. *What was your partner's reaction to the cocoa powder? Why do you think he or she reacted that way?*

4. *What was your partner's reaction to the ascorbic-acid powder? Why do you think he or she reacted that way?*

5. *Do you think these reactions to the basic tastes influence the food choices that we make?*

Name	Date

How Does It Taste?

Using this two-column table, record everything your partner says or does during and after tasting each powder, including facial gestures and sounds your partner makes.

TASTE-TEST OBSERVATIONS	
Substance	**Partner's Reactions**
A	
B	
C	
D	

INVESTIGATING OUR CHOICES : DYNAMIC EQUILIBRIUM : FROM DATA TO HEALTH GOALS : EFFECTS OF OUR CHOICES : MAINTAINING COMPETENCE

Investigating What's in Food

AIM

To investigate fat and sugar content in certain foods.

SCIENTIFIC PROCESSES

- gather data, observe, theorize, apply

OBJECTIVES

Students will be able to:

- explain that human beings have an innate biological preference for fatty foods;

- describe the relationship between biology and food preferences;

- compare the amount of fat and sugar in various foods and beverages to the daily recommended level;

- apply what they have learned to their own food choices.

OVERVIEW

In this lesson, students continue to explore how taste influences our food choices. The lesson begins with a review of the Module and Unit questions and the reading homework assignment. Next, students listen to a scenario to help them visualize the experience of having the smell of French fries motivate them to buy and eat the fried food. Through a class discussion, students compare their responses and discover that most people enjoy eating fried and fatty foods. Students build on what they learned about a predisposition for sweet tastes and learn that humans also have a biological preference for both the smell and "feel" of fat in their mouths. Next, students use play dough and sugar to measure out the amount of fat and sugar in various foods. Students compare the amounts to the daily recommended amount and discuss their observations. Finally, students think about the choices they can make if they want to reduce the amount of fat and sugar they consume.

MATERIALS

For the teacher:
- Homework questions for Lessons 4 and 5 (p. 247)
- *French Fry Visualization* lesson resource
- *Investigating Fat and Sugar in Foods* experiment sheet
- *Play Dough* recipe (p. 281)

For the class:
- *Fat and Sugar Cards* experiment sheet
- Scissors
- Play dough
- 9 paper plates

- 5 plastic cups
- 3 small bowls
- 14 plastic spoons
- 1 pound bag of sugar

For each student:
- **Food and Activity Environments** student reading (p. 197)
- Notes from Lesson 3 homework
- (Optional) *Homework Notes* activity sheet (p. 275)
- LiFE Log

PROCEDURE

Before You Begin:

- Remind students to bring in their notes from their **Fat Tastes Good** homework assignment. Have the homework questions available for discussion.

- Review the *French Fry Visualization* lesson resource and the *Investigating Fat and Sugar in Foods* experiment sheet. Gather materials. Review the *Play Dough* recipe. Gather the materials and make one recipe.

- Make class copies of the *Fat and Sugar Cards* experiment sheet. Cut out the cards.

- Read the **Food and Activity Environments** student reading and homework questions. Make a copy of the reading for each student. If you plan to distribute copies of the *Homework Notes* activity sheet, make enough copies to distribute one copy to each student. Alternatively, students can take notes in their LiFE Logs.

- If you have not done so already, post the Module Question and Unit 1 Question at the front of the classroom.

MODULE QUESTION

How can we use scientific evidence to help us maintain energy balance?

UNIT QUESTION

What influences our food and activity choices?

 THEORIZING

1. Review Module and Unit Questions

Remind students of the Unit and Module questions. Tell them that in this lesson they will continue to investigate human biological preferences for certain foods.

2. Discuss Homework

Have students take out their notes from their **Fat Tastes Good** homework assignment. Engage students in a discussion of the reading. Use the homework questions to guide the discussion.

 **APPLYING TO LIFE**

3. French Fry Visualization

Tell students you are going to describe a scenario. Ask them to close their eyes and imagine themselves in this scene. Read the scenario on the *French Fry Visualization* lesson resource. Feel free to embellish the description.

Have students think about their own experiences with the smell of French fries. Tell them to use a 5-point scale, as indicated on the *French Fry Visualization* lesson resource, to respond to the questions on the lesson resource. Make a table, like the sample table, and record student responses. *What does our data suggest? Are more people in the class tempted to buy French fries when they smell them? What percentage of the class orders French fries after smelling them?* Tell students that human beings have a biological preference for food that's high in fat.

 **EXPERIMENTING**

4. Investigate Fat and Sugar Content

Use the *Investigating Fat and Sugar in Foods* experiment sheet to guide this next part of the lesson. Divide the class into seven groups. Give each group one card and distribute the appropriate materials to each group. Next, demonstrate how to measure the sugar and "fat." Have all the student groups work simultaneously to measure out the fat and sugar according to the instructions on their cards.

Note: In the **Calvin and Carol Take Charge** reading, Calvin looks at a label that has the measurements in grams, as all food labels do. We use teaspoons in this lesson because it is easier for students to measure out in class and it is a standard household measurement unit used when preparing food. Write on the board that 1 teaspoon of sugar equals 4 grams and 1 teaspoon of fat equals 5 grams. Students can use this if they want to be able to convert the amount of fat and sugar in foods they eat into teaspoons. Alternatively, if you have a triple beam balance in your classroom you can have students perform these measurements in grams.

 THEORIZING

5. Present Findings

After students have completed their measurements, have each group present its findings, as described on the **Investigating Fat and Sugar in Foods** experiment sheet. Have each group fold their card and display the portion of the card that lists the amount of fat or sugar in their food item.

Discuss how the various foods compare. *What do you notice about the amounts of fat and sugar in these foods? Were you surprised by what you found?* Use the questions on the **Investigating Fat and Sugar in Foods** experiment sheet to guide the rest of the discussion.

6. Review Homework Questions

Give each student a copy of the **Food and Activity Environments** reading. Post the homework questions for the reading on the

board. Have students copy them onto the **Homework Notes** activity sheet or into their LiFE Logs.

7. LiFE Logs

Have students write at least two paragraphs that answer this question: *How do human biological preferences influence food choices?* After students have completed the writing, invite volunteers to share their thoughts with the class. Remind students to use scientific evidence to support their views.

French Fry Visualization

Tell students you are going to describe a scene to them and then ask them some questions. Ask them to close their eyes and imagine the following:

You and your friends are walking down the street and smell something that makes your mouths water. You smell French fries. They smell hot and delicious. You remember the last time you ate some. They were crisp, just the way you like them, and covered with salt. You are getting hungry just thinking about them. You and your friends follow your noses to the fast-food restaurant that is frying all those potatoes. You decide to go in and order some food. You order French fries to go with your meal. When you get the meal, you find that the French fries taste even better than they smelled. Each one is golden brown and crunchy. You eat all the fries before you eat anything else. They're best when they are piping hot.

Review the 5-point scale with students: 1=never, 2=occasionally, 3=sometimes, 4=often, 5=always.

Ask students to listen to the following questions and to choose a number from 1 to 5 that best represents their personal experience. Make a table, like the one below, on the board. Ask a question, have students hold up the number of fingers that represent their response to the question, count how many 1s, 2s, etc., and record the number for each response on the table.

	1=never	2=occasionally	3=sometimes	4=often	5=always
The smell of French fries and other fried foods makes me want to buy and eat them.					
I order French fries after smelling them in fast-food restaurants.					
French fries and other fried foods taste really good to me.					

Questions

1. *Were you surprised by the class results or were they what you expected?*

2. *What do you like about French fries and other fried foods? What makes them taste so good? What makes you want to eat them?*

3. *If you don't like fried foods, what don't you like about them? What makes you not want to eat them?*

Investigating Fat and Sugar in Foods

This activity helps students visualize the amount of fat and sugar in various foods.

Setup

1. Copy the *Fat and Sugar* cards on pages 54–57. Cut them out.

2. Divide the class into seven groups. Give each group one card.

3. Pour sugar into three small bowls for groups 1, 2, and 7.

4. Distribute the appropriate materials to each group.

> Group 1: 1 plate, 1 cup, small bowl with sugar, 2 teaspoons, play dough
> Group 2: 2 cups, small bowl with sugar, 2 teaspoons
> Group 3: 2 plates, 2 teaspoons, play dough
> Group 4: 2 plates, 2 teaspoons, play dough
> Group 5: 2 plates, 2 teaspoons, play dough
> Group 6: 2 plates, 2 teaspoons, play dough
> Group 7: 2 cups, small bowl with sugar, 2 teaspoons

Procedure

1. Tell students that the play dough represents fat. Demonstrate how to measure out 1 teaspoon of sugar. To measure the sugar, completely fill the spoon, then use your finger to level it off so it is flat across the top. Place the measured sugar into a cup.

2. Next, demonstrate how to measure out the fat. Fill the spoon with play dough until it is flat across the top. Use your thumb to remove the play dough from the spoon. Roll it into a ball and place it on a plate. Explain that the groups that are measuring out the fat can measure out 1 teaspoon and roll it into a ball, as you did. Using this as a model, have them create as many teaspoon-sized balls of play dough as they need. Be sure they make all the balls as close to the same size as possible.

3. Have the groups follow the instructions on their card. Walk among the groups to make sure students understand their assignment.

4. After all the groups have completed their work, have each group present its findings, starting with Group 1.

5. As Group 1 presents, explain that the class will compare the daily recommended amount to the amount of fat and sugar found in various foods. Tell students that not exceeding the daily recommended amount on a regular basis can reduce risk for conditions such as high blood fat and high blood sugar that can lead to cardiovascular disease and Type 2 diabetes.

6. After Groups 2 through 7 have presented, discuss how the various foods compare. Make sure students understand that the larger the soda bottle or glass, the more sugar there is. Engage students in a discussion of what they have learned about the amount of fat in different kinds of food. Challenge them to think about the choices they can make if they want to reduce the amount of fat and sugar they consume.

Questions

1. *This is the daily recommended amount of fat and sugar from all your food throughout the day. What do you think when you see this?*

2. *What do you think is the reason for the difference in the amount of sugar in the two different sizes of soda? Does this make you feel differently about drinking soda and other sweetened beverages?*

3. *What do you think is the reason for the difference in the amount of fat in the two different burgers? What size burger do you think is healthier? Why?*

4. *What do you think is the reason for the difference in the amount of fat in the two different sizes of fries? What are some ways you might be able to eat fewer fries?*

5. *What do you think is the reason for the difference in the amount of fat in the two chicken sandwiches? What cooking methods add fat to food? What cooking methods do not add fat?*

6. *What do you think is the reason for the difference in the amount of fat in a turkey sandwich and a slice of pizza? How will you use this information when you buy snacks or meals for yourself?*

7. *What do you think is the reason for the difference in the amount of sugar in the two different sizes of fruit-flavored sports drinks? Does this make you feel differently about drinking sports drinks?*

Fat and Sugar Cards

What to Do

1. Make 13 teaspoon-sized balls of fat and place them on a plate.

2. Measure out 12 1/2 teaspoons of sugar in a cup.

3. Display the recommendations by the plate of fat and cup of sugar.

Fat and Sugar Recommendations Per Day

(for a person who eats 2,000 calories per day)

FAT: 13 teaspoons per day

SUGAR: 12 1/2 teaspoons per day

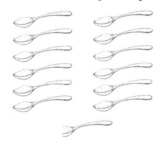

What to Do

Measure as accurately as you can.

1. Measure out 17 teaspoons of sugar in a cup. This represents the amount of sugar in 20 ounces of soda.

2. Measure out 28 teaspoons of sugar into the second cup. This represents the amount of sugar in 32 ounces of soda.

3. Display the side of the card with the amount of sugar by the two cups.

Amount of Sugar in Two Different-Sized Sodas

20 OUNCES OF SODA: 17 teaspoons of sugar

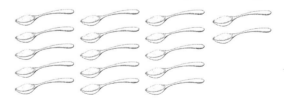

32 OUNCES OF SODA: 28 teaspoons of sugar

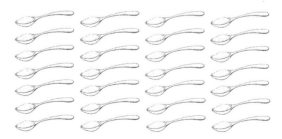

What to Do

1. Place 2 1/2 teaspoon-sized balls of fat on a plate to represent the amount of fat in a small hamburger.

2. Place 6 teaspoon-sized balls of fat on the second plate to represent the amount of fat in a large double cheeseburger.

3. Display the side of the card with the amount of fat by the plates.

Fat in Burgers

SMALL HAMBURGER: 2 1/2 teaspoons of fat

LARGE DOUBLE CHEESEBURGER:
6 teaspoons of fat

What to Do

1. Place 2 teaspoon-sized balls of fat on a plate to represent the amount of fat in a small order of fries.

2. Place 6 teaspoon-sized balls of fat on the second plate to represent the amount of fat in a large order of fries.

3. Display the side of the card with the amount of fat by the plates.

Fat in French Fries

SMALL FRIES: 2 teaspoons of fat

LARGE FRIES: 6 teaspoons of fat

What to Do

1. Place 1 1/2 teaspoon-sized balls of fat on a plate to represent the amount of fat in a grilled chicken-breast sandwich.

2. Place 6 teaspoon-sized balls of fat on another plate to represent the amount of fat in a fried chicken-breast sandwich.

3. Display the side of the card with the amount of fat by the plates.

Fat in Chicken Sandwiches

GRILLED CHICKEN-BREAST SANDWICH:
1 1/2 teaspoons of fat

FRIED CHICKEN-BREAST SANDWICH:
6 teaspoons of fat

What to Do

1. Place 1 teaspoon-sized ball of fat on a plate to represent the fat in a turkey sandwich.

2. Place 3 teaspoon-sized balls of fat on another plate to represent the fat in a slice of pizza.

3. Display the side of the card with the amount of fat by the plates.

Fat in a Turkey Sandwich and in a Slice of Pizza

TURKEY SANDWICH WITH MUSTARD, LETTUCE, AND TOMATO (NO CHEESE OR MAYONNAISE): 1 teaspoon of fat

SLICE OF PIZZA: 3 teaspoons of fat

What to Do

Measure as accurately as you can.

1. Measure out 9 teaspoons of sugar in a cup. This represents the amount of sugar in 20 ounces of a fruit-flavored sports drink.

2. Measure out 19 teaspoons of sugar into the second cup. This represents the amount of sugar in 32 ounces of a fruit-flavored sports drink.

3. Display the side of the card with the amount of sugar by the two cups.

Amount of Sugar in Two Different-Sized Fruit-Flavored Sports Drinks

20 OUNCES OF A FRUIT-FLAVORED SPORTS DRINK: 9 teaspoons of sugar

32 OUNCES OF A FRUIT-FLAVORED SPORTS DRINK: 19 teaspoons of sugar

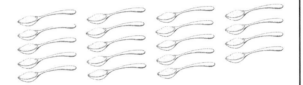

Exploring Food and Activity Environments

AIM

To investigate environmental factors that influence food choices and physical-activity choices.

SCIENTIFIC PROCESSES

• **question, observe, search, analyze**

OBJECTIVES

Students will be able to:

• **identify factors in their food environment that affect food choice;**

• **identify factors in their physical-activity environment that affect activity choices;**

• **develop a method for collecting data about the food or physical-activity environment;**

• **synthesize how biological, social, and environmental factors influence food and physical-activity choices.**

OVERVIEW

This is the last lesson of Unit 1. In this lesson, students think about the ways in which their local environment affects how they make food choices and physical-activity choices. The lesson begins with a review of the Module and Unit questions and the reading homework assignment. Students work in groups to research and investigate different aspects of the food and physical-activity environments around them. They gather data, organize it, and look for patterns and relationships. Then, each group shares its findings with the class. Through a whole-class discussion, students reflect on the influence of the food and physical-activity environments on their personal eating habits and physical-activity choices. To reflect on what they have learned throughout this unit, students write an answer to the Unit 1 Question in their LiFE Logs.

MATERIALS

For the teacher:
• Homework questions for Lessons 5 and 6 (p. 247)
• *Environmental Factors* teacher note
• *Sample Projects* lesson resource

For the class:
• Magazines
• Local map of your school's neighborhood

For each student:
• **Modeling Energy Balance** student reading (p. 200)
• Notes from Lesson 4 homework
• LiFE Log
• (Optional) *Homework Notes* activity sheet (p. 275)

PROCEDURE

Before You Begin:

- Remind students to bring in their notes from their **Food and Activity Environments** homework assignment. Have the homework questions available for discussion.

- Review the **Modeling Energy Balance** student reading and homework questions. Make a copy of the reading for each student. If you plan to distribute copies of the *Homework Notes* activity sheet, make enough to distribute one copy to each student. Alternatively, students can take notes in their LiFE Logs.

- Read the *Environmental Factors* teacher note.

- Review the *Sample Projects* lesson resource. Gather any additional materials you may need, such as maps of fast-food chains and grocery stores in your school's neighborhood, menus from your local area, magazines, and advertisements.

- If you have not done so already, post the Module Question and Unit 1 Question at the front of the classroom.

MODULE QUESTION

How can we use scientific evidence to help us maintain energy balance?

UNIT QUESTION

What influences our food and activity choices?

1. Review Module and Unit Questions

Read the Module Question out loud. Remind students that this question frames everything that they will do throughout this module. To become familiar with the biological, environmental, and personal behaviors that influence food and activity choices, students investigated the Unit 1 Question. Explain to the class that this is the final lesson in the unit, and it is an opportunity to reflect on and synthesize what they have learned about the Unit 1 Question.

2. Discuss Homework

Have students take out their notes from their **Food and Activity Environments** homework assignment. Use the homework questions to guide the discussion. Check for student understanding of environmental factors that influence food and activity choices.

3. Investigate Environment

Divide the class into small groups. Tell students that each group will do an activity related to their food or physical-activity environment. Engage students in a discussion of their food environment and physical-activity environment. *What do you think the term* environment *means when we talk about food and physical activity?* (It means surroundings. It means where we get food or do physical activities.) Remind students what they read in the **Food and Activity Environments** reading. Tell students that they are going to investigate different aspects of the physical environment that influence food and activity choices. For example, some groups may study what kinds of food are available in the school neighborhood. Others may investigate what kinds of physical activities are available. Another group may investigate the information environment — for example, how foods are marketed to young people. If you have time, we encourage you to invite students to design their own investigation. If not, use the *Sample*

Projects lesson resource and modify it as needed to fit your local environment and your students' interests. You may wish to have students complete their projects as homework and report to the class the next day.

 THEORIZING

4. Present Research

When all the groups have finished their investigations, tell them that they are going to share what they have learned with their classmates. Have each group select a reporter to present the information to the class. Encourage students to focus on what their group thought was the most important information to share. Remind students to include a discussion of their methods in their presentation. After all the groups have briefly shared their findings, have a whole-class discussion of the overall impact of their food and physical-activity environments on their food and exercise choices.

5. Review Homework Questions

Give each student a copy of the **Modeling Energy Balance** student reading. Post the homework questions for the reading on the board. Have students copy them onto the *Homework Notes* activity sheet or into their LiFE Logs.

6. LiFE Logs

Have students write an answer to the Unit 1 Question in their own words. Encourage them to write at least two paragraphs. Ask them to include definitions of "food environment" and "physical-activity environment" as part of their answer. Invite students to share what they have learned with their classmates.

Environmental Factors

We all make food decisions throughout the day: when to eat, what to eat, whom to eat with, and how much to eat. We also make similar decisions about what activities we do. In this unit, students have been learning about biologically determined behavioral predispositions such as liking specific tastes. Now they are going to learn how the environment interacts with human biological preferences. Environmental factors are powerful influences on human food and activity choices. But what do we mean by *environmental factors*?

In this lesson, we focus on factors in the physical environment — specifically, *availability*, *accessibility*, and *information* — as strong determinants of our food and activity choices. Our focus is on the physical environment that makes up a student's "world," where she is in control and making her own choices.

By *availability* we mean the array of food and activity options around us. What is available in our community influences what we eat and what we do. By *accessibility* we mean the readiness and convenience of the options. This means food that requires little or no cooking, is packaged in a convenient way so it can be eaten anywhere, and can be stored for some time without spoilage. And it means activity that is safe, seemingly pleasant, and easy to get to. By *information*, we mean the media-saturated environment that surrounds us 24/7.

In developed countries like the United States, the food system makes food and processed-food products available in an ever-widening array of choices. More than 50,000 food items are available in U.S. supermarkets, and about 9,000 new brand-name processed-food products are introduced each year. In addition, many highly processed foods and sweetened beverages are available all around us — from vending machines to mini-markets at gas stations to corner stores — specifically the types of places where middle-school students can be in control and make choices for themselves.

Even though food is abundantly available, accessibility (particularly to more healthful foods) varies. Many people need transportation to reach a supermarket or a farmers' market where fresh, whole foods such as fruits and vegetables are typically available. This limits the accessibility of healthful food for people who do not drive or do not have cars, including middle-school students.

The information that surrounds food is complex as well. Billions of dollars are spent on food advertising every year and much of this is for less-healthful foods. Often the way the media present food and nutrition information is sensationalized and confusing. It takes critical thinking skills to competently navigate the information environment.

Taken together, the food environment pushes middle-school students toward processed-food products, sweetened beverages, and fast foods and pulls them away from water, vegetables, fruit, and other whole foods.

The physical-activity environment is complex as well. The availability and accessibility of cars, buses, appliances, computers, and so forth make it easy for human beings to go through the day with little physical activity. The availability and accessibility of places that promote physical activities such as parks; streets; walking, hiking, and biking paths; and indoor recreation spaces varies from location to location.

The media also influence our physical activity. For middle-school students, time spent on media usage, which is mostly sedentary, is high: eight hours per day if you consider that adolescents often use several media simultaneously. The effect is compounded if the message that viewers get promotes less-healthful choices in both food and activity.

Our goal for students is to have them become more aware of the physical environment around them and how this environment influences their choices. We hope this knowledge will encourage a desire to navigate the environment and make more healthful choices.

Sample Projects

1. DOES OUR SCHOOL ENVIRONMENT PROMOTE PHYSICAL ACTIVITY?

Students survey their classmates to learn about the physical-activity environment at or near their school. Students collect and organize data and create a graphic representation of it. Encourage them to think about the Unit Question and, specifically, *What influences our physical-activity choices?* If you have a map of your school grounds and the local neighborhood, have students locate all the places where they can play sports, ride their bikes, skate, skateboard, climb up and down stairs, and so forth. Here is a sample that students can use or modify.

Date:_____   Interviewer Name: _____

Interviewee Name (or Assign Interviewee a Number): _____

Questionnaire

Please circle the answer that best applies to you and your school.

1. How often does your school have supervised physical activities before school?

    Never   Rarely   Sometimes   Frequently   Always   Don't know

2. How often does your school have supervised physical activities after school?

    Never   Rarely   Sometimes   Frequently   Always   Don't know

3. How often does your school allow students to use play areas or fields after school?

    Never   Rarely   Sometimes   Frequently   Always   Don't know

4. How often does your school allow students to use play areas or fields before school?

    Never   Rarely   Sometimes   Frequently   Always   Don't know

5. How often does your school allow students to use play areas or fields after lunch?

    Never   Rarely   Sometimes   Frequently   Always   Don't know

Do you have any of these at your school? Circle all that apply.

6. Basketball hoop		Yes	No	Don't know
7. Bike rack		Yes	No	Don't know
8. Things to climb up		Yes	No	Don't know
9. Running/walking track		Yes	No	Don't know
10. Tennis court		Yes	No	Don't know
11. Volleyball net		Yes	No	Don't know
12. Playing field (football, baseball, soccer, field hockey, etc.)		Yes	No	Don't know

2. HOW DO YOU GET TO SCHOOL?

Students survey their classmates to learn about how they get to school. Students collect and organize data and analyze any barriers students list that influence whether or not they bike or walk to school. Encourage students to think about the Unit Question and, specifically, *What influences our physical-activity choices?* Tell students to assign each student they interview an identifying number. Emphasize that they are doing this to keep the focus of the investigation on how they get to school. Challenge them to look for patterns and relationships in the responses. Here is a sample that students can use or modify:

Date:_____   Interviewer Name: _____

Interviewee Number: _____

1. How far away do you live from your school?_____

In an average school week, how many days do you use the following kinds of transportation to get to and from school? [Example: If you always ride a bus to and from school, you would circle 5 next to "go by car or bus" in both columns.]

2. Days Per Week **to** School

   a. walk   0 1 2 3 4 5
   b. bicycle   0 1 2 3 4 5
   c. go by car or bus   0 1 2 3 4 5
   d. other_____ 0 1 2 3 4 5

3. Days Per Week **from** School

   a. walk   0 1 2 3 4 5
   b. bicycle   0 1 2 3 4 5
   c. go by car or bus   0 1 2 3 4 5
   d. other_____ 0 1 2 3 4 5

Please tell us how much you agree or disagree with each statement. Put a check in the appropriate box.

	Strongly disagree	Somewhat disagree	Somewhat agree	Strongly agree
4. Other kids my age walk or bike to school by themselves.				
5. Other kids my age walk to school with a parent or other adult.				
6. I enjoy (or would enjoy) walking or biking to school.				
7. I enjoy (or would enjoy) walking or biking to school with my friends.				
8. I enjoy (or would enjoy) walking or biking to school with a parent or other adult.				

Please check the answer that best applies to you.

9. Is your school within a 30-minute walk or bike ride from your home?   ❏ Yes   ❏ No

10. Do you walk or bike to school (alone or with someone)
at least once a week?   ❏ Yes   ❏ No

Please tell us how much you agree or disagree with the following statements:

It is difficult to walk or bike to school (alone or with someone) because…

	Strongly disagree	Somewhat disagree	Somewhat agree	Strongly agree
11. There are too many hills along the way.				
12. There are no sidewalks or bike lanes.				
13. The route does not have good lighting.				
14. There is too much traffic along the route.				
15. There is at least one dangerous crossing.				
16. Others do not walk or bike to school.				
17. It's not considered cool to walk or bike to school.				
18. I have too much stuff to carry.				
19. It is easier for someone to drive me here on the way to something else.				
20. It involves too much planning ahead.				
21. There is nowhere to leave a bike safely.				
22. It is too far.				

3. MAPPING THE FOOD ENVIRONMENT

In this example, students investigate the snack-food environment between their homes and their school. If possible, provide students with a street map of the neighborhood where your school is located. They can use this map to find their school, the sites of the stores and restaurants where they buy their snacks, and the routes to get to these sites. They will be looking for patterns of spatial organization — where snack food is available to students at your school — and relationships between the availability of snack food and their snack-food choices.

Have students begin by developing a questionnaire to learn about their classmates' snack-food choices. Tell students to assign each student they interview an identifying number. Emphasize that they are doing this to keep the focus of the investigation on what the snack-food choices are, not who is eating them. Here is a sample that students can use or modify:

Date:_____   Interviewer Name: _____

Interviewee Number: _____

Snack-Food Choices

1. Do you buy snack food between the time you leave your home in the morning to go to school and the time you get home after school? ☐ Yes ☐ No

2. If yes, list all the places where you buy snacks. For example, food store, cafeteria, vending machine, fast-food chain, sit-down restaurant, school store, and so forth.

_____

_____

_____

_____

3. What kinds of snack foods are sold in the places where you buy snacks? (Circle as many as apply)

Soda or sugary drinks	Candy	"Energy" bars	Fresh vegetables
Fruit juices	Vitamin water	Hamburgers or cheeseburgers	Pizza
Water	Packaged cookies	French fries	Ice cream
Sports drinks	Chips	Fresh fruit	Bagels
Other (please describe)			

_____

_____

4. What kinds of snack foods do you usually choose?

Soda or sugary drinks	Candy	"Energy" bars	Fresh vegetables
Fruit juices	Vitamin water	Hamburgers or cheeseburgers	Pizza
Water	Packaged cookies	French fries	Ice cream
Sports drinks	Chips	Fresh fruit	Bagels

Other (please describe) _____

_____

_____

5. Look at the data you have collected. What kinds of snack foods are available? What kinds of snack foods do you choose? Do you see any patterns between what is available and what is selected?

_____

_____

_____

_____

_____

_____

_____

_____

_____

_____

4. INVESTIGATING MARKETING TO YOUNG PEOPLE

With this project, students explore advertising for food or beverages. Challenge students to stop and think about the number of times that they see advertisements each day. Ask them to think about how often they see colorful images of food or someone eating or drinking something. Next, tell them to think of the number of times that they hear about food. Point out that if they watch TV, read magazines, listen to commercial radio, go to Web sites, or simply walk down a street lined with stores, they are surrounded by media trying to sell something, and often that something is food. Competing sellers are all trying to convince the consumer to buy a specific product. People who work in advertising and marketing use different strategies to try to persuade consumers to buy their products. Challenge students to think about how they do it.

Have students pick an ad from a magazine or from TV. Ask them to think about what it is that attracts them to this ad. Take a look at the list of strategies and techniques below. Were any of them used in this ad? As you do your advertising-and-marketing research, think about the strategies that were used to try to sell the product. Use the questions below to guide your analysis.

Strategies to Persuade

Celebrities: The ad suggests that you can be like these celebrities or sports stars if you eat this product. Celebrities eat this product so it must be the best!

Family: The ad implies that if your family eats this food, you are guaranteed to have a good time.

Fun: The images show people doing fun things. Everyone is happy.

Adventure: That ad implies that if you eat this food, you will be transported to a world of adventure, such as surfing a wave or dancing onstage at a concert with your favorite band.

Repetition: The strategy is to repeat the name of a product so many times that eventually you'll buy it.

Good Feelings: The ad tells a "feel-good" story like a dad cheering up his daughter by taking her out to lunch at her favorite fast-food chain or buying her her favorite food.

Cartoons: The strategy is to use familiar cartoon characters to help you remember a product.

Misleading Words: The ad uses words or phrases that are misleading. For example, it may say "with the taste of real fruit" when the product doesn't actually have any fruit in it.

Friends: The ad shows groups of people enjoying each other and doing things together.

Questions

1. *What food is being advertised?*

2. *Who has sponsored or produced this ad and why?*

3. *Are colors used in the ad? Which ones?*

4. *Does the ad use famous people, like celebrities or sports stars, or cartoon figures? Describe what they are doing. What expressions do they have on their faces?*

5. *Who do you think would be attracted to this ad? Explain your answer.*

UNIT 2

Dynamic Equilibrium

Exploring Dynamic Equilibrium

AIM

To explore the relationship between energy intake and energy expenditure.

SCIENTIFIC PROCESSES

- **experiment, question, theorize, apply**

OBJECTIVES

Students will be able to:

- **explain the relationship between food, energy consumption, and energy expenditure;**

- **discuss why system scientists create models and simulations;**

- **describe what it means to maintain energy balance, or dynamic equilibrium, in their bodies;**

- **define positive and negative energy balance.**

OVERVIEW

This is the first lesson of Unit 2, in which students begin in earnest their exploration of energy balance. In this lesson, students explore the relationship between energy intake (food and drink consumption) and energy expenditure (physical activity). The lesson begins with a review of the Lesson 5 homework reading, which you can use as an opportunity to check student understanding of energy balance. Use the homework questions to guide the discussion. This review is followed by a class demonstration that models the relationship between energy intake and energy output, furthering student understanding of energy balance. This simulation visually demonstrates a state of energy balance between energy coming in and energy going out of the body. Students learn why this balanced state is called *dynamic equilibrium*. The lesson closes with students comparing the caloric value of foods to the physical activity required to burn off those calories.

MATERIALS

For the teacher:
- Homework questions for Lessons 6 and 7 (pp. 247–248)
- *Energy Balance: Bringing Together Science and Nutrition* teacher note
- *Energy In and Energy Out* lesson resource
- *Finding the Balance* experiment sheet

For the class:
- Clock with second hand
- 2 clear plastic cups
- Marker
- Scissors
- 1 large nail (to punch a hole in the bottom of one cup)
- 3–4 cups of water
- Plastic dishpan or basin
- (Optional) food coloring
- (Optional) spoon to stir food coloring in water

For each student:
- **The Digestive System** student reading (p. 203)
- Notes from Lesson 5 homework
- (Optional) 2 copies of the **Homework Notes** activity sheet (p. 275)
- LiFE Log

PROCEDURE

Before You Begin:

- Remind students to bring in their notes from their **Modeling Energy Balance** homework assignment. Have the homework questions available for discussion.

- Read the *Energy Balance: Bringing Together Science and Nutrition* teacher note.

- Review the *Finding the Balance* experiment sheet. Gather the materials and set up the demonstration as described on the experiment sheet.

- Review the *Energy In and Energy Out* lesson resource. Copy and cut out the energy cards.

- Review the two-part **The Digestive System** student reading and homework questions. Make a copy of the reading for each student. If you plan to distribute copies of the *Homework Notes* activity sheet, make enough to distribute two copies to each student. Alternatively, students can take notes in their LiFE Logs.

- If you have not already done so, post the Module Question and Unit 2 Question at the front of the classroom.

MODULE QUESTION

How can we use scientific evidence to help us maintain energy balance?

UNIT QUESTION

How can we make sure that we get the right amount of energy to help our bodies do what we want them to do?

 THEORIZING

1. Review Module and Unit Questions

Invite a student to read the Module and Unit 2 questions out loud. Explain that in this unit, the class is going to learn about the relationship between "energy in" (food and drink) and "energy out" (physical activity).

2. Discuss Homework

Have students take out their notes from their **Modeling Energy Balance** homework assignment. Engage students in a discussion of the reading. Use the homework questions to guide the discussion. Check for student understanding of energy balance.

 EXPERIMENTING

3. Investigate Energy Balance

Use the *Finding the Balance* experiment sheet to conduct the demonstration. Introduce the demonstration by explaining that human bodies work best when they are in what is called *a balanced state*. Tell students that this demonstration will provide them with a visual representation of energy being taken in through eating and drinking and energy being released through physical activity and body functions. Point out the cup that is marked "Human Body." *Why do we use a cup to represent the human body?* Prompt students with a reference to Calvin and Carol and what they learned from Christian. Tell students that the water represents energy. Conduct the demonstration.

 THEORIZING

4. Discuss Energy Balance

Explain to students that sometimes scientists call this balanced state *dynamic equilibrium*. Write the term on the board. *What does equilibrium mean?* Accept all answers. Explain that when something is in equilibrium, it is in a state of balance. Point out that in the simulation the class just observed with the water and the plastic cups, they saw that in order to keep the level of the water constant, it was necessary to find a balance between energy in and energy out. Explain that this is an example of dynamic balance. Tell students that just like the water in the cup, human bodies are very dynamic, but they work best when the energy in and the energy out are balanced, keeping the body in equilibrium. Invite a few students to explain dynamic equilibrium in their own words. Ask students to share thoughts on how they might be able to use what they have learned about dynamic equilibrium in their own lives.

 APPLYING TO LIFE

5. Find Your Balance

Remind students that depending on many factors, our bodies need a certain number of daily calories in order to maintain an energy balance. Emphasize that there are many factors that make one person's body different from another's. Point out that living things need energy to grow, which means that as children grow, they need more energy. Explain that when people exercise on a regular basis, they need more energy. However, participating in activities such as watching television or using the computer requires less energy. Emphasize that it is important to examine what level of energy in and energy out keeps your body in balance, so you can control the amount of energy you need to take in to balance the amount of energy you use. Stress that there is no one body size that indicates whether a person is healthy or in a balanced state. Healthy bodies come in many shapes and sizes.

6. Investigate Calories

In this activity, students compare the caloric value of foods to the physical activity required to burn off those calories. Use the *Energy In and Energy Out* lesson resource to conduct this activity. Stress that people do not need to "burn off" all the food they take into their bodies through exercise because in addition to burning calories through exercise, we burn calories all the time in order to keep our bodies functioning. The point of this activity is for students to contrast the different amounts of energy in different foods through comparing the walking distances that equal the amount of energy in the food.

 THEORIZING

7. Review Homework Questions

Give each student a copy of the **Digestive System** student reading. Post the homework questions for the reading on the board. Point out that there are two parts to the reading and two sets of questions. Have students copy them onto the *Homework Notes* activity sheets or into their LiFE Logs.

8. LiFE Logs

Ask students to take out their LiFE Logs and think about their own energy in and energy out. Have students write a few paragraphs briefly describing their energy in, or diet, and their energy out, or activity. Then have them explain whether they think they are in balance, and if not, what they think they may have to adjust to find their dynamic equilibrium.

Energy Balance: Bringing Together Science and Nutrition

Energy balance is key to maintaining our health, yet students spend little time directly learning about this topic. Energy balance means that the energy you take in in the form of food is equal to the energy, or calories, you expend through both physical activity and body functioning. If you take in more food energy than your body needs, you will gain weight. This is a positive energy balance. If you expend more energy or calories than you take in, you will lose weight. This is negative energy balance.

While students may learn about the importance of a "balanced diet" in nutrition education, it is typically taught through the lens of eating all the "food groups," without focusing on understanding energy balance. Additionally, although equilibrium is an important scientific concept, it is seldom taught in the context of the human body. An important take-away message for students learning about energy balance in humans is that it is a long-term process. On any given day it is perfectly fine to be in positive or negative balance, as long as balance is achieved over the long term. Obesity is one of the consequences of long-term energy imbalance.

Obesity is a chronic metabolic condition that results when someone is in positive energy balance over a long period of time. Gaining extra body fat comes about from a complex interaction among genes, environment, and personal behavior. The percentage of overweight children and adults in the United States has dramatically increased over the past few decades. In this module, students learn why obesity rates are rising. One reason is that the human species has evolved from a time when food was scarce, and our hominid ancestors needed survival mechanisms that would allow them to store extra energy taken in during times when food was plentiful. Today, however, in the United States, there are ample sources of relatively inexpensive energy-dense foods. These foods tend to be ones that are high in fat and added sugars and low in fiber. Some examples are cheeseburgers, soda, potato chips, and candy. The combination of today's food and activity environment with our genetics has caused a societal weight change. We emphasize the role the environment plays in food and activity choices as well as societal shifts in weight in order to reduce guilt; that is, we take a system-blaming approach instead of a victim-blaming approach.

In this module, students also learn some of the health consequences related to obesity. Through inquiry-based activities, students learn that obesity increases the risk of developing many conditions, including heart disease and stroke, high blood pressure, and high blood sugar. Fortunately, maintaining energy balance can reduce the risk of many of these negative consequences. This is where personal behavior comes in. Adopting more healthful food and activity behaviors can help students achieve energy balance. Indeed, adopting such habits is important for anyone at any weight. The *Choice, Control & Change* food and activity goals were developed to help adolescents achieve energy balance as they make choices in today's complex food and activity environment.

Adolescents and Energy Balance

During adolescence, is a time when children enter a stressful, confusing, and sometimes frightening time of social, emotional, and physical development. They may experience problems in their family environment. Some teenagers may develop eating disorders as a result of complex psychological, environmental, and genetic factors. Many adolescents do not understand the changes that are occurring during this time, including the weight gain associated with growth and sexual development. There is peer pressure to fit in and gain acceptance. Teenagers may worry excessively about what others think of them, especially their physical appearance. The media and popular culture don't help, with their emphasis on thinness in girls, promoting pencil-thin models and celebrities as the "ideal" body image. In this curriculum, an important objective is for adolescents to be motivated to adopt healthful food and activity habits and to recognize that healthy bodies come in a variety of shapes and sizes.

Motivation to Act

What's wrong with the way I eat? Why do I have to change? I'm not fat, so why do I need to change what I eat and do? Your students may have already asked questions like these, or they may be thinking similar thoughts. How do you go about making them think seriously about why to take action now about eating more fruits and vegetables, getting more physical activity, and eating less fast food and fewer processed snacks and sweetened beverages if they see no reason to change? They can probably tell you the "pluses" of their current habits: the foods they eat taste good, are easy to find, are what all their friends are eating, and are inexpensive. In terms of physical activity, hanging out with friends playing video games may be considered fun and a cool thing to do.

So how can you motivate your students to take action? The first crucial step is for your students to become aware of a need to change and to see what's in it for them. In our research, we have found that learning about societal weight increases, why these are occurring, the challenge that our current food environment presents, and the consequences of not being in energy balance increase students' perception of risk and their willingness to make a change. They are then ready to learn the health reasons and personal benefits of maintaining energy balance.

Skills to Act

Once students become motivated to want to change, this brings up a whole host of new questions. How do I change my habits? Will it be hard? Will I be able to do it? What will my friends and family think? How will I keep at it? Will I have to eat foods that I don't like — such as vegetables? Research has shown that these are important questions because many people want to make healthier choices, but some barrier gets in the way. Class discussions will help students work with each other to overcome the barriers they face as they make changes. The combination of learning the science for why to change along with skills in how to change can help students develop the competence they need to maintain healthy habits throughout middle school and beyond.

Energy In and Energy Out

In this activity, students compare the amount of stored energy in different kinds of foods.

Distribute Cards

Ask for eight volunteers. Give each student one of the food cards.

Action

1. Have each student volunteer read the name of the food item on his or her card.

2. Taking one type of food at a time, ask students how many steps they think each volunteer will have to take to balance the number of calories for the food. Allow students time to make predictions. Record the predictions on the board or on chart paper.

3. After students have made their predictions, explain that for every 2,000 steps an adult takes, he will burn approximately 100 calories. Walking 2,000 steps equals about one mile. Point out that people who weigh less will burn fewer calories and people who weigh more will burn more calories. Tell students that the precise number of calories burned and steps taken in a mile varies from person to person.

4. Using the formula that it takes 2,000 steps to burn 100 calories, have students calculate the number of miles for each food.

5. Hold up an energy card. Tell students that each energy card represents walking 1/4 mile. Count out the number of energy cards for each food, based on students' calculations. As you count out the energy cards, dramatically emphasize the energy differences among the different foods.

6. Remind students that some calories are burned just to keep the human body functioning. We do not need to "walk off" all the calories we consume.

Continued

Use the **Energy In/Energy Out** chart below to help with this activity. Note that calories vary in foods. This table also provides the approximate amount of fat and sugar in the foods. This information is included since these are the calories that are of concern in the development of risk factors that can lead to Type 2 diabetes, heart disease, and other diet-related diseases.

ENERGY IN/ENERGY OUT						
Food	Calories	Miles	Energy Cards[a]	Steps	Fat Grams (calories rounded)	Sugar Grams (calories rounded)
Cheeseburger (1/4 lb.)	500	5	20	10,000	25 (175 Cal)	9 (35 Cal)
Large French fries	525	5.25	21	10,500	30 (270 Cal)	0
Baby carrots (1 cup)	75	.75	3	1,500	0	10[b] (40 Cal)
Low-fat yogurt (1 cup)	150	1.5	6	3,000	1.5 (15 Cal)	28[c] (110 Cal)
Pepperoni pizza slice	475	4.75	19	9,500	20 (180 Cal)	4 (15 Cal)
Turkey sandwich with mustard	250	2.5	10	5,000	4 (35 Cal)	6 (25 Cal)
Cupcakes (pack of 2)	400	4	16	8,000	14 (125 Cal)	38 (150 Cal)
Apple	75	.75	3	1,500	0	16[b] (65 Cal)

[a]each energy card represents walking 1/4 mile

[b]the sugar in carrots and apples is natural sugar

[c]yogurt has a combination of natural sugar and added sugar

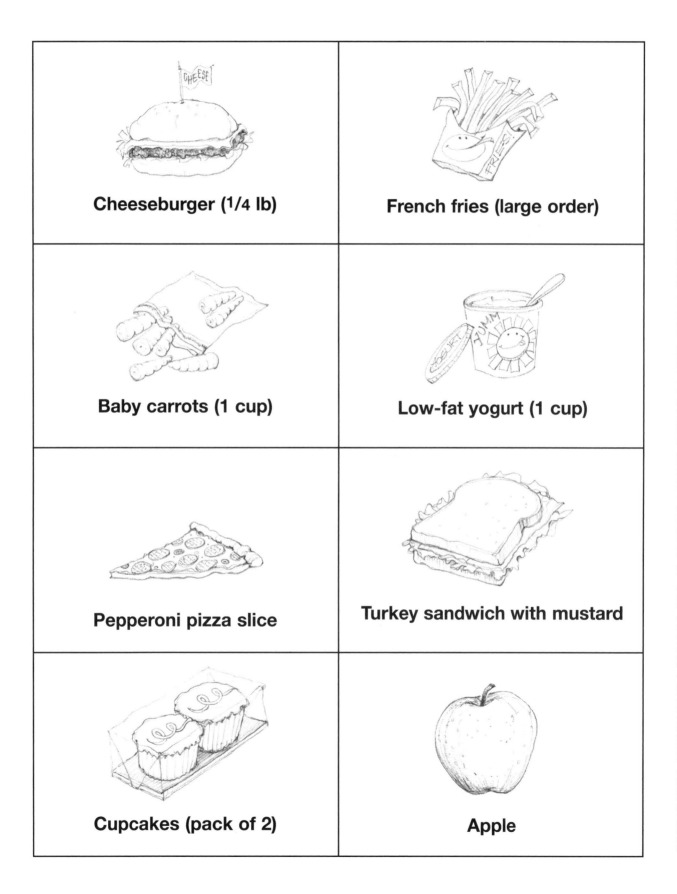

Cheeseburger (1/4 lb)

French fries (large order)

Baby carrots (1 cup)

Low-fat yogurt (1 cup)

Pepperoni pizza slice

Turkey sandwich with mustard

Cupcakes (pack of 2)

Apple

Energy	**Energy**	**Energy**	**Energy**
Energy	**Energy**	**Energy**	**Energy**
Energy	**Energy**	**Energy**	**Energy**
Energy	**Energy**	**Energy**	**Energy**
Energy	**Energy**	**Energy**	**Energy**
Energy	**Energy**	**Energy**	**Energy**

Finding the Balance

Students observe a simulation of the relationship between energy intake and energy output in this model of the human body. Depending upon the size of your class and the amount of time you have, either do this as a demonstration at the front of the room or have students work in small groups to carry out the simulation.

Setup

1. Gather the materials.

2. With a dark permanent marker, draw a line about an inch from the rim of one cup. This line marks the energy-balance level. Write "Human Body" on the side of this cup. Use the nail to punch a small hole in the center of the bottom of the cup. Use the marker to label the bottom "Energy Out." Label the other plastic cup "Energy In."

3. Put 3–4 cups of water in a plastic dishpan or basin.

4. If you opt to dye the water, add the food coloring. This makes it easier to see the water in the cup.

Procedure

1. Ask for three student volunteers. Assign one student the job of "energy in," assign another the job of "energy out"; the third student is the timer.

2. Tell the class that in this simulation of energy balance, the water represents energy and the plastic cup with the hole in it represents the human body.

3. Have the "energy out" student place a finger over the hole at the bottom of the plastic cup so no water/energy can escape. Have the "energy in" student fill this cup to the top with water.

4. Have the "energy out" student hold the water/energy-filled plastic cup over the dishpan or basin containing water, then take his finger away from the hole so that water/energy flows out of the cup. At the same time, have the "energy in" student pour water into the cup so that the level of the water stays between the energy-balance line and the top of the cup. The goal is to keep the water at the energy-balance line and not to let it get below the line or to overflow. Tell students to keep the energy balanced for 20 seconds. Have the timer watch the clock.

5. Repeat the simulation. This time, once the "Human Body" cup is full, have "energy in" pour water/energy in as slowly as she can, so that the water flows out of the hole at a faster rate than she is pouring it into the cup. The water will drop below the energy-balance mark on the cup.

6. Repeat the simulation again. Have "energy in" pour the water/energy in as fast as she can, so that the water flows into the cup faster than it flows out of the hole. The cup will overflow.

Questions

1. *What did we have to do to make sure the water/energy stayed in energy balance for 20 seconds?*

2. *What action can we take to make the "energy in" less than the "energy out"? What evidence do you have?*

3. *What action can we take to make the "energy in" greater than the "energy out"? What evidence do you have?*

4. *Based on the evidence from the simulation, if we want to maintain energy balance, what should we do?*

Digesting Food

AIM

To gain an understanding about how food is digested and distributed throughout the body.

SCIENTIFIC PROCESSES

- **construct knowledge, investigate, think through, apply**

OBJECTIVES

Students will be able to:

- **explain how food gets digested;**

- **discuss the role of the digestive system in obtaining nutrients and removing waste;**

- **describe how the circulatory system distributes nutrients throughout the body.**

OVERVIEW

In this lesson, students continue to explore energy balance. The lesson begins with a review of the Lesson 6 homework reading, which you can use as an opportunity to check student understanding of the digestive system. Use the homework questions to guide the discussion. Following the review, students participate in a whole-class simulation of the journey of food through the digestive tract. By actively moving "food" from the mouth through all parts of the digestive tract, into the blood, and finally to cells in the body, students have a visual demonstration of what happens to food when we eat it. Through participation in the simulation, students gain an understanding of the function of the digestive system and its parts as well as the role of the circulatory system. As a post-activity assessment, students write a story that describes the journey of an apple from Carol's mouth to a muscle cell in her leg.

MATERIALS

For the teacher:
- Homework questions for Lessons 7 and 8 (p. 248)
- *Human-Body Simulation* lesson resource

For the class:
- 3 spray bottles
- Water (to fill bottles)
- Newspaper
- Construction paper (enough sheets to make 1 label for each student)
- Markers
- Classroom wastebasket
- Tape
- (Optional) Yarn or string

For each student:
- **Energy in Food** student reading (p. 208)
- Notes from Lesson 6 homework
- *Digestive System Review* activity sheet
- (Optional) 2 copies of the *Homework Notes* activity sheet (p. 275)
- LiFE Log

PROCEDURE

Before You Begin:

- Remind students to bring in their notes from their **The Digestive System** homework assignment. Have the homework questions available for discussion.

- Review the **Energy in Food** student reading and homework questions. Make a copy of the reading for each student. If you plan to distribute copies of the *Homework Notes* activity sheet, make enough to distribute two copies to each student. Alternatively, students can take notes in their LiFE Logs.

- Make a copy of the *Digestive System Review* activity sheet for each student.

- Review the *Human-Body Simulation* lesson resource. Gather materials and make the labels.

- If you have not done so already, post the Module Question and Unit 2 Question at the front of the classroom.

MODULE QUESTION

How can we use scientific evidence to help us maintain energy balance?

UNIT QUESTION

How can we make sure that we get the right amount of energy to help our bodies do what we want them to do?

 THEORIZING

1. Review Module and Unit Questions

Remind students of the Module and Unit questions and tell them that in this lesson, to be able to understand how we can get the right amount of energy, we are going to learn about what happens inside Calvin's body when he eats food.

2. Discuss Homework

Have students take out their notes from their **The Digestive System** homework assignment. Engage students in a discussion of the reading. Use the homework questions to guide the discussion. Check for student understanding of the digestive system and energy balance. Close the discussion by telling students that they are going to conduct the simulation that they read about in their homework assignment.

 **EXPERIMENTING**

3. Conduct Simulation

Follow the procedure on the *Human-Body Simulation* lesson resource. Assign students different roles and give them the appropriate label to identify their role. Have students tape the labels to their chests. Explain that the classroom represents Calvin's body. His head is at one end and his feet are at the other. Have students distribute themselves throughout the "body." Use the *Human-Body Simulation* lesson resource to guide their placement. Modeling the digestive system will help students gain knowledge of how food moves through the body. It will also help students begin to develop an understanding of how nutrients in food are distributed throughout the body.

 THEORIZING

4. Discuss Digestion and Absorption

After the class has completed modeling the human digestive system and how it works, distribute a copy of the *Digestive System Review* activity sheet to each student. Tell the class to use this activity to review what they have learned about digestion. Give students a few minutes to add their notes to the diagram, then pose the following questions for discussion. *How does the digestive system work? How does food get into the circulatory system? What happens once nutrients get into the blood? Why does every cell in the body need nutrients and energy from food? Does it matter what we eat? What evidence do you have to support your point of view?* Encourage students to refer to the notes they made on the **Digestive System Review** activity sheet for this discussion. Tell them to correct their notes or modify them if they learn new information.

5. Review Homework Questions

Give each student a copy of the **Energy in Food** student reading. Post the homework questions for the **Energy in Food** student reading on the board. Have students copy them onto the **Homework Notes** student page or into their LiFE Logs. Remind them to bring their notes to the next class.

6. LiFE Logs

To assess student understanding of what happens during the digestion of food, have the class take out their LiFE Logs and write a story that describes the journey of an apple from Carol's mouth to a muscle cell in her leg. Have students include the organs of the digestive system as well as the blood vessels in their stories. Encourage students to include illustrations if they would like. Have students use their notes from the **Digestive System Review** activity sheet to help them with this assignment.

Human-Body Simulation

This simulation of the human digestive system helps students gain an understanding of how food moves through the digestive tract, as well as how the nutrients in food are distributed throughout the body.

Make Labels

1. Use nine sheets of construction paper to make labels: Mouth, Esophagus, Stomach, Small Intestine, Large Intestine, Rectum, Digestive Juices (Mouth), Digestive Juices (Stomach), Digestive Juices (Small Intestine).

2. Use five sheets of construction paper to make labels to represent blood. Label each sheet Blood.

3. Use the remaining sheets of construction paper to make labels for cells found in different parts of the body, such as Cell (Heart), Cell (Brain), Cell (Arm Muscle), Cell (Kidney), Cell (Big Toe), and so forth. Make certain every student has a role in the simulation and a label.

4. Label each of the spray bottles filled with water Digestive Juices.

Simulation of Human Digestive System

Part One

1. Assign each student to a different role in this simulation. Distribute the labels and have students tape the labels to their chests.

2. Explain that the classroom represents Calvin's body. His head is at one end, his feet are at the other end, and his hands and arms are at either side. You may wish to use string or yarn to outline the body.

3. Have the students playing the role of digestive-system organs line up in the following order: Mouth, Esophagus, Stomach, Small Intestine, Large Intestine, and Rectum. Tell the Digestive Juices to stand next to the appropriate organ.

4. Students playing the roles of Blood and Cells observe this part of the simulation.

5. Give the Mouth one sheet of newspaper and tell him to tear it into pieces and mold them into the shape of a ball.

6. Have the Digestive Juices (Mouth) lightly spray the paper with water until it is damp all over (about four squirts). Remind students that digestion begins in the mouth as the salivary glands spray the food with saliva and the teeth grind it up, making it a big, wet, mushy ball.

7. The Mouth passes the "food" to the Esophagus, who makes wavelike motions, mimicking the muscle action of the esophagus. The Esophagus passes the food on to the Stomach.

8. The Stomach tears up the newspaper into smaller pieces. The Digestive Juices (Stomach) sprays more water on the newspaper as it is being torn. Once the paper is a mushy, wet ball, the Stomach passes this food on to the Small Intestine.

9. The Small Intestine mashes and rips up the newspaper even more. The Digestive Juices (Small

Intestine) sprays the food until it is soggy. The Small Intestine continues to tear the newspaper into smaller pieces and passes about half of the mushy paper to the Large Intestine, holding on to the remaining half.

10. The Large Intestine holds the mushy paper over a wastebasket and squeezes as much water out as she can. After squeezing out the water, the Large Intestine passes what's left to the Rectum.

11. The Rectum throws the squeezed-out newspaper into the wastebasket.

Part Two

12. Tell the Cells to go to the appropriate parts of the body — Cell (Kidney) to the approximate area of the kidneys, Cell (Big Toe) to the approximate area of the big toe, and so forth. Make sure there are cells at points near and far from the digestive system.

13. Have the Blood stand around the Small Intestine. Tell the Small Intestine to take about two-thirds of the food and distribute small pieces to each student playing Blood. Have the Blood bring it to one of the Cells stationed around Calvin's body. Explain that this action mimics the digested nutrients' being absorbed through the small intestine and traveling via the blood through the blood vessels (part of the circulatory system) to cells throughout the body. In addition to carrying nutrients, blood carries the oxygen that humans inhale to all of the body's cells and takes away waste including carbon dioxide.

14. Have the Cells take the pieces of digested food from the Blood. Explain that this action represents the blood traveling through the blood vessels and delivering the nutrients from the digested food to the cells. The cells use these nutrients for energy, growth, and maintenance.

Name	Date

Digestive System Review

Study this diagram. Think about what you have learned about the digestive system from your reading and from the human-body simulation. Write notes on this page to help you remember how the digestive system works and what roles the organs play. Use these notes to help you with your LiFE Log writing assignment.

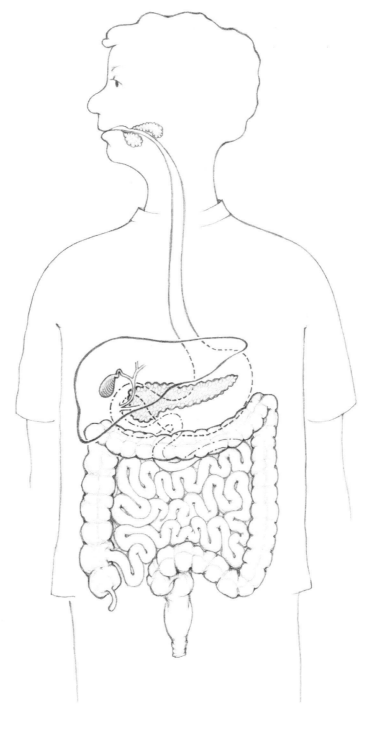

Burning Up

AIM

To further student understanding of how cells release the energy from food through metabolism.

SCIENTIFIC PROCESSES

• experiment, question, construct knowledge, theorize, apply

OBJECTIVES

Students will be able to:

• define the term *calorie*;

• investigate energy transfer;

• describe how cells convert the chemical energy from food into energy the body can use;

• explain metabolism.

OVERVIEW

In this lesson, students continue to investigate energy in food. The lesson begins with a review of the Lesson 7 homework reading, which you can use as an opportunity to check student understanding of energy. Use the homework questions to guide the discussion. Following the review, in a teacher-led demonstration, students burn a peanut to measure the energy content of food. Then, using a simplified calorimeter, they convert chemical energy in a peanut to heat energy and warm a beaker of water. They measure the amount of energy in the peanut by calculating how much the water is heated. Through these demonstrations and class discussion, students learn that when we eat food, our bodies convert the energy stored in food to energy that the body needs to grow and survive. Finally, students review what they have read about metabolism and cellular respiration.

Alert: Before you begin this lesson, make sure no students are allergic to peanuts. See the **Energy Burn** experiment sheet for other options.

MATERIALS

For the teacher:
• Homework questions for Lessons 8 and 9 (p. 248)
• *Calculating Calories in a Peanut* lesson resource
• *Energy Burn* experiment sheet
• *Calorimetry* experiment sheet

For the class:
• 10 peanuts
• Several paper clips
• 1 potato
• Beaker stand
• Beaker holder
• Thermometer
• Thermometer holder
• 250 milliliters beaker
• 50 milliliters of water

• Clock with second hand
• Matches
• (Optional) aluminum foil
• (Optional) 5 mini-marshmallows
• (Optional) coarse-weave wheat cracker

For each student:
• *Peanut-Burning Data* activity sheet
• **Visualizing Change** student reading (p. 214)
• Notes from Lesson 7 homework
• (Optional) *Homework Notes* activity sheet (p. 275)
• LiFE Log

PROCEDURE

Before You Begin:

- Remind students to bring in their notes from their **Energy in Food** homework assignment. Have the homework questions available for discussion.

- Review the *Energy Burn* and *Calorimetry* experiment sheets and *Calculating Calories in a Peanut* lesson resource. Gather the materials. Prepare the potato-and-paper-clip setup and the calorimeter setup for the experiments. If you are burning the peanut on a table or desk that is flammable, place foil under the area where you will be burning the peanut.

- Review and make copies of the *Peanut-Burning Data* activity sheet for students.

- Review the **Visualizing Change** student reading and homework questions. Make a copy of the reading for each student. If you plan to distribute copies of the *Homework Notes* activity page, make enough copies to distribute one to each student. Alternatively, students can take notes in their LiFE Logs.

- If you have not already done so, post the Module Question and Unit 2 Question at the front of the classroom.

MODULE QUESTION

How can we use scientific evidence to help us maintain energy balance?

UNIT QUESTION

How can we make sure that we get the right amount of energy to help our bodies do what we want them to do?

 THEORIZING

1. Review Module and Unit Questions

Remind students of the Module and Unit questions. Explain that in this lesson, they are going to further their understanding of food energy. They are going to learn about how the body's cells use the nutrients in food through a process called metabolism.

2. Discuss Homework

Have students take out their notes from their **Energy in Food** homework assignment. Engage them in a discussion of the reading. Use the homework questions to guide the discussion. Check for student understanding of energy and metabolism.

 EXPERIMENTING

3. Conduct Experiment

Distribute the *Peanut-Burning Data* activity sheets to students. Ask for student volunteers to help with the demonstrations. As you set up the peanut-burning experiment, review the process of science inquiry. *What is the question we want to answer? What do you predict?* Review the materials and methods with students. Ask students to record what they observe on the *Peanut-Burning Data* activity sheet.

 THEORIZING

4. Discuss Observations

Use the questions on the experiment sheet to guide this discussion. If necessary, burn another peanut and conduct a guided discussion. As the peanut is burning, remind students that they are seeing the stored energy in the peanut being released as heat and light. Help students understand that burning the peanut is one way to demonstrate that the peanut has stored energy.

EXPERIMENTING

5. Conduct Experiment

Write the term *calorimetry* on the board. Tell students that calorimetry is the measurement of heat and a calorimeter is the apparatus used to measure the heat. Point out the calorimeter that you will use with the experiment. Ask for student volunteers to help with the demonstration. Review the materials and methods with students. Ask students to record what they observe on the **Peanut-Burning Data** activity sheet.

Follow the procedure on the **Calorimetry** experiment sheet. After you complete the demonstration, explain that how much the water is heated identifies the amount of energy, or number of calories, in the peanut. Use the **Calculating Calories in a Peanut** lesson resource as a guide to calculate how many calories were in the peanut. Explain that scientists use calorimeters to determine the caloric content of food. Tell students that a food that has more chemical, or stored, energy will have more energy to convert to heat and thus will raise the temperature of the water more when it is burned. If time permits, repeat this demonstration so students have two sets of data to compare.

Depending upon student interest and time, you may wish to compare the energy in different foods, such as a miniature marshmallow and about 1/4 of a coarse-weave wheat cracker. Both burn well and both are about the same weight as a peanut — about 1 gram.

Note: You do not need to calculate the caloric

content of food with your students. The important concept for them to understand is that calories represent stored energy.

THEORIZING

6. Review Homework Questions

Give each student a copy of the **Visualizing Change** student reading. Post the homework questions for this student reading on the board. Have students copy them onto the **Homework Notes** activity sheet or into their LiFE Logs. Remind them to bring their notes to the next class.

7. LiFE Logs

Have students add on to the journey of an apple from Lesson 7. Tell students to write several paragraphs that explain what happens once the apple enters a cell in the body and how it is metabolized. Encourage them to refer to the Lesson 7 **Energy in Food** homework reading for ideas.

Calculating Calories in a Peanut

The word *calorie* may bring to mind images of food labels with the number of calories per serving, or it may make you think of calorie counting to monitor weight loss or gain...but what exactly is a calorie? In physical science, a calorie is defined as the amount of heat energy needed to raise the temperature of 1 gram of water by 1 degree Celsius. When it comes to food, however, nutritionists refer to kilocalories (kcals). Calorie, with a capital C, often is used interchangeably with kilocalorie:

1 Calorie = 1 kilocalorie = 1,000 calories (lower case c)

In this lesson, you and your class will burn a peanut to determine its approximate number of calories. You will be releasing the energy stored in the peanut and then measuring that energy. The energy is released as heat, and that heat raises the temperature of the water in the beaker.

If you know the amount of water you are heating, the initial temperature of the water, and the final temperature of the water after burning the peanut, you have enough information to calculate the approximate number of calories in the peanut.

In one classroom we worked with, we had the following results. We used 50 grams (50 milliliter) of water. The starting temperature of the water was 25 degrees Celcius. The peanut burned for 3 minutes 18 seconds, at which time we measured the temperature again. The ending temperature of the water was 58 degrees Celcius. There was a temperature increase of 33 degrees Celcius.

We used the following equation to calculate the approximate number of calories in the peanut.

calories in the peanut = 33°C x 50 g = 1,650 calories

It may seem like there's an error. How can one little peanut possibly have so many calories? Are the food labels wrong? Remember that food labels actually report the number of kilocalories, so 1,650 calories equals 1.65 kcal. On a nutrition label, this would be written as 1.65 Cals.

Finally, because the peanut in this demonstration is burned out in the open and not in a calorimeter that traps all the heat, much of the heat is lost. Therefore, this is an approximation of the energy released from burning the peanut.

Energy Burn

Warning: Before you bring peanuts into your classroom, make sure no one is allergic to them. If you have a student with a peanut allergy, try burning a tree nut (Brazil nut or cashew), mini-marshmallow, or cracker.

This demonstration will help students understand that peanuts, a food, contain energy. When the peanut burns, it releases the stored energy as heat energy and light energy. A similar thing happens in our bodies when we eat food. Through the process of metabolism, the energy stored in food is converted into heat and potential energy that the body can use to grow and survive.

Setup

1. Place the paper clip on a flat surface.

2. Bend the top half of the paper clip up and straighten the lower half, as shown in the drawing.

3. Make the bottom half of the paper clip as straight as possible.

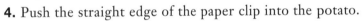

4. Push the straight edge of the paper clip into the potato.

5. Place one peanut in the "cradle" formed by the bent paper clip.

Procedure

1. Make sure the peanut is secure in the "cradle." Have students record their observations of the peanut.

2. Tell students you are going to light a match. Ask the class to predict whether or not the peanut will catch on fire, and if it will, how long it will burn.

3. Ask students to record their observations during the demonstration. Invite a student volunteer to record the amount of time it takes for the peanut to burn.

4. Light the match. It takes two to four matches to ignite the peanut. Once it is ignited, the peanut will burn for two to three minutes.

5. Watch the peanut carefully through the entire burning. If it looks as if it might fall off the cradle, blow it out.

6. After the fire extinguishes itself, have students record their observations on the ***Peanut-Burning Data*** activity sheet. Encourage students to be as descriptive as possible. Reinforce the idea that food has energy that can be converted into heat and potential energy that the body can use to grow and thrive.

Questions

1. *When something burns, what is released? Think about what you feel when you stand close to a fire.*
2. *Watch the peanut burn. What do you think is going on?*
3. *Where do the light and heat come from?*
4. *What changes did you notice in the peanut? What do you think is happening that caused the changes?*

Calorimetry

In this demonstration, the class uses a simple calorimeter to measure the amount of energy in a peanut. Burning the peanut converts stored chemical energy to heat energy, which is measured in units called calories. A calorie is the amount of heat used to raise the temperature of 1 gram of water 1 degree Celsius.

Setup

1. Place a new peanut in the potato stand. Follow the setup on page 90. Place the peanut setup on the beaker stand.

2. Adjust the height of the beaker holder so that it is about 1/2 inch above the peanut.

3. Pour 50 milliliter of water in the 250 milliliter beaker and place it on the beaker holder.

4. Place the thermometer in the holder so that it is dipping into the water and near the bottom of the beaker. Make certain it is not touching the bottom or the sides of the beaker.

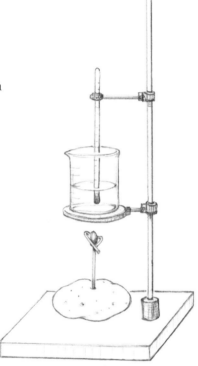

Procedure

1. Make sure the peanut is secure in the "cradle."

2. Record the beginning temperature of the water.

3. Light the match. It takes two to four matches to ignite the peanut.

4. Time how long the peanut burns.

5. When the flame goes out, record the ending temperature of the water.

6. Calculate the temperature change.

7. Use this formula to calculate the number of calories in the peanut:

calories = milliliters of water x degrees of temperature change

Questions

1. *What caused the change in the temperature of the water?*

2. *How many calories were in the peanut?*

3. *If we burned a food that heated the water more, or less, than the peanut did, what would that mean about the amount of energy in the food?*

4. *Did the calorimeter trap all the heat coming from the peanut?*

5. *How could the setup be changed to trap more heat?* (Put aluminum foil around the burning peanut or use a container that would keep in all the heat. This makes the calorimeter able to capture more heat. Scientists who are determining the number of calories in food use a container that traps all the heat).

Name   Date

Peanut-Burning Data

Use these tables to record your observations.

Visual Observations: In the space below, draw what the peanut looks like at each stage of the experiment. Label your diagrams with details such as texture, color, shape, size, different materials, and so forth.

Peanut Before Burning	Peanut While Burning	Peanut After Burning

Written Observations: Write down everything you notice about the peanut before, during, and after the experiment. Record the amount of time it took for the peanut to burn completely.

Peanut Before Burning	Peanut While Burning	Peanut After Burning

Amount of time it took for the peanut to burn: _____

Continued

Name   Date

Peanut-Burning Data, *Continued*

Calorimetry

In this experiment, you measure the amount of heat that is produced when a peanut is burned. If you have time, try burning other foods.

Food	Starting Temperature	Ending Temperature	Temperature Change	Burn Time
peanut				

Was there a change in the water temperature? _____

_____

What was the change for each food burned? _____

_____

_____

What does the change in temperature tell you? _____

_____

_____

_____

Creating Self-Portraits

AIM

To synthesize and communicate what energy balance means and to gain appreciation for why maintaining energy balance is personally important.

SCIENTIFIC PROCESSES

• **question, research, apply**

OBJECTIVES

Students will be able to:

• **communicate why it is personally important to them for their body to perform well;**

• **explain concepts learned in Unit 2 about how the body obtains and uses energy from food and maintains energy balance.**

OVERVIEW

In this lesson, students pull together what they have learned in Unit 2. The lesson begins with a review of the Lesson 8 homework reading. Use the homework questions to guide the discussion. Next, using what they have learned about energy balance, students create a self-portrait that illustrates what they have learned about the human body and energy as it relates to body function. They think about what is particularly important to them about their own body performance and communicate this by creating a work of art of themselves doing something that they like to do. After completing their self-portraits, students write a short paragraph in their LiFE Logs that answers the Unit 2 Question. For homework, students read **Bite, Write, Learn,** answer the homework questions, and complete the ***Bite and Write Food Log*** activity sheet.

MATERIALS

For the teacher:
• Homework questions for Lessons 9 and 10 (pp. 248–249)
• *Self-Portrait Tips* lesson resource
• *Keeping a Food Log* lesson resource

For the class:
• Scissors
• Markers, crayons, pastels, charcoals, etc.
• Paint
• Paper
• Cutting materials
• Collage materials
• Adhesives
• Sculpting materials
• Cleanup supplies

For each student:
• *Self-Portrait* activity sheet
• *Bite and Write Food Log* activity sheet (p. 276)
• **Bite, Write, Learn** student reading (p. 216)
• Notes from Lesson 8 homework
• (Optional) *Homework Notes* activity sheet (p. 275)
• LiFE Log

PROCEDURE

Before You Begin:

- Remind students to bring in their notes from their **Visualizing Change** homework assignment. Have the homework questions available for discussion.

- Review the **Bite, Write, Learn** student reading and homework questions. Make a copy of the reading for each student. If you plan to distribute copies of the *Homework Notes* activity sheet, make enough to distribute one copy to each student. Alternatively, students can take notes in their LiFE Logs.

- Review the *Self-Portrait Tips* and *Keeping a Food Log* lesson resources. Gather materials for the self-portrait assignment. The lesson resource lists options for you to consider.

- Review the *Self-Portrait* activity sheet. Make enough copies of the **Bite and Write Food Log** activity sheet to distribute one copy to each student.

- If you have not already done so, post the Module Question and Unit 2 Question at the front of the classroom.

MODULE QUESTION

How can we use scientific evidence to help us maintain energy balance?

UNIT QUESTION

How can we make sure that we get the right amount of energy to help our bodies do what we want them to do?

 THEORIZING

1. Review Module and Unit Questions

Remind students of the Module and Unit questions and explain that this is the last lesson of Unit 2. Tell them that this lesson is about visualizing their future. They will create a self-portrait that illustrates how they imagine themselves to be in the future. In creating their illustrations, they will review and synthesize what they've learned so far and think about how they want to apply what they've learned.

2. Discuss Homework

Have students take out their notes from their **Visualizing Change** homework assignment. Engage students in a discussion of the reading. Use the homework questions to guide the discussion. Check for student understanding of energy balance.

3. Review Unit 2

Review the key ideas covered in Unit 2. You may wish to conduct a whole-class discussion or ask small groups of students to make a list of what they remember doing and learning in this unit. Encourage students to look back at the Calvin and Carol readings to refresh their memories. *Why did Calvin and Carol go to the LiFE Center? What did they learn about themselves? How does the digestive system work? How do cells use the energy in food?* Summarize by pointing out that maintaining an energy balance keeps us in dynamic equilibrium, which is how our bodies are best able to do what we want them to do.

 **APPLYING TO LIFE**

4. Create a Self-Portrait

Distribute the *Self-Portrait* activity sheet. Engage students in a brief discussion about self-portraits. *Why do artists create self-portraits? What kinds of questions can a self-portrait attempt to answer?* (Who am I? How do I want other people to see me? What is distinctive about me?) Accept all answers. Tell students that they are going to create self-portraits. By visualizing themselves doing something they like to do, students reflect on how a healthy diet and regular physical activity help them feel better and learn and work more effectively. Thus students apply what they are learning to long-term goals. In the second part of this activity, students write an answer to the Unit 2 Question in their LiFE Logs, further communicating what they have learned about the human body and energy as it relates to body function.

To begin, have students make a quick sketch of their self-portrait. Walk among the students and check in to make sure they understand the assignment and are comfortable with it. After students have completed their sketches, hand out the materials for their final works of art and let the students create them.

5. Discuss Self-Portraits

Consider your students and then decide if a whole-class discussion or small-group discussions will work best. You may have students who are uncomfortable discussing their self-portraits with the whole class. Emphasize that there is no right or wrong answer. This is a personal reflection and visualization. Draw the activity to a close.

 THEORIZING

6. Review Homework Questions

Give each student a copy of the **Bite, Write, Learn** student reading. Post the homework questions for the student reading on the board. Have students copy them onto the *Homework Notes* activity sheet or into their LiFE Logs. Remind them to bring their notes to the next class.

7. LiFE Logs

Have students refer to the writing assignment on the *Self-Portrait* activity sheet. As a class, review the Unit 2 Question. Use the questions on the activity sheet to guide student thinking. After students have written their paragraphs, invite volunteers to read their responses to the class.

 **EXPERIMENTING**

8. Review Bite and Write Food Log

Explain that now that students have a general understanding of how the human body works in relation to eating and exercise, in Unit 3 they are going to begin to focus more on their own individual bodies. They will collect data on their own eating habits (energy in) and physical activity levels (energy out). Students will use this data to analyze whether the choices they are making enable their body to function the way they want it to, and what kinds of changes they might want to make if not.

Review the instructions on the *Keeping a Food Log* lesson resource. Encourage students to carry their food logs with them and record what they eat at the time they are eating it.

Self-Portrait Tips

The idea for this activity is simple: students communicate, through art, how they see themselves doing something they like to do and want to be good at. It can be a drawing, a painting, a collage, or a sculpture. It's up to you and the resources that you have. Old magazines are a great resource for collages, and a plain sheet of paper will work for a drawing. If you want to encourage sculpture, make some play dough using the recipe on page 281. Papier-mâché and painting require more setup and cleanup time and can get messy. The point of the activity is to offer students a nonverbal way to communicate how they would like to see themselves.

Here are some tips to guide the process:

1. You may find that when they are finished with their self-portraits, students would feel more comfortable sharing their thoughts, feelings, and artwork in small groups than they would in a whole-class discussion.

2. If you don't have a sink in your classroom, have a dish basin with water for students to wash sticky hands.

3. If you use a wet medium, be sure to plan ahead, especially if your classroom must be immediately cleaned up for the next class. Where will students be able to place their artwork until it is dry?

Materials

Choose from any of the materials below:

- **Paint:** acrylic paint is a good choice since it is water-based. Be sure to have cups for paint, brushes, brush cleaner, plates for mixing colors, and something to stir the paint.

- **Dry media:** wax crayons, felt-tip pens, oil pastels, charcoal, colored pencils, markers

- **Paper:** construction paper, white paper, tracing paper, brightly colored paper, card stock (white and colored), scraps of unusual paper (found at craft stores), rolls of newsprint

- **Cutting materials:** scissors, circle cutters, hole punches

- **Collage materials:** old magazines, fabrics, textured materials

- **Miscellaneous:** bits of thread, embroidery floss, beads, stickers, ribbon, buttons

- **Adhesives:** collage glue, craft glue, fabric glue, rubber cement, glue sticks, tape

- **Sculpting materials:** play dough (p. 281), papier-mâché, clay

- **Cleanup supplies:** rags, paper towels, plastic bags, tarps, drop cloths, surface cleaner

Keeping a Food Log

A food log is one way to study what we eat each day. Looking at this information, we can decide what food choices we might want to change. In this lesson, as homework, students keep a one-day food log. From the time they leave class one day until the time they return to class the next day, they record everything they eat and drink on the *Bite and Write Food Log* activity sheet (p. 276). Students use the food log to help them choose an energy-intake goal in Lesson 10.

When you introduce students to the food-log activity, emphasize that they will need to be diligent about recording what they eat. Explain that food logs can teach us a lot about what we eat, when we eat it, and how much we eat. Tell students to be as accurate as possible. Encourage them to carry the food log with them at all times so they can record the data at the time they eat rather than trying to rely on their memories. Tell students if they are not sure what to record in the "How much" column, they can be descriptive. In Lesson 10, they will learn some skills that will help them record how much they ate more accurately. For this homework assignment, encourage them to do the best they can.

Use the sample entries on the following page to model several examples for students. Point out that the more details they write on the food log, the more they will be able to learn about their eating in the future. Here are some tips to guide students with this activity:

Time: Each time you eat or drink something, write down the time that you ate or drank it.

Place: Write down where you ate or drank the food or beverage. For example, "in my kitchen," "in the cafeteria," "in the park," "in my dining room," "in front of the TV," "in my bedroom while doing my homework," and so forth.

What I ate: Be as detailed as you can in describing the foods. If the food has a specific name on the package, then write this down. If the food comes in different types (for example, milk comes as whole milk, 2 percent, 1 percent, or fat-free), record the type. If you made the food at home, such as a sandwich, be detailed about what you put on it. Don't forget to include all the parts of the sandwich, such as kind of bread, kind of meat, kind of cheese, mayonnaise, lettuce, and tomatoes.

How much: Be as exact as you can with how much. You will use different units for different food. For example, when recording beverages, use ounces as the unit. For some foods you may count the number that you have, such as slices of pizza. For packaged snacks (such as chips or candy), record the amount as accurately as you can. If you ate the entire package, record the size of the package (it can usually be found on the package). If you ate a portion of the package, estimate what portion you ate. You can also look at the nutrition-facts label to see the serving size and estimate how many servings you ate. If you get confused, bring in the packaging from what you ate and discuss it in class.

Sample 24-Hour Bite and Write Food Log

Date: _25 October_   Day of the Week: _Tuesday_

Time	Place	What I Ate	How Much?
3:30 p.m.	On the way home from school	1 can of root-beer soda and potato chips	12-oz can and small bag
5:30 p.m.	Sitting in front of the TV	1 green apple	Medium sized, about the size of a baseball
7:30 p.m.	Double-Quick-Eats fast-food place	Cheeseburger with lettuce and tomatoes and bun, French fries, cola	Small, I think, they were from the dollar menu
10 p.m.	My kitchen	Glass of water	Not sure exactly how much, but it filled the blue cups we have in our kitchen
11 p.m.	My kitchen	Glass of cola	Not sure exactly how much, but it filled the blue cups we have in our kitchen
7:30 a.m.	My kitchen	Banana; packaged cinnamon bun; water	Large; medium sized bun; 1 cup
11:30 a.m.	Cafeteria	Chicken nuggets; green beans; bread roll; grape soda	6 nuggets; 1/2 cup; 1 small roll; 20-oz bottle.

Name   Date

Self-Portrait

In this activity, you communicate, through art, how you would like to see yourself.

1. Think about the Unit 2 Question: *How can we make sure that we get the right amount of energy to help our bodies do what we want them to do?* Now, think about what you really want to be able to do. Think about what you like to do, who you are, and the things that are important to you. List two or three things that you like to do and that are important to you to be good at. **Hint:** Are athletics important to you? Do you like to garden? Are you a good cook? Do you like to write, play a musical instrument, or take photographs? These are just a few ideas. Now think about what's important to you.

2. Make a quick sketch of yourself doing one or more of these things. Try to make your sketch show who you are, what you like about yourself, what you are proud of, and how you see yourself. If you were going to use your portrait as a way to introduce yourself to a new friend, to show your new friend what you are good at and what you like to do, what would you show? After you finish your sketch, your teacher will give you materials to create your final artwork. Have fun and be creative!

3. Now that you've made your self-portrait, think about how you can make sure you get the right amount of energy to do whatever you pictured yourself doing. Write a short paragraph in your LiFE Log that answers the Unit 2 Question. Here are some other questions to guide your thinking:

   a. *What happens to food after it enters my body?* Remember the human-body simulation. Be sure to include the words *digestive system*, *blood*, *blood vessels*, and *cells* in your answer.

   b. *What do my cells do to release the energy from my food and to build the molecules my body needs?* Be sure to include the word *metabolism* in your answer.

   c. *What does it mean to be in energy balance?* Remember the simulation with the water and the plastic cup. Be sure to include the words *energy balance*, *energy in*, and *energy out* in your answer.

From Data to Health Goals

Collecting Food-Intake Data

AIM

To learn to gather, record, and analyze data about food intake.

SCIENTIFIC PROCESSES

- **question, research, design, experiment, apply**

OBJECTIVES

Students will be able to:

- **gather and record data on 24 hours of energy intake, keeping in mind the C3 goals;**

- **use familiar objects as nonstandard units of measurement;**

- **understand how to interpret items on a food label;**

- **apply data-collection skills to their own eating habits;**

- **understand the importance of collecting reliable scientific data.**

OVERVIEW

In this lesson, students begin to work with data they have collected about their own eating habits. In introducing the Unit 3 Question, remind students that they are scientists gathering data. Challenge them to think about the questions they are trying to answer and what kind of information they need to gather. As you work through these activities, remind students that they are using mathematics to quantify what they need to know. This lesson provides students with the skills to record detailed data about specific foods and beverages they consume. Through this inquiry-based investigation, students develop an in-depth understanding of the rationale for taking action. For homework, students continue to practice recording detailed data about food and answer questions about the reading.

Note: In this lesson, students use data they collected on the *Bite and Write Food Log.* If students have not yet completed this assignment, have them do so before beginning the lesson.

MATERIALS

For the teacher:
- Homework questions for Lessons 10 and 11 (p. 249)
- *Measuring Food Intake* lesson resource
- *Measuring Centers* experiment sheet
- Chart paper and markers

For the class:
- *Fast-Food Data* lesson resource
- *Processed-Snack Data* lesson resource
- *How Much?* lesson resource
- 2 apples
- Small bowl
- Sharp knife
- Measuring cups
- Empty beverage containers: 12-ounce soda can, 16-ounce bottle, 20-ounce bottle
- 2 clear cups, each large enough to hold 12 ounces of water

- Food coloring
- (Optional) 2 carrots, 3 large stalks of celery, 2 pears

For each student:
- *24-Hour Food Intake* activity sheets
- Completed *Bite and Write Food Log* activity sheet (p. 276)
- *Calculating Calories, Fat, and Sugar* activity sheet
- Notes from Lesson 9 homework
- **Steps** student reading (p. 220)
- (Optional) *Practicing How Much* activity sheet
- (Optional) *Analyzing Calvin's Data* activity sheet
- (Optional) *Homework Notes* activity sheet (p. 275)
- LiFE Log

PROCEDURE

Before You Begin:

- Make sure students have completed the **Bite and Write Food Log** homework assignment from Lesson 9. Students need the information they recorded about what they ate during a 24-hour period to complete this lesson. They will also use this information to choose a goal in Lesson 12.

- Remind students to bring in their answers from their **Bite, Write, Learn** homework questions. Have the homework questions available for discussion.

- Review the **Steps** student reading and homework questions. Make a copy of the reading for each student. If you plan to distribute copies of the **Homework Notes** activity sheet, make enough copies to distribute one to each student. Alternatively, students can take notes in their LiFE Logs.

- Review the **Fast-Food Data, Processed-Snack Data,** and **How Much?** lesson resources. Make copies to put out in the measuring centers. Make enough copies of the **How Much?** lesson resource so that each student gets one card. Cut out the **How Much?** cards.

- Gather the materials and set up the measuring centers.

- Review the **Bite and Write Food Log** and **24-Hour Food Intake** activity sheets.

- Review the **Calculating Calories, Fat, and Sugar** activity sheet and make copies for each student.

- (Optional) Review the **Practicing How Much** and **Analyzing Calvin's Data** activity sheets. Make copies of the two activity sheets for students.

- If you have not done so already, post the Module Question and Unit 3 Question at the front of the classroom.

MODULE QUESTION

How can we use scientific evidence to help us maintain energy balance?

UNIT QUESTION

How can we use personal data to help us make healthy food and activity choices?

 THEORIZING

1. Review Module and Unit Questions

Review the Module Question and introduce the Unit 3 Question. Remind students that the Module Question is the big question they are studying. Point out that this unit focuses on students' learning more about their own food and activity habits through collecting personal data on their energy in and energy out.

2. Discuss Homework

Have students take out their notes from their **Bite, Write, Learn** homework questions. Engage them in a discussion of the reading. Use the homework questions to guide the discussion.

Invite students to share their experiences recording what they ate for the past 24 hours on their **Bite and Write Food Log** activity sheets. *What was the easiest data to record? What was the most difficult?* You may find that students had difficulty with the "How Much?" column. Tell students that the point of the **Bite and Write Food Log** homework assignment was to introduce them to food logs and to help them identify skills that they might need to practice.

E X P E R I M E N T I N G

3. Measure Food Intake

The *Measuring Centers* experiment sheet describes four ways that students can gather standardized data related to the *Choice, Control & Change* food and activity goals. Using the *Measuring Centers* experiment sheet, review different ways students can measure how much they eat. Have them take notes in their LiFE Logs. Distribute a *How Much?* card to each student. Discuss the various ways to visually estimate serving sizes. *If you are in a restaurant and you don't have a cup to measure, what's another way that you can estimate a serving size of fruits or vegetables?* (A fist is about the size of a cup. I can visualize a baseball, which is also about the same size as a cup, and compare my serving size to it.) *What can you use to estimate the serving size of a processed snack?* (Use the *How Much?* card.) Point out that the *How Much?* card is 3"x5" — which is about a medium-sized portion of a processed snack. Smaller than the card is a small portion and larger than the card is a large portion. Encourage students to carry the *How Much?* card with them at all times.

If you plan to do this activity using centers, divide the class into small groups. Have groups rotate through the centers. After all groups have completed this work, hold a whole-class discussion using the questions listed for each center.

4. Discuss Data

Challenge students to think about how they might use and interpret the data that is based on these measurements. *How can you use personal data about fruit and vegetable consumption? How can you use personal data about the kind of beverages you drink and how much you drink?* (I can compare how much I eat to the dietary guidelines. I can see how many ounces of sweetened beverages I drink.) *Is it important to record your data in a consistent way? Why is it important to measure your fruits and vegetables in cups and beverages in ounces?* (Those are the units of measurement that are

used with the dietary guidelines and the *Choice, Control & Change* food goals. I need to use the same units of measurement so I can compare my data to the guidelines.)

Discuss the methods and units of measurement the students used in their 24-hour food logs. Make the point that measurements need to be made using the same units of measurement so the data can be compared.

5. (Optional) Apply Measuring Skills

If your students need more practice applying their measuring skills, have them practice determining what to write in the "How Much" column for various foods by completing the *Practicing How Much* activity sheet. They can look at the illustrations and try to correctly record how much for each food (cheeseburger: 4-ounce meat patty, 1/2 cup vegetables and bun; fries: large order; apple: 1 cup; cupcakes: 1 medium processed snack; beverage in a can: 12 ounces; and beverage in a bottle: 20 ounces).

Students can use the *Analyzing Calvin's Data* activity sheet as practice before they complete the *24-Hour Food Intake* activity sheet with their own data. Have students refer to the information in Calvin's Food Log on p. 218. Tell them to use this data to figure out how many cups of fruits and vegetables Calvin ate and how many ounces of sweetened beverages he drank.

6. Record Personal Data

Now that students have practiced their measuring skills, have them apply the skills to their own data. Distribute the *24-Hour Food Intake* activity sheets. Tell students they are going to transfer the data from their *Bite and Write Food Log* activity sheets to these data tables. Be sure to allow enough time for students to complete these sheets in class. Tell students that the *24-Hour Food Intake* activity sheets focus on food and beverages included in the *Choice, Control & Change* goals. (These are: eat more fruits and vegetables, drink fewer sweetened beverages, drink more water, eat less fast food, and eat fewer processed snacks.) Emphasize that it is important for the students to record their food-intake data as accurately as possible, along with thoughtfully answering the questions below each data table, because they will use this information to choose a food goal in Lesson 12.

7. Review Processed-Snacks Homework

Review the *Calculating Calories, Fat, and Sugar* activity sheet with students. Point out that processed snacks often are sold in containers that are typically consumed in a single sitting, but contain more than one recommended serving.

Through this activity, students learn about how many calories and how much fat and sugar are in processed snacks. Remind students that the recommendation is for the average *adult* to have 2,000 calories per day and no more than 65 grams of total fat and 50 grams of total sugar. Processed snacks in the sizes that are typically sold for people to eat in one sitting can contribute significant fat and sugar to the diet. Students often find this information shocking and become motivated to choose smaller portions of processed snacks. You may wish to assign some students to chips, some to candy, and some to baked goods. With this approach, students will collect a wide variety of data. Have students share their findings in Lesson 12.

8. Review Homework Questions

Give each student a copy of the **Steps** student reading. Post the homework questions for the

reading on the board. Have students copy them onto their *Homework Notes* activity sheets or into their LiFE Logs. Remind them to bring their notes to the next class.

9. LiFE Logs

Have students practice measuring amounts of food at home. Tell them to record their measurements in their LiFE Logs. Ask them to select three to five food items that they often eat for dinner or for a snack. Have them list these foods along with the amount they ate. Tell them to draw a two-column table like the ones on the *24-Hour Food Intake* activity sheet. They can measure how much they ate using any of the methods they learned about in this lesson, including measuring cups, their fist, food labels, or the *How Much?* card.

Measuring Food Intake

This lesson explores the practical application of nonstandard measurement units to gathering personal food-intake data. You may need to remind students that there are standard and nonstandard units of measurement. Point out that standard units have high accuracy and nonstandard units are less accurate but more readily available. In this module, there are times when standard measurement units, like cups and ounces, are used. However, for the purpose of keeping a food log, nonstandard units are generally more convenient for quantifying food intake. Emphasize that what is important is becoming more conscious of the food choices students make. Engage them in thinking about how they are going to use and interpret the data that is based on these measurements. In our work with teachers, we have found that students are more receptive to this activity after they have tried to keep a food log and realize how challenging it can be. You may wish to have students repeat the Lesson 9 ***Bite and Write Food Log*** homework assignment after they have practiced measuring food and beverage intake.

Standardizing Measurements

Dietary guidelines from the United States Department of Agriculture (USDA) use cups to measure fruits and vegetables and ounces to measure beverages. Since the *Choice, Control & Change (C3)* food and activity goals are based on these federal guidelines, we use the same units of measurement. For students to be able to compare their personal data to the *C3* food and activity goals, it is important for them to try to use cups and ounces as units of measurement as well. However, since standard units of measurement are not practical in most eating situations, we have included the ***How Much?*** card (p. 110) to help students find a close approximation. What is important is consistency of data over time and increased awareness of how much they are eating.

In measuring fast-food servings, students specify the size they ordered, such as small cheeseburger, quarter-pounder, large French fries, two-piece fried-chicken combo meal with large French fries, or chicken Caesar salad with an entire packet of dressing.

Processed snacks include candy, chips, and baked goods, such as cookies, cake, and brownies. Have students use the ***How Much?*** card to approximate the size of the processed snack. The unit of measurement is small, medium, or large.

Students can also use the amount of energy (calories) in the processed snack to determine the size. Assuming a 2,000-calorie diet (the general recommendation for adults), a snack of about 150–300 calories is about medium-sized, less than that is small, and more than that is large.

Our experience has been that when students understand the big picture — eat more fruits and vegetables, drink more water, and consume fewer processed snacks, fast foods, and sweetened beverages — and use the more readily available nonstandard measuring tools, they are more likely to transfer what they have learned to their food choices.

Summary

The table below summarizes the categories of food that students are measuring and the standard and nonstandard units of measurement they can use to report how much they eat.

Food Category	Unit of Measurement	Measuring Tools
Fruits and vegetables	Cup	Measuring cup, fist, visual estimation (a cup is about the size of a baseball, etc.)
Beverages	Fluid ounce	Beverage-container label, measuring cup, visual estimation
Fast food	Size	Serving size from order menu
Processed snacks	Size	3" x 5" index card, *How Much?* card, nutrition facts on food's package labels

Fast-Food Data

These sample figures were collected from nutrition information given by the restaurants online. Use them to become familiar with different portion sizes of fast foods and how to describe them. If you have Internet access in your classroom, encourage students to do their own research.

McDonald's[1]	Serving size	Calories
Hamburger	3.5 oz (100 g)	250
Cheeseburger	4 oz (114 g)	300
Premium Grilled Chicken Classic Sandwich	8 oz (226 g)	420
French Fries (small)	2.5 oz (71 g)	230
French Fries (medium)	4.1 oz (117 g)	380
French Fries (large)	5.4 oz (154 g)	500
Chicken McNuggets (4 pieces)	2.3 oz (64 g)	190
Premium Southwest Salad with Grilled Chicken	12.3 oz (350 g)	320
Chocolate-Chip Cookie	1 cookie (33 g)	160
Burger King (BK)[2]		
Hamburger	N/A	290
Cheeseburger	N/A	340
Tendercrisp Chicken Sandwich	N/A	800
French Fries (small)	N/A	340
French Fries (medium)	N/A	480
French Fries (large)	N/A	580
Crown-shaped Chicken Tenders (4 pieces)	N/A	180
Tendercrisp Garden Salad (with chicken)	N/A	670
Carl's Jr.[3]		
Kid's Hamburger	102 g	230
Kid's Cheeseburger	118 g	290
Charbroiled BBQ Chicken Sandwich	239 g	380
Natural-cut French Fries (small)	119 g	320
Natural-cut French Fries (medium)	169 g	460
Natural-cut French Fries (large)	184 g	500
Chicken Strips (3 pieces)	108 g	370
Charbroiled Chicken Salad	410 g	250
Chocolate-Chip Cookie	1 cookie (71 g)	370

[1] *http://nutrition.mcdonalds.com/nutritionexchange/nutritionfacts.pdf* (retrieved July 2, 2010)

[2] *www.bk.com/en/us/menu-nutrition/index.html* (retrieved October 22, 2009)

[3] *www.carlsjr.com/menu* (retrieved October 22, 2009)

Processed-Snack Data

On average, adults need 2,000 calories a day, with no more than 65 grams of fat and 50 grams of sugar.

Examples of Processed Snacks	Calories	Fat (grams)	Sugar (grams)
Chocolate-Chip Cookie (30 g: small)	90	5	6
Chocolate-Chip Cookie (60 g: medium)	180	10	11
Chocolate-Chip Cookie (120 g: large)	360	20	22
Potato Chips (1/2 oz: small bag)	80	5	0
Potato Chips (1 oz: medium bag)	160	10	0
Potato Chips (2 oz: large bag)	320	20	0
Chocolate Peanut-Butter Cup (1: small)	105	7	11
Chocolate Peanut-Butter Cup (2: medium)	210	13	21
Chocolate Peanut-Butter Cup (3: large)	315	21	32

To convert grams to teaspoons: **5 grams of fat = 1 teaspoon**
4 grams of sugar = 1 teaspoon

Calorie Comparison of Packaged Snacks

To calculate the number of calories in a packaged snack, use this formula:

calories x servings per container = total calories in the packaged snack

Cookies
Nutrition Facts
Serving Size: 2 Cookies (60 g)
Servings Per Container: 2
Amount Per Serving
Calories: 180   Calories from Fat: 90

Total Calories: 360 (180 x 2)
Total Calories from Fat: 180 (90 x 2)

Chips
Nutrition Facts
Serving Size: 1 ounce (30 g)
Servings Per Container: 5
Amount Per Serving
Calories: 160   Calories from Fat: 90

Total Calories: 800 (160 x 5)
Total Calories from Fat: 450 (90 x 5)

Snack-Sized Chocolate Bar
Nutrition Facts
Serving Size: 1 ounce (30 g)
Servings Per Container: 1
Amount Per Serving
Calories: 170   Calories from Fat: 90

Total Calories: 170 (170 x 1)
Total Calories from Fat: 90 (90 x 1)

King-Sized Chocolate Bar
Nutrition Facts
Serving Size: 1 ounce (30 g)
Servings Per Container: 4
Amount Per Serving
Calories: 170   Calories from Fat: 90

Total Calories: 680 (170 x 4)
Total Calories from Fat: 360 (90 x 4)

How Much?

Use this lesson resource to make a *How Much?* card for students. Make a copy of this page for each student in your class. Have student volunteers help you. Cut out the card along the solid line. Fold it on the dotted line, making a 3"x5" card. Glue or tape the sides together. You may wish to laminate the cards. If you do, trim them to keep the cards as close to 3"x5" as possible so they can be used to get accurate measurements of the serving size of processed snacks.

PROCESSED-SNACKS SERVING SIZE

Using this 3"x5" card:

- Smaller than this card = small
- Same size as this card = medium
- Larger than this card = large

Using calories:

- Less than 150 calories = small
- 150–300 calories = medium
- More than 300 calories = large

FAST-FOOD SERVING SIZE

Use the sizes listed on the menu. If you want to know specific amounts of calories, fat, sugar, sodium, or other nutrients in fast foods, ask for nutrition information when purchasing the food, or look up the information online.

FRUITS AND VEGETABLES SERVING SIZE

1 cup = **1 baseball** = **1 fist**

SWEETENED BEVERAGES SERVING SIZE*

8 oz.   **12 oz.**   **20 oz.**   **1 liter (33.8 oz.)**

*At home, use a measuring cup to find out how much your cups and glasses hold.

Measuring Centers

In this experiment, you can set up these activities as centers or do them as classroom demonstrations. If your students are already comfortable with measuring and using close approximations, doing a demonstration will work. However, if your students need more time to become familiar with this type of measurement, set these up as centers and give students ample time to practice measuring. The directions that follow are for centers.

CENTER ONE: FRUITS AND VEGETABLES

Students use different measuring tools to measure fruits and vegetables to develop a visual sense of different portion sizes. Have small groups of students take turns moving through the center.

Setup

1. Take two apples that are approximately the same size. Cut one up and leave the other whole. Place the cut-up apple in a 1-cup measuring cup.

2. Repeat Step 1 using other fruits and vegetables, such as carrots, pears, or celery.

Procedure

1. Tell each group to spend time exploring ways to visualize how much a 1-cup serving of fruits and vegetables is.

2. Have students put the chopped fruit or vegetable onto a plate and look closely at how much of the plate is filled by the 1-cup serving. Tell them to try to create a mental image of that 1-cup serving.

3. Have students take turns holding up the whole apple and using their fists as the unit of measurement. Tell them that the size of their fist is approximately 1 cup.

4. Have students hold their fists near the 1-cup serving of cut-up apple on the plate.

Questions

1. *What unit of measurement can you use to record the amounts of fruits and vegetables you eat?*

2. *What is the most accurate way to measure servings of fruits and vegetables?*

3. *What can you use to reach a close approximation of the number of cups of fruits and vegetables that you eat?*

CENTER TWO: BEVERAGES

Students explore different ways to measure the amount of liquids they drink each day. Have small groups of students take turns moving through the center.

Setup

1. Label one clear cup 8 Fluid Ounces and the other clear cup 12 Fluid Ounces.

2. Pour 8 ounces of water into the first cup and 12 ounces into the second cup. Tint each cup of water by stirring in several drops of food coloring.

3. Put out a 12-ounce can of soda, a 20-ounce bottle, and the two cups of tinted water.

4. Have a cloth or paper towels at this center to clean up any spills.

Procedure

1. Have students look at the can of soda and try to determine how many ounces of liquid are in the can. If students are puzzled, point out where they can find the information printed on the can.

2. Have students look to see how many ounces are in the bottle.

3. Tell students to compare the two cups of water. Have them look closely at the two cups to try to create a mental image of each amount so they can estimate how much they are drinking if they don't know the exact amount.

Questions

1. *How many fluid ounces are there in 1 cup?* (8 fluid ounces = 1 cup)

2. *How many fluid ounces does a standard can of soda or sweetened beverage contain?*

3. *How many fluid ounces does a standard bottle of soda or sweetened beverage contain?*

4. *Where can you find the number of fluid ounces of liquid in a bottle of soda?*

CENTER THREE: FAST FOODS

Students become familiar with different portion sizes of fast foods. Have small groups of students take turns moving through the center.

Setup

1. Make copies of the *Fast-Food Data* lesson resource. Place them in the center for students to review.

2. If you have Internet access in your classroom, set up a computer for students to research additional fast-food data. You may wish to set up "favorites" for students to visit so they can learn more about the fat and sugar in fast foods.

Procedure

Have students compare several of the same items from each of the fast-food chains.

Questions

1. *Are all the small portions of French fries the same? Do they weigh the same amount? Do they have the same number of calories?*

2. *What do you notice about other products, like hamburgers, that come from different fast-food chains? Are they the same? What similarities or differences do you see?*

3. *What do you notice about the beverages that are listed? Are you surprised by anything you see?*

CENTER FOUR: PROCESSED SNACKS

Students explore different ways to measure portion sizes of processed snacks. Have small groups of students take turns moving through the center.

PROCESSED-SNACKS SERVING SIZE

Using this 3"x5" card:

- Smaller than this card = small
- Same size as this card = medium
- Larger than this card = large

Using calories:

- Less than 150 calories = small
- 150–300 calories = medium
- More than 300 calories = large

FAST-FOOD SERVING SIZE

Use the sizes listed on the menu. If you want to know specific amounts of calories, fat, sugar, sodium, or other nutrients in fast foods, ask for nutrition information when purchasing the food, or look up the information online.

Front

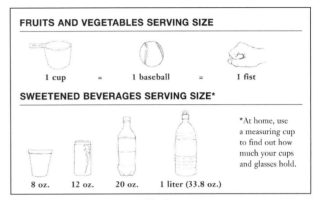

FRUITS AND VEGETABLES SERVING SIZE

1 cup = 1 baseball = 1 fist

SWEETENED BEVERAGES SERVING SIZE*

8 oz.   12 oz.   20 oz.   1 liter (33.8 oz.)

*At home, use a measuring cup to find out how much your cups and glasses hold.

Back

Setup

1. Make several copies of the **Processed-Snack Data** lesson resource. Place them in the center for students to review.

2. Make copies of the **How Much?** card. Cut them out and place them in the center for students to use.

3. Set out several examples of packaged snacks, such as chips, cookies, or candy.

Procedure

1. Have students use the **How Much?** card to estimate serving sizes of different packaged snacks.

2. Tell students to read the labels and look for the serving size of each snack.

Questions

1. *Is the serving size of all the packaged snacks the same?*

2. *Describe the relationship between the size of the snack and the number of calories it contains.*

3. *What do you notice about the food labels on the packaged snacks? In addition to calories, what other information do the labels contain?* (Hint: Remember Lesson 4, **Investigating What's in Food**. What did you learn about fat and sugar?)

| Name | Date |

Practicing How Much

Now that you know how to measure food intake, try out your skills. Look at the illustrations. For each food or beverage, record what you estimate the portion size to be. Don't forget to include the appropriate units (such as ounces, cups, size) in your measurement.

Food/Drink	How Much?
1. Cheeseburger	
2. French fries	
3. Cupcakes	
4. Beverage in a can	
5. Beverage in a bottle	
6. Apple	

LESSON 10: COLLECTING FOOD-INTAKE DATA

Name   Date

Analyzing Calvin's Data

Calvin's doctor recommended that he add more fruits and vegetables to his diet. How can Calvin tell if he is getting enough fruits and vegetables throughout the day? Look at Calvin's Food Log in the **Bite, Write, Learn** student reading and list all the fruits and vegetables and their amounts. Add up the total number of cups of fruits and vegetables Calvin ate.

Fruits and Vegetables	Amount (cups)

Total: _____ cups

Calvin's doctor also said that there was an increase in Calvin's blood-sugar levels — that they are higher than they should be. One change Calvin said he wanted to make to become healthier was to reduce the sweetened beverages he drank — like soda, sports drinks, and juice with sugar added. How can Calvin find out how many ounces of sweetened beverages he really drinks? How can he come up with ideas about how he can reduce this amount? Look back at Calvin's Food Log in the reading. List all the sweetened beverages and their amounts. Add up the total number of ounces of sweetened beverages that Calvin drank during the day.

Sweetened Beverages	Amount (ounces)

Total: _____ ounces

Name

Date

24-Hour Food Intake

In this activity, you use the personal data you collected for the **Bite and Write Food Log** homework assignment and the measuring skills you just learned to complete the tables and answer the questions below. You will use this data in Lesson 12, when you select which of the *Choice, Control & Change* food goals you want to work on. To select the food goal that is right for you, you need to compare what you eat and how much you eat to the recommendations. Be as detailed and accurate as you can. It will help you in choosing your goal.

FRUITS AND VEGETABLES

List all the fruits and vegetables you ate in the past 24 hours.

Fruits and Vegetables	Amount (cups)
	Total (cups)

1. Is this the amount you would normally consume? _____ YES _____ NO

2. If NO, explain how today was different from other days. Do you usually eat more or fewer fruits and vegetables? Are there other fruits and vegetables you often eat?

_____

_____

_____

_____

Continued

Name	Date

24-Hour Food Intake, *Continued*

WATER

List all the water you drank in the past 24 hours.

Water	Amount (ounces)
	Total (ounces)

1. Is this the amount of water you would normally drink? _____ YES _____ NO

2. If NO, explain how today was different from other days. Do you normally drink more or less water?

_____

_____

_____

_____

Continued

Name	Date

24-Hour Food Intake, *Continued*

SWEETENED BEVERAGES

Sweetened beverages include soda, sports drinks, sweetened iced teas, and fruit-flavored drinks. List all the sweetened beverages you drank in the past 24 hours.

Sweetened Beverages	Amount (ounces)
	Total (ounces)

1. Is this the amount you would normally drink?   _____ YES   _____ NO

2. If NO, explain how today was different from other days. Do you usually drink more sweetened beverages, fewer sweetened beverages, or different sweetened beverages?

_____

_____

_____

_____

Continued

Choice, Control & Change
©2010 Teachers College Columbia University

Name

Date

24-Hour Food Intake, *Continued*

FAST FOODS

Fast-food restaurants are places where you order cooked and ready-to-eat food over the counter or at a drive-through. Fast-food chains, take-out pizza places, and take-out Chinese restaurants are examples. List all the foods you ate from fast-food restaurants in the past 24 hours.

Fast Foods	Amount (size)

1. Is this what you would normally eat at a fast-food place?   _____ YES   _____ NO

2. If NO, please explain what you usually eat at fast-food places.

_____

_____

Usual Number of Times Eating at Fast-Food Places in a Week

3. How many times did you eat in a fast-food place in the last week? _____

4. Is this how many times you would normally eat fast food in a week? _____ YES _____ NO

5. If NO, explain why this week was different from other weeks. Do you usually eat more or less often at fast-food places?

_____

_____

Continued

Name   Date

24-Hour Food Intake, *Continued*

PROCESSED SNACKS

Processed snacks are foods like chips, candy, cookies, and cakes. To determine the portion size of your processed snacks, use the ***How Much?*** card. List all the processed snacks you ate in the past 24 hours.

PROCESSED-SNACKS SERVING SIZE

Using this 3"x5" card:
- Smaller than this card = small
- Same size as this card = medium
- Larger than this card = large

Using calories:
- Less than 150 calories = small
- 150–300 calories = medium
- More than 300 calories = large

FAST-FOOD SERVING SIZE

Use the sizes listed on the menu. If you want to know specific amounts of calories, fat, sugar, sodium, or other nutrients in fast foods, ask for nutrition information when purchasing the food, or look up the information online.

Front

FRUITS AND VEGETABLES SERVING SIZE

1 cup   =   1 baseball   =   1 fist

SWEETENED BEVERAGES SERVING SIZE*

8 oz.   12 oz.   20 oz.   1 liter (33.8 oz.)

*At home, use a measuring cup to find out how much your cups and glasses hold.

Back

Processed Snacks	Amount (size)
Total (per day)	

1. Is this the amount of processed snacks you would normally eat?   _____ YES   _____ NO

2. If NO, explain why today was different from other days. Do you usually eat more or fewer processed snacks?

_____

_____

Name	Date

Calculating Calories, Fat, and Sugar

Remember that the average adult needs about 2,000 calories a day. The recommendation is to consume no more than 65 grams of fat and 50 grams of sugar in a day. It is important to know how much fat and sugar are in the processed snacks you eat. Look at the labels of three different processed snacks such as chips, candy, and baked goods (cookies, cakes, brownies). Choose snacks that you think are sold with the intention that a person would eat the entire package at one time.

1. Write the name of each kind of snack that you studied under "Food #1," "Food #2," and "Food #3."

2. Use the Nutrition Facts section of the food label to complete the "Data from Nutrition Facts Label" section of the table.

3. Calculate the number of calories in each package. To get this number, multiply the "Calories per Serving" by the "Servings per Container." Write the total in the column "Calories in Container."

4. Calculate the total grams of fat in each package. To get this number, multiply the "Total Fat (grams)" by the "Servings per Container." Write the total in the column "Total Fat in Container (grams)."

5. Calculate the total grams of sugar in each package. To get this number, multiple the "Sugars (grams)" by the "Servings per Container." Write the total in the column "Total Sugar in Container (grams)."

6. Look at the calculations you made. Were you surprised by what you found? What surprised you the most? How will you use what you have learned the next time you want a snack? Write your answers in your LiFE Log.

Data from Nutrition Facts Label	Food #1:	Food #2:	Food #3:
Serving Size			
Servings per Container			
Calories per Serving			
Total Fat (grams)			
Sugars (grams)			
Calculations of Calories, Fat, and Sugar in Container			
Calories in Container			
Total Fat in Container (grams)			
Total Sugar in Container (grams)			

INVESTIGATING OUR CHOICES : DYNAMIC EQUILIBRIUM : FROM DATA TO HEALTH GOALS : EFFECTS OF OUR CHOICES : MAINTAINING COMPETENCE

Investigating Physical Activity

AIM

To gain experience in recording data on physical activity through the use of pedometers.

SCIENTIFIC PROCESSES

• **question, research, gather data, display data, apply**

OBJECTIVES

Students will be able to:

• **describe the benefits of regular physical activity;**

• **use a pedometer to accurately record step-count data;**

• **demonstrate their appreciation for how a pedometer can motivate increased physical activity.**

OVERVIEW

In this lesson, students gather personal data that they will use to help them make healthy physical-activity choices. The lesson begins with a review of the Lesson 10 homework reading, which you can use as an introduction to pedometers and to review the benefits of physical activity. Next, students learn that a pedometer needs to be calibrated, like any piece of scientific equipment, and used in the correct way so that the data collected is valid. Students will use pedometers to track their personal activity levels. From this point forward in the curriculum, they will record the number of steps they take each day. For homework, in addition to reading, they will do research comparing the step counts of different activities. This information will be used in Lesson 13. These inquiry-based investigations help students develop an in-depth understanding of how they can take action to meet their goals.

Note: An inexpensive pedometer (less than $2) can be purchased from Pedometers USA or Amazon.com. We used these pedometers in our field tests and they provide a level of accuracy that will work with this lesson. If you do not have pedometers for your class, please refer to the **24-Hour Activity Log.**

MATERIALS

For the teacher:
• Homework questions for Lessons 11 and 12 (p. 249)
• *Keeping Track of Physical Activity* lesson resource
• *Great Reasons to Stay Active* lesson resource
• *Calibrating Pedometers* experiment sheet
• Pedometer
• (Optional) chart paper
• (Optional) permanent marker
• (Optional) *How to Use the 24-Hour Activity Log* lesson resource

For each group:
• Chart paper and markers

For each student:
• Pedometer
• **Choosing a Goal** student reading (p. 223)
• Notes from Lesson 10 homework
• *Step and Write* activity sheet (p. 277)
• *Comparing Activities* activity sheet
• (Optional) 2 copies of the **Homework Notes** activity sheet (p. 275)
• (Optional) *24-Hour Activity Log* activity sheet (p. 279)
• LiFE Log

PROCEDURE

Before You Begin:

- Remind students to bring in their notes from the **Steps** homework questions. Have the questions available for discussion.

- Review the **Choosing a Goal** student reading and homework questions. Make a copy of the reading for each student. If you plan to distribute copies of the *Homework Notes* activity sheet, make enough copies to distribute two to each student. Alternatively, students can take notes in their LiFE Logs.

- Read the *Keeping Track of Physical Activity* and the *Great Reasons to Stay Active* lesson resources.

- Review the *Calibrating Pedometers* experiment sheet. Place a pedometer on your waistband.

- (Optional) If you do not plan to use pedometers, review the *How to Use the 24-Hour Activity Log* lesson resource. Make a copy of the *24-Hour Activity Log* activity sheet for each student. Reproduce the sample activity log on chart paper to post during class discussion.

- Make copies of the *Step and Write* and *Comparing Activities* activity sheets for each student.

- If you have not already done so, post the Module Question and Unit 3 Question at the front of the classroom.

MODULE QUESTION

How can we use scientific evidence to help us maintain energy balance?

UNIT QUESTION

How can we use personal data to help us make healthy food and activity choices?

 THEORIZING

1. Review Module and Unit Question

Remind students of the Module and Unit questions. Explain that in the last lesson they explored the "energy in" part of the energy-balance equation by collecting data on what they ate. In this lesson, they will learn more about the "energy out" part of the equation by learning one way to collect data about the level of their daily physical activity.

2. Discuss Homework

Have students take out their notes from their **Steps** homework assignment. Engage students in a discussion of the reading. Use the homework questions to guide the discussion. Check for student understanding of how being active benefits the human body. *What happens to us when we are physically active on a regular basis?* (We feel more energetic. We have the energy to do the things we want to do. We get fit. We feel good.) Summarize the benefits of physical activity.

3. Discuss Reasons to Stay Active

Have students work in small groups. Give each group a sheet of chart paper. Ask students to generate a list of reasons to stay active and record them on the chart paper. If they have difficulty coming up with ideas, use the *Great Reasons to Stay Active* lesson resource to prompt them. Don't dwell on the number of reasons — what's important is that they have a chance to reflect on why physical activity is important and that the reasons resonate for them.

EXPERIMENTING

4. Introduce Pedometers

Draw attention to the pedometer on your waistband. Ask students if they are familiar with this instrument. Explain that it is called a pedometer, and that it is used to count the number of steps you take. *Why would you use a pedometer instead of counting the steps yourself?* (You can lose count. It's more accurate. It makes it easier to keep track of your physical activity.)

Use the *Keeping Track of Physical Activity* lesson resource to discuss guidelines for using a pedometer. Emphasize that the pedometer is an important data-collection tool and that shaking it can artificially increase step count and, more important, damage it. Remind students to take good care of their pedometers.

Note: If you do not have pedometers for students to use, substitute the *24-Hour Activity Log* activity sheet. The *How to Use the 24-Hour Activity Log* lesson resource will guide this work. Post the sample activity log at the front of the classroom.

5. Collect Step-Count Data

Use the *Calibrating Pedometers* experiment sheet to instruct students in pedometer use and guide class discussion. You may find that some students try to wear the pedometers on their pockets, shoelaces, or other places that do not provide accurate step counts. This is a good time for students to discover that where the pedometer is placed does make a difference. After students have had time to experiment, check to make sure they place the pedometer in the correct location, on their waistband. Emphasize that wearing the pedometer on a high or low waistband produces data that is not as accurate as data produced by one worn on a waistband that falls at the waistline, with the pedometer halfway between the belly button and the hip bone. Check in with students to make sure they understand how to calibrate the pedometer.

6. Record Physical-Activity Data

Distribute the *Step and Write* activity sheets. Explain that for the remainder of the curriculum, students are expected to wear a pedometer every day. Review the activity sheet and check for understanding. Point out that in addition to selecting food goals in Lesson 12, students have an activity goal to take 10,000 steps per day. Remind them that they are collecting personal data and analyzing it to choose a goal that works for them. This is not a competition. Each person has different needs and goals.

7. Compare Activities

For the next few days, as homework, students gather personal data to compare the number of steps they take during different activities as they go about their daily routine. The purpose of collecting this data is to help them identify ways to meet their step-count goals. Review the *Comparing Activities* activity sheet with them. Make certain they all know how to record their average step rates. Tell them that this homework must be completed before Lesson 13. They use the data in Lesson 13.

 THEORIZING

8. Review Homework Questions

Give each student a copy of the **Choosing a Goal** student reading. Post the homework questions for the reading on the board. Have students copy them onto the *Homework Notes* activity sheet or into their LiFE Logs. Remind them to bring their notes to the next class.

9. LiFE Logs

Students have learned that they should aim to walk at least 10,000 steps a day. Have them write a few paragraphs in their LiFE Logs explaining why it is personally important for them to try to reach this goal. Ask them to explain why they believe getting ample physical activity will help their body do what they want it to do.

Keeping Track of Physical Activity

We all know that physical activity is important for health, but how can you tell if you're getting enough? Engaging in regular physical activity helps you make sure you have enough extra oxygen in your body to fuel your energy needs. Think about the last time you made a mad dash to catch a bus or train or make a meeting on time. Your breathing increased, your heart beat faster — what was going on? Your lungs, heart, and blood vessels were all working together to get more oxygen into your body. This helped you have enough energy to perform well...and catch that bus or make that meeting!

The amount of oxygen you take in and use greatly affects how well your body performs and how energetic you feel. With regular exercise, your lungs and heart get stronger. Your heart can pump out more blood and your lungs can bring in more oxygen. Walking is one type of daily physical activity that can help to increase your capacity to bring in and use oxygen. Staying physically active lays the foundation for being sure your body can perform well for you.

Pedometers

In this lesson, students are introduced to the pedometer, a tool that will help them measure and keep track of their physical activity each day. The pedometer is a small device that calculates the number of steps taken throughout the day. Once you calibrate it to the length of your stride, the little machine will keep track of how far you walk. Some also calculate distance and calories burned. Press "reset" each morning, and the pedometer starts all over again.

For the rest of the curriculum, students will be keeping track of their physical activity and trying to walk 10,000 steps a day. It's important for them to learn how to calibrate the pedometer, and why. They will be using the pedometers to track their personal data. Be sure to emphasize that the accuracy of their personal data is what counts. This is not a competition. Remind students that they are scientists collecting data.

We have provided a *24-Hour Activity Log* activity sheet as an alternative to pedometers. You also can use the log data to complement pedometer data. The *How to Use the 24-Hour Activity Log* lesson resource will guide this work.

Using the Pedometer

The best place to wear the pedometer is on your waist, attached to your waistband or belt. If your pedometer has a cover, make sure it is closed and that it is not hanging at an angle. Keep the pedometer as straight as possible. Remind students to put it on when they get dressed in the morning and to take it off when they go to bed at night, and to reset it to zero each day. Pedometers work like pendulums, moving back and forth with each step that is taken.

Encourage students to test the limits of their pedometers. Challenge them to design investigations to see how accurate the pedometer is when they run, bike, or climb stairs, or if they carry it in a pocket. Remind them to keep careful records of their investigations.

Join your students — clip on a pedometer and see how active you are each day! How close do you come to the 10,000-step goal?

Great Reasons to Stay Active

- **To build muscles**

- **To decrease body fat**

- **To build bone mass**

- **To have better concentration**

- **To get over "the blues"**

- **To control weight**

- **To be more flexible**

- **To be better at what is important to me**

- **To spend time being active with friends**

- **To make my heart and lungs stronger**

- **To be more alert**

- **To increase my self-confidence**

- **To increase my energy level**

- **To have fun**

- **To feel good about myself**

How to Use the 24-Hour Activity Log

If you do not have pedometers to use with this lesson, students can gather data about their physical activity by using the *24-Hour Activity Log* activity sheet. You also can use this log to gather additional information to complement the *Step and Write* data.

Recording sheets similar to the *24-Hour Activity Log* are often used in research on physical activity. They can provide accurate and useful information. Encourage students to record their data as they go through their day.

Here's how to use it. The log covers a time period of 24 hours — from noon of one day until noon the next day. Students record what they do every half hour. Tell them to record what they did in short phrases, using action verbs. Point out that there will be times when there is activity overlap within a half hour. For example, walking to the next class and sitting in the classroom. Use the sample on the next page to review with students what they should do. Because they need to fill this out every half hour while they are awake, remind them to carry the log with them at all times. In the "Level" column, students rate their activity level during each half-hour period, using a 5-point scale. For half-hour periods that included different levels of activity, tell students to choose the level that best represents what their overall activity level was during this time.

5-Point Scale for Level of Activity

1: Mostly lying or sitting still
2: Some moving but minimal, such as working on a computer, doing homework, or eating
3: A combination of some sitting and some standing or walking
4: Walking or light physical activity
5: Very active, running or playing sports that make you breathe hard and elevate your heart rate

If you meet with your class before noon, tell students to start the log at noon. If you meet with your class after noon, give them a few minutes during class to record their data, starting at noon. This will give you the opportunity to check their activity logs and provide guidance on collecting complete and accurate data.

24-Hour Activity Log Follow-Up (For Use in Lesson 13)

Once students have completed their logs, tell them to mark the times when they had control over their activities and could make changes. Have them mark these times with a star or a highlighter pen. Activities that students could control might include watching television and playing video games or getting from one place to another. Have students think about ways they could increase their activity level during the times they are in control. For example, they could stretch and do simple exercises while watching television. Or they could play an interactive video game that includes standing and moving. They could walk, bike, or ride a scooter or skateboard instead of riding in a car. They could take stairs instead of using the elevator.

Have students record their plans for what changes they will make in their LiFE Logs. You may wish to have them periodically complete the activity log again to create follow-up data they can compare with their original activity log in order to track their progress.

Time	Main Activities	Level
12:00 noon	Sitting in class at school	1
12:30 p.m.	Playing volleyball in school gym	5
1:00 p.m.	Sitting in class at school	1
1:30 p.m.	Sitting in class at school and walking to next class	1
2:00 p.m.	Sitting in class at school	1
2:30 p.m.	Walking to computer lab; working on computers	1
3:00 p.m.		1
3:30 p.m.	Walking home from school	4
4:00 p.m.	Eating a snack	2
4:30 p.m.	Skateboarding with my friends	5
5:00 p.m.		5
5:30 p.m.		5
6:00 p.m.	Eating dinner at home with my family	2
6:30 p.m.		2
7:00 p.m.	Taking the dog for a walk around the neighborhood	4
7:30 p.m.	Sitting at my desk at home doing homework	2
8:00 p.m.		2
8:30 p.m.		2
9:00 p.m.		2
9:30 p.m.		2
10:00 p.m.	Playing video games	2
10:30 p.m.	Sleeping	1
6:30 a.m.	Waking up, getting up, and getting dressed	1
7:00 a.m.	Eating breakfast	2
7:30 a.m.	Riding the bus to school	1
8:00 a.m.	Sitting in class at school	1
8:30 a.m.	Sitting in class at school and walking to next class	1
9:00 a.m.	Sitting in class at school	1
9:30 a.m.	Sitting in class at school and walking to next class	1
10:00 a.m.	Sitting in class at school	1
10:30 a.m.	Sitting in class at school and walking to next class	1
11:00 a.m.	Sitting in class at school and walking to lunch	1
11:30 a.m.	Eating lunch with my friends	2
12:00 noon	Sitting in class at school	3

Calibrating Pedometers

In this activity, students calibrate pedometers and learn how to use these science tools to collect physical-activity data.

Setup

1. Clear an area in the classroom where students can walk 100 steps in a straight line. Alternatively, plan to take students into the hallway or outside on the playground.

2. Distribute pedometers to students. We have found it helpful to write each student's initials on the pedometer with a permanent marker.

Procedure

1. Very gently move the pedometer up and down. Observe how it records movement. Establish a rhythm so the pedometer continues to count. Do not vigorously shake the pedometer. It is delicate.

2. Choose a place on your body to clip on the pedometer. Record the location in your LiFE Log. Do a quick sketch of where you placed it on your body. Describe the location in detail. This is important information so you can replicate exactly what you did.

3. Reset the pedometer to zero. Walk in a straight line and count out about 100 steps.

4. Record the number of steps you counted and the number of steps that were recorded on your pedometer.

5. Now place the pedometer at your waist, halfway between your belly button and hip bone. Record the location in your LiFE Log. Do a quick sketch of where you placed it on your body and describe the location in detail.

6. Reset the pedometer to zero. Walk in a straight line and count out about 100 steps.

7. Record the number of steps you counted and the number of steps that were recorded on your pedometer.

After you have walked 100 steps, if your pedometer is calibrated accurately, it will read between 90 and 110. If it does not, change the placement and try again. Use the 100-step test anytime you want to make sure your pedometer is working properly. You may find you need to move it if the waistband on the clothes you wear varies. For example, if a waistband is tight or loose, or falls above or below your waistline, this will change where your pedometer is located and can affect the results.

Questions

1. *What do you notice when you move the pedometer up and down?*

2. *What do you have to do to make the pedometer continue to count? Is this similar to what happens when you wear a pedometer and you walk or run? What's similar?*

3. *Where did you place your pedometer? Did the location affect the accuracy of the count?*

4. *Did you observe any factors that made the pedometer more or less accurate?*

5. *Why is it important to calibrate the pedometer? Could it have an influence on your investigation of physical activity? Explain your answer.*

Name   Date

Comparing Activities

In this activity, you investigate the question *Which physical activities will help me reach my goal of taking 10,000 steps a day?* You will spend several days collecting data on three different activities. Organize your data into a table like the example below. You will use these data tables to help you compare the activities.

Name of Activity: Walking the Dog

	Steps	Time
Before	2,107	10:08
After	3,563	10:36
Difference	1,456	28 minutes

Steps per minute: 1,456 ÷ 28 = 52 steps per minute

1. Complete the following three activity tables. Choose any three activities you do on a regular basis, such as cleaning your room, playing video games, walking home from school, playing basketball, and so forth.

2. Before you start each activity, record the time and the number of steps on your pedometer.

3. When you are finished, record the time and the number of steps on your pedometer.

4. To find the total number of steps you took during the activity, subtract the number of steps at the beginning from the number of steps at the end.

5. To find out how much time you spent doing the activity, subtract the time at the beginning from the time at the end, or use a clock.

6. To find the average number of steps per minute of each activity, divide the number of steps by the number of minutes spent on each activity.

Name of Activity: _____

	Steps	Time
Before		
After		
Difference		

Steps per minute: _____ ÷ _____ = _____ steps per minute

Continued

Name	Date

Comparing Activities, *Continued*

Name of Activity: _____

	Steps	Time
Before		
After		
Difference		

Steps per minute: _____ ÷ _____ = _____ steps per minute

Name of Activity: _____

	Steps	Time
Before		
After		
Difference		

Steps per minute: _____ ÷ _____ = _____ steps per minute

Summary of Activities

Complete this table using the data you collected from all three activities. You will use this information in Lesson 13.

Name of Activity	Steps per Minute

Selecting Food Goals

AIM

To use personal data to select a *Choice, Control & Change* food goal.

SCIENTIFIC PROCESSES

- question, hypothesize, gather data, apply

OBJECTIVES

Students will be able to:

- compare their own dietary behaviors with the *Choice, Control & Change* food goals;

- select food goals using personal data and other scientific reasoning;

- create a plan for how to implement their goal;

- implement their goal and track their progress.

OVERVIEW

In this lesson, students begin **The C3 Journey**, a series of readings and activity sheets that they will use and refer to for the rest of the module. This "booklet" summarizes the scientific basis for taking action; the why-to, which is followed by tips and strategies; and the how-to of making healthful choices. Students use personal data to choose a food goal, create concrete action plans, and then collect data so they can track and analyze their progress toward reaching their goal. One tool that students use to communicate is the bar graph. As one of our field-test teachers pointed out to her students, the bar graph is a great visual tool that can be used to compare what the *C3* food and activity goals are to what is actually going on in students' daily lives. Encourage students to take the time to really examine what the bar graphs communicate. Make sure they continue to use bar graphs to chart their progress as they work toward reaching their goal.

MATERIALS

For the teacher:
- Homework questions for Lessons 12 and 13 (p. 249)
- *The Story behind the* **C3** *Goals* lesson resource
- *Analyzing Personal Data* teacher note

For each student:
- *The C3 Journey* (pp. 251–274)
- **Step Success** student reading (p. 229)

- Notes from Lesson 11 homework
- (Optional) *Homework Notes* activity sheet (p. 275)
- Completed *24-Hour Food Intake* activity sheets (pp. 116–120)
- LiFE Log

PROCEDURE

Before You Begin:

- Remind students to bring in their notes from their **Choosing a Goal** homework assignment. Have the homework questions available for discussion.

- Review the *Story behind the C3 Goals* lesson resource and the *Analyzing Personal Data* teacher note.

- Remind students to bring in their completed *24-Hour Food Intake* activity sheets.

- Review and make copies of *The C3 Journey* for each student. Students will be referring to this guide for the remainder of the module. You may wish to staple the pages to keep them together, or have students keep them in a three-ring binder.

- Review the **Step Success** student reading and homework questions. Make a copy of the reading for each student. If you plan to distribute copies of the *Homework Notes* activity sheet, make enough to give one to each student. Alternatively, students can take notes in their LiFE Logs.

- If you have not already done so, post the Module Question and Unit 3 Question at the front of the classroom.

MODULE QUESTION

How can we use scientific evidence to help us maintain energy balance?

UNIT QUESTION

How can we use personal data to help us make healthy food and activity choices?

 THEORIZING

1. Review Module and Unit Questions

Remind students of the Module and Unit questions. Explain that in this lesson each student is going to use his or her personal data from the *24-Hour Food Intake* activity sheets to select a *Choice, Control & Change* food goal.

2. Discuss Homework

Have students take out their notes from their **Choosing a Goal** homework assignment. Engage them in a discussion of the reading. Use the homework questions to guide the discussion. Check to make sure students understand that their food logs record what they ate for a specific period of time, but represent food choices over a long period of time.

 SEARCHING

3. Review Goals

Distribute a copy of *The C3 Journey* to each student. In a whole-class discussion, review the material up through the section *Choice, Control & Change* **Food and Activity Goals.** Remind students of what they learned in the Lesson 4 reading in *Calvin and Carol Take Charge. What's MyPyramid?* (It's the national food-guidance system developed by the U.S. Department of Agriculture. It provides Americans with guidelines on how to make healthy food choices and be active every day.) *How do the* Choice, Control & Change *goals relate to MyPyramid?* (MyPyramid recommends a strong base of food that comes from plants, including fruits and vegetables, and reduced amounts of foods that have added fats and sugars. The *C3* food and activity goals also emphasize eating more fruits and vegetables and eating smaller amounts of foods that have added fats and sugars.) Review the six *C3* food and activity goals with students.

4. Review Scientific Evidence

Have students work in six small groups. Assign each group a different *Choice, Control & Change* food and activity goal from **The C3 Journey** reading (pp. 255–260). For the purpose of this review, include the physical-activity goal. However, in this lesson students will choose only a food goal. In Lesson 13, they will focus on the physical-activity goal. Allow students time to review the why-to (the scientific evidence) and the how-to (tips for taking action for their assigned goal). These readings summarize medical science research that relates to each goal. Feel free to use these readings whatever way best suits your class. We have had success in having small groups become experts on one goal and then share what they have learned with the class. Students will come back to information in **The C3 Journey** throughout the remainder of the module. Make sure they bring it with them to class.

5. Analyze Personal Data

Have students turn to the **Analyze Food Data** section of **The C3 Journey** (p. 261). Review the instructions with them. Have them compare their food and beverage intake to the *C3* food goals. Allow time for students to complete the bar graphs.

6. Choose a Goal

Have students complete the "Choose a Food Goal" portion of **Analyze Food Data** (p. 261). Tell them to circle one goal to work on. After they have chosen goals, have them develop an action plan (p. 267).

7. Introduce the *C3* Tracker

After students have completed their action plan, have them turn to **The *C3* Tracker** (p. 268). Explain to them that each time they make a try at their goal, they should record it on the tracker. Review the table with them. Discuss what information goes in the different columns. *What information would you include in the "How I Did" column?* (I'd record if I was successful or not at meeting my specific goal.) *What would you record in the "Triumphs and Challenges" column?* (I'd record things that helped me be successful and how success made me feel. These would be my triumphs. Things that made it hard for me would be my challenges.) Point out that the information that is recorded in **The *C3* Tracker** is important data that will help students become more successful at navigating the food and activity environment so they can take action and make choices that will improve their health and help their bodies perform better.

8. Review Homework Questions

Give each student a copy of the **Step Success** student reading. Post the homework questions for this reading on the board. Have students copy them onto the *Homework Notes* activity sheet or into their LiFE Logs. Remind them to bring their notes to the next class.

9. LiFE Logs

In this lesson students have learned about setting goals for their food intake. Ask them to think about the importance of setting goals. Have them write two paragraphs in their LiFE Logs about a time when they set a goal in the past and were successful in achieving it. Urge them to elaborate on what they did to achieve that goal and how they felt when they did achieve it.

The Story behind the C3 Goals

As we developed this curriculum, we were often asked where the *Choice, Control & Change (C3)* food and activity goals came from and why we chose them in particular. The quick answer is that they came in part from the federal government's recommendations, specifically the U.S. Department of Agriculture's MyPyramid.

If you look at the illustration below, you'll see that MyPyramid divides basic foods into groups: grains, vegetables, fruits, oils, milk, and meat & beans. Two of the food groups that many people do not eat enough of are fruits and vegetables. MyPyramid also recommends a strong base of food that comes from plants (grains, beans, fruits, vegetables), with some foods that come from animals, and reduced amounts of foods that have added fats and sugars. With these recommendations and the eating habits of middle-school students in mind, we developed the *C3* food and activity goals.

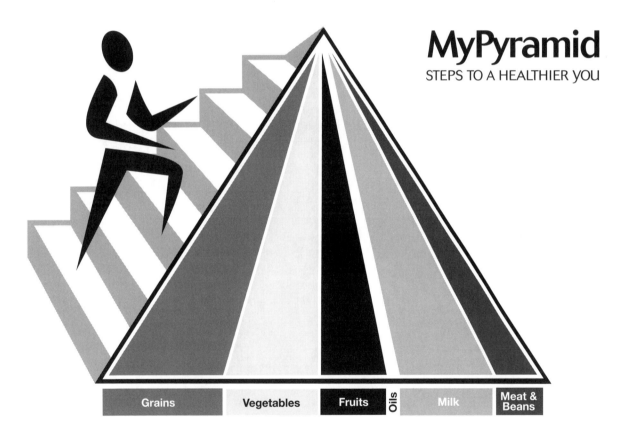

MyPyramid
STEPS TO A HEALTHIER YOU

Grains | Vegetables | Fruits | Oils | Milk | Meat & Beans

C3 Food and Activity Goals

- **Eat more fruits and vegetables.**
- **Drink more water.**
- **Walk more, including stairs.**
- **Drink fewer sweetened beverages.**
- **Eat less frequently at fast-food places.**
- **Eat fewer processed snacks.**

Choice, Control & Change is a behaviorally focused curriculum that addresses energy-balance-related behaviors related to obesity risk. While young children make their food choices based primarily on what they like, by middle school their cognitive-motivational processes also influence food choice through their increasing ability to link consequences to their actions. Inquiry-based science education is ideal for developing deep understandings of the scientific basis, or outcome expectations, for why to take action.

The energy-balance-related behaviors targeted in the curriculum: drinking fewer sweetened beverages, eating less fast food, eating fewer processed snacks, eating more fruits and vegetables, drinking more water, and getting more physical activity. These food and activity goals are supported by the recommendations of the federal government's MyPyramid and by a panel of experts on childhood obesity from 15 professional organizations.[1]

The aim of *Choice, Control & Change* is to help youth acquire motivations and skills to become competent navigators as they make choices within their food and activity environment despite the current food system and sedentary environment. Rather than focusing on weight per se, this curriculum focuses on behaviors over which middle-school students have a large degree of control. It uses a process of guided goal-setting, whereby the curriculum sets out several behaviors from which students can choose one. They create concrete action plans and collect data so that they can track and analyze their progress toward their goal. Through this approach youth learn the why-to and how-to of making healthful choices. They learn that they have *choices*, can take *control*, and can *change*.

---

[1] Barlow, 2007

Analyzing Personal Data

In this lesson, students make bar graphs to compare their food and beverage intake to the *C3* goals. Graphing was a suggestion from one of our field-test teachers. Once the bar graphs were added, the overwhelming consensus was that they work as a particularly effective visual tool to engage students in thinking about the importance of their daily choices.

For example, although looking at total amounts on the ***24-Hour Food Intake*** activity sheets from Lesson 10 tells students what they ate, it doesn't help them see where they are in relationship to the *C3* food goals. By making bar graphs to compare what they ate and drank to the *C3* food goals, students connect what they are learning with their lives. Analyzing food intake data challenges students to think deeply.

You also can use the bar graphs to engage students in a class discussion. Remind students of the Unit 3 Question, *How can we use personal data to help us make healthy food and activity choices?* This is a great time to emphasize that with this activity students are using personal data to help them make a healthy food choice. One of our field-test teachers challenged students to look at the graphs they made and see if anything really jumped out at them. Did they see anything that made them stop and think, "I'm way off here — I'm not even close to what the recommended amount is for something."

Before leaving the graphing activity, ask students if there were any variables that might have influenced their data. For example, during the 24 hours that they analyzed their food intake, did they eat out more often than they usually do? Was the weather hotter than usual or were they more active so they drank more? They can also look at how they answered the questions that follow the data tables on the ***24-Hour Food Intake*** activity sheet to determine if their data truly represents their usual food intake. Challenge students to think like scientists as they analyze their data. Point out that collecting data on food intake that represents what we really eat is hard. You can also challenge your students to design their own data collection methods and to defend why their collection method will produce accurate and complete data.

Creating Daily Activity Goals

AIM

To analyze daily activities and create an action plan to increase physical activity.

SCIENTIFIC PROCESSES

• gather data, analyze, apply

OBJECTIVES

Students will be able to:

• discuss the monitoring data from **The C3 Tracker**;

• use bar graphs to analyze the steps per minute of various activities;

• synthesize and draw conclusions about the step-per-minute data;

• create a personal plan for increasing physical activity in their lives;

• explain what they have learned about using personal data to make healthy food and activity choices.

OVERVIEW

In this lesson, students use their step-count data to explore ways to increase their activity levels so they can reach the *C3* activity goal. Before beginning the analysis of their physical-activity data, students review **The C3 Tracker** and discuss the personal data they have gathered so far in their efforts to meet their new food goal. The lesson continues with a review of the Lesson 12 homework reading, which you can use as an introduction to using personal data to create a plan to increase physical activity. Next, students work in small groups to compare and synthesize their results from the data they collected to determine steps per minute for different activities. Each group shares its findings with the whole class. Students then work individually to develop action plans for increasing the amount of physical activity in their lives, through adding activities with high numbers of steps per minute. The lesson closes with a short writing assignment in which students use what they have learned throughout this unit to write an answer to the Unit Question.

Note: If students used the *24-Hour Activity Log,* they will use the data they collected on the log. See the follow-up on the *How to Use the 24-Hour Activity Log* lesson resource.

MATERIALS

For the teacher:
• Homework questions for Lessons 13 and 14 (pp. 249–250)
• (Optional) *How to Use the 24-Hour Activity Log* lesson resource (p. 127)

For each student:
• Completed *Comparing Activities* activity sheet (pp. 130–131)
• *The C3 Journey* (pp. 251–274)
• **Move, Move, Move** student reading (p. 232)
• Notes from Lesson 12 homework
• *Paragraph Planner* activity sheet
• *Cardiovascular System Review* activity sheet
• (Optional) *Homework Notes* activity sheet (p. 275)
• (Optional) completed *24-Hour Activity Log* activity sheet (pp. 279–280)
• LiFE Log

PROCEDURE

Before You Begin:

- Review **Analyze Daily Activities** in the *The C3 Journey* (p. 270) and the "Develop an Activity Action Plan" (p. 272) section.

- Remind students to bring in their completed *Comparing Activities* activity sheet, their copies of *The C3 Journey,* and their notes from their **Step Success** homework assignment. Have the homework questions available for discussion.

- Review the **Move, Move, Move** student reading and homework questions. Make a copy of the reading for each student. If you plan to distribute copies of the *Homework Notes* activity sheet, make enough to distribute one to each student. Alternatively, students can take notes in their LiFE Logs.

- Make a copy of the *Paragraph Planner* and *Cardiovascular System Review* activity sheets for each student.

- (Optional) If students used the *24-Hour Activity Log* activity sheets rather than pedometers, review the follow-up section in the *How to Use the 24-Hour Activity Log* lesson resource (p. 127). Remind students to bring in their completed *24-Hour Activity Log* activity sheets.

- If you have not already done so, post the Module Question and Unit 3 Question at the front of the classroom.

MODULE QUESTION

How can we use scientific evidence to help us maintain energy balance?

UNIT QUESTION

How can we use personal data to help us make healthy food and activity choices?

 APPLYING TO LIFE

1. Discuss The *C3* Tracker

Have students take out their copies of *The C3 Journey* and turn to **The *C3* Tracker** (p. 268). Check to make sure that they are making entries on the tracker. If they are not, you may wish to give them a few minutes to work on it. However, encourage students to make their entries at the time they are attempting to reach their goal. Engage students in a discussion of how their work is going. Invite volunteers to share their experiences with the class. Acknowledge students' successes. Brainstorm as a class different ways to overcome challenges. If students need a reminder as to why the *C3* food and activity goals are important, refer to pages 255–260 in *The* C3 *Journey*. Draw this discussion to a close.

 THEORIZING

2. Review Module and Unit Questions

Remind students of the Module and Unit questions and tell them that this is the last lesson in Unit 3. Explain that in this lesson they will be comparing different physical activities and developing plans to help them reach their step-count goals.

3. Discuss Homework

Have students take out their notes from their **Step Success** homework assignment. Engage students in a discussion of the reading. Use the homework questions to guide this work. Check to make certain students understand how to compare steps in different activities.

4. Analyze Daily Activities

Divide the class up into small groups of three or four students. Have students take out their completed *Comparing Activities* activity sheet from Lesson 11. Tell them to turn to **Analyze Daily Activities** in *The* **C3** *Journey*. Have students follow the procedure to use the totals they calculated on their *Comparing Activities* activity sheet to make bar graphs that illustrate the number of steps per minute for each of their activities. Give them time to compare their bar graphs within their groups and to discuss what they have learned by comparing the different activities.

5. Synthesize Step-Count Data

Ask a representative from each student group to share the group's findings. *What are some examples of activities that you compared?* Record their responses on the board or on chart paper. Have students compare the steps per minute for the different activities. If some students had the same activity but different average steps per minute, discuss how people can do the same activity at different levels of intensity. For example, some people may walk more slowly than others. Through a whole-class discussion, draw some conclusions about the kinds of activities that result in the fewest steps counted per minute, the ones that offer the most, and the ones that are in the middle.

 APPLYING TO LIFE

6. Develop an Action Plan

Instruct students to turn to the "Develop an Activity Action Plan" section of **Analyze Daily Activities.** Have them use their personal data, as well as the ideas the class generated, to develop a specific plan for increasing the amount of physical activity in their lives. Remind students to make their plan specific. Tell them to include details regarding the exact activity and which days of the week and times

of day they can add that activity to their lives. Encourage them to think carefully about the strategies they plan to use to help them overcome any roadblocks. Invite a few students to share their plans with the class.

 THEORIZING

7. Review Homework Questions

Give each student a copy of the **Move, Move, Move** student reading and the *Cardiovascular System Review* activity sheet. Post the homework questions for the reading on the board. Have students copy them onto the *Homework Notes* activity sheet or into their LiFE Logs. Remind them to bring their notes to the next class.

Go over the *Cardiovascular System Review* activity sheet with students. Review the questions and check for student understanding. Tell students to complete this activity sheet for homework and to bring it the next time your class meets.

8. LiFE Logs

This is the last lesson in Unit 3, in which students explored the question *How can we use personal data to help us make healthy food and activity choices?* To assess what students have learned, ask them write at least a two-paragraph answer to the Unit Question. Distribute a copy of the *Paragraph Planner* activity sheet to each student. Read the Unit Question out loud. Review the activity sheet with students. Point out that this activity sheet is to help them organize their thoughts. Tell them to provide details from their own experience working with their personal data. They may wish to look back at Lessons 10, 11, and 12 to help them with their response.

Name   Date

Cardiovascular System Review

Think about why the human body needs a heart. Look back at your notes and what you learned in the human-body simulation activity in Lesson 7. Use this sheet to help you organize your thoughts.

Questions

1. Why does the body need a heart to stay alive?

2. How does blood get to every cell in the body?

3. Why is it important for blood to get to every cell?

What I Have Learned

a. _____

b. _____

c. _____

d. _____

a. _____

b. _____

c. _____

d. _____

a. _____

b. _____

c. _____

d. _____

Name	Date

Paragraph Planner

Your assignment is to answer the Unit 3 Question. Use this graphic organizer to help you plan your answer. Look at your notes from Lessons 10, 11, and 12 for supporting details.

UNIT 3 QUESTION: *How can we use personal data to help us make healthy food and activity choices?*

Topic sentence: _____

_____

_____

_____

_____

Supporting details:

1. _____

_____

_____

_____

2. _____

_____

_____

_____

3. _____

_____

_____

_____

Concluding sentence:

_____

_____

_____

_____

INVESTIGATING OUR CHOICES : DYNAMIC EQUILIBRIUM : **FROM DATA TO HEALTH GOALS** : EFFECTS OF OUR CHOICES : MAINTAINING COMPETENCE

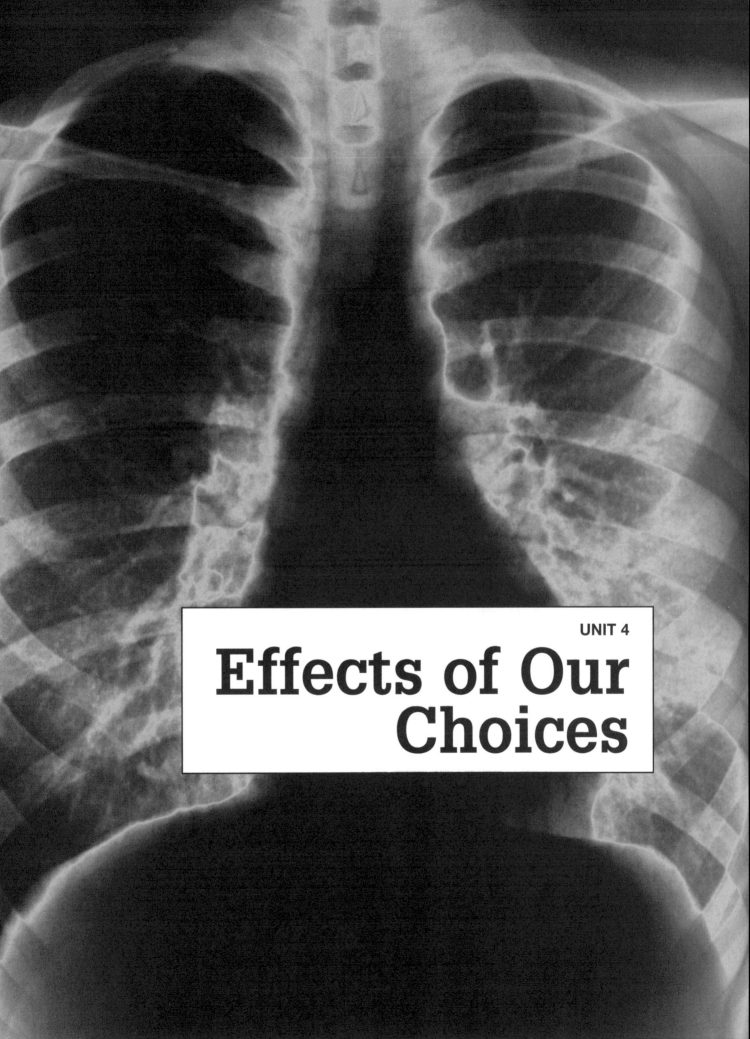

UNIT 4

Effects of Our Choices

Keeping It Pumping

AIM

To investigate the effect of physical activity on cardiovascular function and fitness.

SCIENTIFIC PROCESSES

- question, design experiments, construct knowledge, apply

OBJECTIVES

Students will be able to:

- describe and define the three components of fitness: endurance, flexibility, and strength;

- calculate the recovery time of their heart rate and breathing rate after exercise;

- describe how physical activity affects heart rate, breathing rate, and the function of the cardiovascular system.

OVERVIEW

In Unit 3, students gathered personal data, examined their own eating and activity behavior, chose a food goal, and investigated ways to increase their physical-activity levels. In this lesson, students investigate the effects of physical activity on the cardiovascular system and begin to explore the Unit 4 Question, *Why are healthy food and activity choices important for our bodies?* The lesson begins with students sharing their triumphs and challenges in meeting their food and physical-activity goals. This is followed by a review of what students have already learned about the cardiovascular system. Next the class discusses the Lesson 13 homework reading, which can be used as an introduction to a class discussion of physical fitness. After the discussion, students collect personal data to assess their endurance levels. They discuss why the measurement of recovery rate determines cardiovascular fitness. The lesson closes with a short writing assignment in which students reflect on the progress they are making in meeting their physical-activity goal.

MATERIALS

For the teacher:
- Homework questions for Lessons 14 and 15 (p. 250)
- *Cardiovascular Fitness* experiment sheet
- *Great Reasons to Stay Active* lesson resource (p. 126)

For the class:
- Clock with second hand

For each student:
- *The C3 Journey* (pp. 251–274)
- Completed *Cardiovascular System Review* (p. 141)

- *Recording Heart Rate and Breathing Rate* activity sheet
- **Healthy Hearts** student reading (p. 234)
- Notes from Lesson 13 homework
- (Optional) *Homework Notes* activity sheet (p. 275)
- LiFE Log

PROCEDURE

Before You Begin:

- Review the *Cardiovascular Fitness* experiment sheet and the *Recording Heart Rate and Breathing Rate* activity sheet.

- Remind students to bring in their copies of *The C3 Journey,* including **The C3 Tracker** showing their efforts to reach their food and physical-activity goals, their completed *Cardiovascular System Review* activity sheet, and their notes from the **Move, Move, Move** homework assignment. Have the homework questions available for discussion.

- Review the **Healthy Hearts** student reading and homework questions. Make a copy of the reading for each student. If you plan to distribute copies of the *Homework Notes* activity sheet, make enough to distribute one to each student. Alternatively, students can take notes in their LiFE Logs.

- If you have not already done so, post the Module Question and Unit 4 Question at the front of the classroom.

MODULE QUESTION

How can we use scientific evidence to help us maintain energy balance?

UNIT QUESTION

Why are healthy food and activity choices important for our bodies?

1. Discuss The *C3* Tracker

Have students take out their copies of *The C3 Journey* and turn to **The C3 Tracker** (p. 268). Check to make sure that they are making entries on the tracker. If they are not, you may wish to give them a few minutes to work on it. However, encourage students to make their entries at the time they are attempting to reach their goal. Engage students in a discussion of how their work is going. Invite volunteers to share their experiences with the class. Acknowledge students' successes. Brainstorm as a class different ways to overcome challenges. If students need a reminder as to why the *C3* food and activity goals are important, refer to pages 255–260 of *The C3 Journey*. Draw this discussion to a close.

2. Review Module and Unit Questions

Remind students of the Module Question. Introduce the Unit 4 Question, *Why are healthy food and activity choices important for our bodies?* Explain that this unit goes into more depth about why the C3 goals are important for good health and that in this lesson students will learn about the effects of physical activity on the body.

3. Review Cardiovascular System

Have students take out their notes from their **Move, Move, Move** homework assignment and their completed *Cardiovascular System Review* activity sheets from Lesson 13. Engage them in a whole-class discussion. *Why does the body need a heart to stay alive? What did we learn when we did the human-body simulation? How did blood get to every cell in the body? Why was this important?* Prompt students to discuss how the blood carries digested nutrients from food to all the cells in the body. Remind them that these nutrients are used for energy and to build the molecules the body needs to grow and function. Blood also contains oxygen, taken in through the lungs, which every cell in the body needs so that cellular respiration, part of metabolism, can take place. Cellular respiration releases the energy stored in food, changing it into forms the body can use. The heart pumps blood with oxygen to all the cells and takes away the carbon dioxide, which is a by-product of cellular respiration.

4. Discuss Homework

Have students take out their notes from the **Move, Move, Move** homework assignment. Engage them in a discussion of the reading. Use the homework questions to guide the discussion. Check for student understanding of how being active benefits the human body.

5. Investigate Endurance

Distribute one copy of the ***Recording Heart Rate and Breathing Rate*** activity sheet to each student. Follow the procedure on the ***Cardiovascular Fitness*** experiment sheet.

6. Discuss Fitness Level

As a class, discuss the question on the experiment sheet: *Why does the recovery rate determine the fitness level or health of the cardiovascular system?* Remind students that endurance is also called cardiovascular fitness. It is a measure of the health of the cardiovascular system. *How does the body respond when a person is physically fit?* (The muscles and cells become more efficient at taking up the oxygen and other nutrients they need from the blood. When the body is able to get what it needs quickly, the heart rate returns to its resting state quickly after exercising.) *Are the lungs affected?* (The lungs also become more efficient at taking in oxygen and releasing carbon dioxide.) *How does this affect you?* (When I exercise, I don't need to breathe as quickly to

take in the extra oxygen my body needs. This means my breathing rate returns to normal soon after I finish exercising.) Have a group discussion about some of the benefits of regular physical activity. You may wish to use the ***Great Reasons to Stay Active*** lesson resource to prompt student discussion.

7. Review Homework Questions

Give each student a copy of the **Healthy Hearts** student reading. Post the homework questions for this reading on the board. Have students copy them onto the ***Homework Notes*** activity sheet or into their LiFE Logs. Remind them to bring their notes to the next class.

8. LiFE Logs

Remind students that they have all set a physical-activity goal. Ask them to write a few sentences in their LiFE Logs reflecting on the progress they have made in meeting their goal. Tell them to reflect on what they learned in this lesson and to answer the following questions: *Will what you learned today help motivate you to achieve your goal? Why or why not?*

Cardiovascular Fitness

In this investigation, students measure their heart rate and breathing rate under different conditions to gain an understanding of cardiovascular fitness. They record their data on the **Recording Heart Rate and Breathing Rate** activity sheet.

Setup

1. Clear a space in the room so students can do jumping jacks without bumping into each other. Alternatively, take them outside or to the gymnasium.

2. Copy and distribute the activity sheet to students.

Procedure

1. Have students find their pulse on their wrist.

2. Tell them to count the number of times their heart beats in 15 seconds. Have them record this number on the **Recording Heart Rate and Breathing Rate** activity sheet table under "Resting Heart Rate."

3. Tell students to count the number of breaths they take in 15 seconds (breathing in and out counts as one breath). Have them record this number on the activity sheet table under "Resting Breathing Rate."

4. Have students calculate the heart rate and breathing rate per minute. To get these numbers, they should multiply the 15-second counts by 4.

5. Ask them to predict what will happen to their heart and breathing rates if they engage in physical activity.

6. Tell students to do 50 jumping jacks. If some are struggling and cannot do 50, encourage them to do as many as they can without overexerting themselves.

7. Immediately after they complete the jumping jacks, have them count their heartbeats and breaths for 15 seconds. Tell them to record those numbers under "Post-Activity Heart Rate" and "Post-Activity Breathing Rate."

8. Have students wait 5 minutes, then count their heartbeats and breaths again and record those numbers under "5-Minute Recovery Heart Rate" and "5-Minute Recovery Breathing Rate."

9. Have them determine their endurance level. Tell them to subtract the resting heart rate from the 5-minute recovery heart rate. Have them do the same calculations using their breathing rates.

Question

Why does the recovery rate determine the fitness level or health of the cardiovascular system?

Name   Date

Recording Heart Rate and Breathing Rate

Measuring your heart rate and breathing rate is a good way to determine how well your cardio-vascular system is working. Record your data in the table below.

Heart-Rate and Breathing-Rate Data

Resting Heart Rate (15 sec.)	Resting Breathing Rate (15 sec.)	Post-Activity Heart Rate (15 sec.)	Post-Activity Breathing Rate (15 sec.)	5-Minute Recovery Heart Rate (15 sec.)	5-Minute Recovery Breathing Rate (15 sec.)

Heart and Breathing Rate per Minute

Calculate your heart rate per minute. To get this number, multiply the 15-second Resting Heart Rate count by 4.

Heart rate per minute = _____

Calculate your breathing rate per minute. To get this number, multiply the 15-second Resting Breathing Rate count by 4.

Breathing rate per minute = _____

Predict what will happen to your heart and breathing rates if you engage in physical activity:

_____

_____

_____

Continued

LESSON 14: KEEPING IT PUMPING

INVESTIGATING OUR CHOICES : DYNAMIC EQUILIBRIUM : FROM DATA TO HEALTH GOALS : EFFECTS OF OUR CHOICES : MAINTAINING COMPETENCE

Name   Date

Recording Heart Rate and Breathing Rate, *Continued*

Calculating My Cardiovascular Fitness

Write the numbers in the appropriate blanks below. By subtracting the resting heart and breathing rate from the 5-minute recovery time, you can estimate your endurance level.

Heart-Rate Recovery*

5-minute recovery heart rate minus (-) resting heart rate =

_____ - _____ = _____

Breathing-Rate Recovery*

5-minute recovery breathing rate minus (-) resting breathing rate =

_____ - _____ = _____

*The closer your recovery rate is to zero (0), the faster you recovered from the activity. One indicator of cardiovascular fitness is how quickly the heart rate and breathing rate return to the resting level after exercise.

Keeping the Flow

AIM

To investigate the effect of diet on cardiovascular function and the development of cardiovascular disease.

SCIENTIFIC PROCESSES

- **question, experiment, construct knowledge, apply**

OBJECTIVES

Students will be able to:

- **explain how cardiovascular disease disrupts the function of the cardiovascular system;**

- **explain how diet affects cardiovascular health;**

- **state ways in which they plan to maintain cardiovascular health.**

OVERVIEW

In this lesson, students continue to learn more about the cardiovascular system. The lesson begins with the class sharing its triumphs and challenges in meeting the food and physical-activity goals. This is followed by a review of the Lesson 14 homework reading. Use the homework reading and notes to guide student discussion in this lesson. Next, students work in pairs to investigate the effect that clogged blood vessels have on the flow of blood in the human body. Through a class discussion, students discover how cardiovascular disease develops over time and learn about ways to maintain a healthy cardiovascular system. The lesson closes with a discussion of the homework reading and an assignment to interview family members to find out about diet-related health conditions they might have.

MATERIALS

For the teacher:
- Homework questions for Lessons 15 and 16 (p. 250)
- *Go with the Flow* experiment sheet
- Red food coloring
- (Optional) cornstarch
- (Optional) stove, microwave, or other heat source
- 3-inch piece of 3/4-inch clear plastic (PVC) tubing
- 2 tablespoons of yellow play dough

For each pair of students:
- (Optional) *Go with the Flow* experiment sheet
- 2 3-inch pieces of 3/4-inch clear plastic (PVC) tubing
- 2 tablespoons of yellow play dough (p. 281)

- 1 cup of cornstarch "blood" (p. 282) or red-tinted water
- 1 small plastic bowl
- Pencil
- Paper towel
- Newspapers or other surface covering

For each student:
- *The C3 Journey* (pp. 251–274)
- **Type 2 Diabetes** student reading (p. 237)
- Notes from Lesson 14 homework
- *Interviewing My Family* activity sheet
- (Optional) *Homework Notes* activity sheet (p. 275)
- LiFE Log

PROCEDURE

Before You Begin:

- Review the *Go with the Flow* experiment sheet. Gather materials. Make one clogged blood vessel as a sample for students and make the cornstarch "blood" (p. 282). Alternatively, you may wish to simply tint some water red for "blood."

- (Optional) If you decide to have students work in pairs, make copies of the *Go with the Flow* experiment sheet for each student pair.

- Remind students to bring in their notes from the **Healthy Hearts** homework assignment. Have the homework questions available for discussion.

- Review the *Interviewing My Family* activity sheet, the **Type 2 Diabetes** student reading, and the homework questions. Make copies of the activity sheet and student reading for each student. If you plan to distribute copies of the *Homework Notes* activity sheet, make enough to distribute one to each student. Alternatively, students can take notes in their LiFE Logs.

- If you have not already done so, post the Module Question and Unit 4 Question at the front of the classroom.

MODULE QUESTION

How can we use scientific evidence to help us maintain energy balance?

UNIT QUESTION

Why are healthy food and activity choices important for our bodies?

 APPLYING TO LIFE

1. Discuss The *C3* Tracker

Have students take out their copies of *The* **C3**

Journey and turn to **The *C3* Tracker** (p. 268). Check to make sure that they are making entries on the tracker. If they are not, you may wish to give them a few minutes to work on it. However, encourage students to make their entries at the time they are attempting to reach their goal. Engage students in a discussion of how their work is going. Invite volunteers to share their experiences with the class. Acknowledge students' successes. Brainstorm as a class different ways to overcome challenges. If students need a reminder as to why the *C3* food and activity goals are important, refer to pages 255–260 in **The C3 Journey**. Draw this discussion to a close.

 THEORIZING

2. Review Module and Unit Questions

Remind students of the Module and Unit questions and explain that in this lesson, they are going to learn about how diet affects the cardiovascular system.

3. Discuss Homework

Have students take out their notes from the **Healthy Hearts** homework assignment. Engage them in a discussion of the reading. Use the homework questions to guide the discussion. *What happens when the heart has to pump hard to push blood through clogged blood vessels? What is cholesterol? Why are healthy food choices important for a healthy heart?*

 EXPERIMENTING

4. Compare Blood Flow

Remind students of the simulation they read about in **Healthy Hearts.** *What did Dr. Floyd* *want Christian to simulate?* Explain that the students will do this same simulation in class. Tell them that they will compare two models of blood vessels: one that is very clogged with fat and cholesterol and has developed a lot of plaque, and one that is not clogged with plaque. Show students the sample clogged blood vessel that you made. Explain that this is what the clogged blood vessel should look like. Follow the procedure on the *Go with the Flow* experiment sheet.

 THEORIZING

5. Review Clogged Vessels

Use the questions on the *Go with the Flow* experiment sheet to lead a class discussion. Encourage students to refer to their homework notes from the **Healthy Hearts** reading. *What have we already learned about the cardiovascular system?* (The blood carries digested nutrients from food to all the cells in the body.) *What happens if there are clogged blood vessels?* (It will make it more difficult to deliver the oxygen and nutrients the body needs.) *The body still needs to have blood flow, so what will happen?* (The heart will have to pump harder to get the blood through. Blood going through clogged vessels causes increased pressure within the blood vessels, or high blood pressure.) *What happens if the coronary artery becomes completely clogged?* (This causes a heart attack.)

6. Discuss Diet and Cardiovascular Disease

Engage students in a discussion of how diet affects the function of the cardiovascular system. Have them think about what they observed in the *Go with the Flow* experiment and what they have learned in the **Healthy Hearts** reading. *Why do blood vessels get clogged with plaque? What can be done to keep them from getting clogged? How does diet affect the function of the cardiovascular system? What can happen if you eat a diet rich in animal fat? What can happen if you don't get enough exercise? What can you do to reduce the risk of*

cardiovascular disease?

Explain that it takes a long time for blood vessels to become clogged with plaque. Emphasize that eating a hamburger one day does not result in blood vessels covered in fat the next day. *Do you think young people can have clogged blood vessels?* (Fat accumulates in blood vessels with age. However, this does not mean that young people cannot have clogged blood vessels.) *If you have clogged blood vessels, can you do anything to change the situation? Think about what you have learned about eating and physical activity — do you think you can improve the health of your heart and circulatory system? What can you do?* (I can change my eating and activity habits to be more "heart friendly.")

7. Review Homework Reading

Distribute one copy of the **Type 2 Diabetes** student reading to each student. Tell students that for their homework reading and in the next lesson, they will be learning about Type 2 diabetes. Post the homework questions for the reading on the board. Have students copy them onto the *Homework Notes* activity sheet or into their LiFE Logs. Remind them to bring their notes to the next class.

 SEARCHING

8. Discuss Family Interview

Distribute one copy of the *Interviewing My Family* activity sheet to each student. Point out that Type 2 diabetes is often associated with a cluster of factors, including abdominal obesity, high blood pressure, high blood glucose levels, high LDL cholesterol, high blood triglycerides, and low HDL cholesterol. Tell students that they will be surveying their family members to find out if they have any of these conditions. Remind students to bring the completed activity sheet to the next class.

Go with the Flow

In this experiment, students compare the flow of "blood" in clogged and unclogged model blood vessels.

Setup

1. Gather materials.

2. Make simple "blood" by mixing red food coloring with water. If you wish to have thicker "blood," follow the *Cornstarch "Blood"* recipe (p. 282).

3. Cover work surfaces with newspaper or other covering so any "blood" that might spill will not stain.

Procedure

1. Have students work in pairs.

2. Give each pair of students two plastic tubes. Tell them that these tubes represent blood vessels.

3. Distribute the yellow play dough to each student pair. Tell them that this play dough represents plaque, which comes from the fat and cholesterol in the foods we eat.

4. Have them set aside one plastic tube. Tell them that this represents a blood vessel that has not been clogged with plaque.

5. Have them use the second plastic tube to make a blood vessel that is clogged with a lot of plaque and only has a small opening for blood to flow through. Demonstrate how to do this. Use your hand to roll the play dough into two long, thin logs. Make them slightly smaller in diameter than the plastic tube. Stuff one log into each end of the tube. Stick a pencil through the middle of the play dough in the tube so that there is a small opening from one end to the other.

Steps for making a plaque-filled blood vessel:

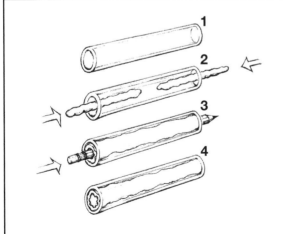

1) Take one of the clear tubes.

2) Roll the play dough into two logs thin enough to insert into the tube. Stuff one log into each end of the tube so it is filled with play dough.

3) Use a pencil to make a narrow hole all the way through the tube. Twist the pencil to help it pass through the play dough.

4) Remove the pencil. Now the tube models a plaque-filled blood vessel

---

6. After the student pairs have made the plaque-filled blood vessel, distribute the "blood" — a cup to each pair.

7. Instruct the pairs to have one student hold the unclogged blood vessel over the plastic bowl. Tell the other student to pour the "blood" through the blood vessel as quickly as possible. Have the partner holding the blood vessel count the seconds it takes for the blood to flow through. Tell them to record the time in their LiFE Logs.

8. Have students pour the "blood" back into the cup. Students should now switch roles. This time, have one hold the clogged blood vessel over the plastic bowl. Have the other pour the blood through while the partner holding the blood vessel counts out the seconds. Tell them to record the time in their LiFE Logs.

9. After they have completed this experiment, have them clean the play dough out of the clogged blood vessel by pushing a paper towel through the tube with a pencil.

Questions

1. *What did you observe when the blood flowed through the unclogged blood vessel?*

2. *What did you observe when the blood flowed through the clogged blood vessel?*

3. *Did you observe any differences in the way the blood flowed through the two different blood vessels? Describe what you observed.*

4. *What do you think would happen if your heart had to pump blood through very clogged blood vessels?*

Name	Date

Interviewing My Family

Ask five adults in your family who are over the age of 21 if they have any of the conditions listed below. Place a check beside all the conditions they say they have. The adults in your family could include parents, grandparents, aunts, uncles, or cousins. If you are not able to talk to five adults, you can also ask younger family members.

FAMILY HISTORY

Name	Condition
	❑ None ❑ High blood sugar ❑ High blood cholesterol or triglycerides ❑ High blood pressure ❑ Low good cholesterol (HDL*) ❑ Fat in the stomach area (abdominal obesity)
	❑ None ❑ High blood sugar ❑ High blood cholesterol or triglycerides ❑ High blood pressure ❑ Low good cholesterol (HDL*) ❑ Fat in the stomach area (abdominal obesity)
	❑ None ❑ High blood sugar ❑ High blood cholesterol or triglycerides ❑ High blood pressure ❑ Low good cholesterol (HDL*) ❑ Fat in the stomach area (abdominal obesity)
	❑ None ❑ High blood sugar ❑ High blood cholesterol or triglycerides ❑ High blood pressure ❑ Low good cholesterol (HDL*) ❑ Fat in the stomach area (abdominal obesity)
	❑ None ❑ High blood sugar ❑ High blood cholesterol or triglycerides ❑ High blood pressure ❑ Low good cholesterol (HDL*) ❑ Fat in the stomach area (abdominal obesity)

*HDL=High-density lipoprotein

Fighting Type 2 Diabetes

AIM

To explore how Type 2 diabetes develops.

SCIENTIFIC PROCESSES

- **experiment, question, theorize, apply**

OBJECTIVES

Students will be able to:

- **identify the factors that are involved in Type 2 diabetes;**

- **describe what happens in the body when a person has Type 2 diabetes;**

- **state actions that can be taken to prevent the onset of Type 2 diabetes.**

OVERVIEW

In this lesson, students investigate Type 2 diabetes. The lesson begins with students sharing their triumphs and challenges in meeting their food and physical-activity goals. This is followed by a review of the Lesson 15 homework reading. Use the homework questions to guide student discussion in this lesson. Next, students analyze the data on risk factors for chronic disease that they collected as homework. Using both the **Type 2 Diabetes** homework reading and the family interviews, the class shares what they have learned about chronic disease. After the discussion, they work in small groups to model how Type 2 diabetes develops over time in response to the blood constantly trying to remove extra sugar. Students reflect on the scientific evidence they already know and the new evidence they have just learned. The lesson closes with students answering the Unit Question in their LiFE Logs.

MATERIALS

For the teacher:
- Homework questions for Lessons 16 and 17 (p. 250)
- *Risk Factors for Chronic Disease* lesson resource
- *Exploring Family Data* lesson resource

For each group of five:
- *Investigating Blood Sugar* experiment sheet
- 4 plastic cups
- Plastic spoon
- Plastic fork
- 1 cup sand
- Paper
- Marker
- Tape
- Scissors

For each student:
- *The C3 Journey* (pp. 251–274)
- *Step and Write* activity sheet (p. 277)
- **Sharing Information** student reading (p. 240)
- Completed *Interviewing My Family* activity sheet
- Notes from Lesson 15 homework
- (Optional) *24-Hour Activity Log* activity sheet (p. 279)
- (Optional) *Homework Notes* activity sheet (p. 275)
- LiFE Log

PROCEDURE

Before You Begin:

- Read the *Risk Factors for Chronic Disease* lesson resource.

- Review the *Investigating Blood Sugar* experiment sheet. Gather the materials. If you have students working in groups of five, make a copy of the experiment sheet for each group. Alternatively, you may wish to set this up as a demonstration.

- On the board or a piece of chart paper, write the five conditions listed on the *Interviewing My Family* activity sheet: "High blood sugar"; "High blood cholesterol or triglycerides"; "High blood pressure"; "Low good cholesterol (HDL)"; "Fat in the stomach area (abdominal obesity)." Be sure to include "None" on the list.

- Remind students to bring in their notes from their **Type 2 Diabetes** homework assignment and their completed *Interviewing My Family* activity sheet. Have the homework questions available for discussion.

- Review the **Sharing Information** student reading and homework questions. Make a copy of the reading for each student. If you plan to distribute copies of the *Homework Notes* activity sheet, make enough to distribute one to each student. Alternatively, students can take notes in their LiFE Logs.

- If you have not already done so, post the Module Question and Unit 4 Question at the front of the classroom.

MODULE QUESTION

How can we use scientific evidence to help us maintain energy balance?

UNIT QUESTION

Why are healthy food and activity choices important for our bodies?

1. The *C3* Tracker and Activity-Log Discussion

Have students take out their copies of *The* **C3** *Journey* and turn to **The C3 Tracker** and the *Step and Write* activity sheet (or the *24-Hour Activity Log* activity sheet). Check to make sure that they are making entries on the tracker and the activity log. If they are not, you may wish to give students a few minutes to work on them. However, encourage students to make their entries at the time they are attempting to reach their goals. Engage the class in a discussion of how the work is going. Invite volunteers to share their experiences. Acknowledge all successes. Brainstorm as a class different ways to overcome challenges. If students need a reminder as to why the *C3* food and activity goals are important, refer to pages 255–260 of *The* **C3** *Journey*. Draw this discussion to a close.

2. Review Module and Unit Questions

Remind students of the Module and Unit questions. Have them turn to **Scientific Evidence that Supports My Goals** in *The* **C3** *Journey* (p. 273). Engage the class in a brief discussion of what they already know about why healthy food and activity choices are important for the human body. Tell students that with this lesson they are going to gather more scientific evidence about the effects of food and activity choices on the human-body system.

3. Discuss Homework

Have students take out their notes from the **Type 2 Diabetes** homework assignment. Engage them in a discussion of the reading. Use the homework questions to guide the discussion. *What is Calvin doing to decrease his risk of getting diabetes? What are the two main kinds of diabetes? What happens when a person has Type 2 diabetes? What food choices can a person with Type 2 diabetes make to be as healthy as possible?* Check for student understanding of Type 2 diabetes.

4. Discuss Risk-Factor Data

Refer to the conditions on the board. Point out that people often have several of these conditions at the same time. Have students take out their completed family interviews. *What can we do with the data we collected? What kinds of patterns can we look for?* (We can look at the class as a whole and see how common these conditions are in our families. Students can also analyze their own data for patterns and trends. We can see how many people have at least one risk factor.) Tell students that they are going to explore different patterns in their data. Use the **Exploring Family Data** lesson resource to guide this discussion.

Did anything surprise you as we looked at your data? (There were more people than I expected with risk factors for chronic disease. [Or] There were fewer people than I expected with risk factors for chronic disease.) Tell students that health professionals are becoming alarmed that an increasing number of people are developing Type 2 diabetes, especially children and teenagers. Point out that the percentage of people with Type 2 diabetes or related health problems has been increasing at a greater rate each year.

Reinforce the fact that there are two kinds of influences that contribute to the likelihood of a person developing Type 2 diabetes: genetic and environmental. *What do we mean by genetic factors?* (Genetic factors are things we are born with that we inherit from our families.) *What do we mean by environmental factors?* (Environmental factors are factors we can control through our behaviors, such as eating foods high in fat, sugar, and calories and not getting enough physical activity.) Bring this discussion to a close.

5. Discuss Weight

Address the issue of weight with students. Point out that excessive weight gain, when that weight is mostly an increase of stored fat, is associated with certain factors that may be related to Type 2 diabetes. However, this does not mean that you can look at a person and determine how healthy he or she is, or whether he or she has diabetes. *Do you remember Rosanna from your Calvin and Carol readings? What did Carol learn from Rosanna?* (You can't tell about a person's health by their physical appearance. Rosanna looks skinny but the fat in her blood is a little high. She is working on her energy balance, too.)

Challenge the class to think about messages that popular culture gives about the "ideal" body size. *When you think of an ideal body size, what image comes to mind? Do you think of a particular celebrity, sports star, or model? Where do you see images of these people? Do you think genetics plays a part in how tall, short, heavy, or thin a person might be? What other factors have you learned about that might influence body size?* (My food and physical-activity choices can affect my energy balance, and therefore my health.) *Does being underweight have health consequences?* (It can lead to malnutrition. Just because someone is thin does not mean that he or she is healthy. Just because a person is overweight does not mean that he or she is unhealthy.) Remind students that adolescence is a time when their bodies are going through changes, and it is normal for both boys and girls to gain weight as they get taller. How each person's body achieves this growth is unique — some people gain weight and then grow taller, and some people grow taller and then gain weight.

EXPERIMENTING

6. Investigate Blood Sugar

Depending on the amount of time you have, either set this up as a demonstration or have students work in groups of five. If you set this up as group work, distribute the *Investigating Blood Sugar* experiment sheet to each group. Distribute materials to each group and follow the procedure on the experiment sheet. You may wish to review each scenario before the groups begin the investigation. Use the questions on the experiment sheet to engage students in a discussion of what they observed.

Have students turn to **Scientific Evidence that Supports My Goals** in *The C3 Journey* (p. 273). Tell them to think about the class discussions and the blood-sugar investigation. Have them add what they have learned to the "Additional Scientific Evidence that I Learned" column.

THEORIZING

7. Review Homework Questions

Distribute one copy of the **Sharing Information** student reading to each student. Post the homework questions for the reading on the board. Have students copy them onto the *Homework Notes* activity sheet or into their LiFE Logs. Remind them to bring their notes to the next class.

8. LiFE Logs

This is the last lesson of Unit 4. To wrap up the unit and assess what students have learned, have them write two paragraphs in their LiFE Logs that answer the unit question, *Why are healthy food and activity choices important for our bodies?* Tell students that they can refer to the

scientific evidence chart in **Scientific Evidence that Supports My Goals** and their Calvin and Carol readings to answer the question.

Risk Factors for Chronic Disease

For homework, students interviewed adult family members to find out if any of them had risk factors for chronic disease. In this lesson, you will use the data students collected to see how prevalent these factors are in their families and to look for patterns. One pattern that health researchers have observed is that the incidence of risk factors for chronic disease has been increasing in adults. In fact, many adults have three, four, and sometimes all of the factors listed below. When a person has three or more of these risk factors, he or she is considered to have metabolic syndrome. The group of conditions associated with metabolic syndrome put you at risk for heart disease, stroke, and diabetes. More than 45 million adults in the United States have metabolic syndrome. However, what researchers find even more troubling is that these conditions are also being seen in adolescents and young adults at rapidly increasing rates. Make sure that students understand that, while there are medications available to control these conditions, it is possible to lower your risk of heart disease and diabetes by eating healthy food, getting enough physical activity, and staying in energy balance.

RISK FACTORS FOR CHRONIC DISEASE

Condition	What It Means to Have This Condition
High blood sugar	Insulin, a hormone, helps move sugar from the blood into the cells. When the body cannot use insulin effectively, sugar builds up in the blood. This can lead to Type 2 diabetes.
High blood cholesterol or triglycerides	There is an elevated level of the blood fat called triglycerides. Blood vessels get clogged with fat, and the resulting plaque buildup can prevent blood from flowing through the vessels. This increases the risk for heart attack or stroke.
High blood pressure	Blood pressure refers to the pressure of the circulating blood against the walls of the blood vessels. It is given as two numbers, the systolic measurement over the diastolic measurement. High blood pressure is a systolic measurement higher than 130 millimeters of mercury (mm Hg) or a diastolic measurement higher than 85 mm Hg.
Low good cholesterol (HDL)	High-density lipoprotein (HDL) cholesterol removes fat and cholesterol from the blood so it cannot build up on the walls of the blood vessels. Not having enough HDL cholesterol increases the chances of developing heart disease.
Fat in the stomach area (abdominal obesity)	There is extra fat in the body's midsection, particularly around the waist. This is often described as being "apple shaped." Extra fat tissue in the abdominal area interferes with the body's ability to get and use energy from food. This increases the risk of heart disease and Type 2 diabetes.

Exploring Family Data

You can use the data students gathered with their *Interviewing My Family* activity sheets to explore how prevalent these factors are in your students' families. Use the following questions to guide the investigation. The questions at the end of this lesson resource give different ways students can explore their own family data.

We've had success using the following method to tally results. Tell students you are going to use visual cues to keep track of their responses to the questions that you are going to ask about their data.

Begin with the entire class standing up. Tell students there are actions they will take if their response to a question is "yes." With the first "yes," students sit down and raise a finger. If their response to another question is also a "yes," they raise another finger, making their fingers a tally of their yes responses. They keep their finger(s) up until the end of the questioning. By the end of the questions, some students may be seated with five fingers in the air. Others may still be standing (no affirmative answers).

Questions

1. *Does anyone in your family have high blood sugar?* (Sit if yes and raise a finger.)

2. *Does anyone in your family have high blood cholesterol or triglycerides?* (Sit if yes and raise a finger. If you are already sitting and the answer is yes, raise another finger.)

3. *Does anyone in your family have high blood pressure?* (Sit if yes and raise a finger. If you are already sitting and the answer is yes, raise another finger.)

4. *Does anyone in your family have low good cholesterol (high-density lipoprotein, or HDL)?* (Sit if yes and raise a finger. If you are already sitting and the answer is yes, raise another finger.)

5. *Does anyone in your family have excessive fat in their abdominal area?* (Sit if yes and raise a finger. If you are already sitting and the answer is yes, raise another finger.)

In all likelihood at the end of this activity you will find that most of your students are sitting with at least one finger raised, and a large percentage of them will have two, three, or four fingers raised. Tell students that health researchers are observing that there are an increasing number of people with more than one risk factor for chronic disease throughout the United States. If any students are still standing, have them sit down.

You can also use this data to have students look in greater depth at their family. Students can think of their own questions to explore. Here are some possible questions: *Is one condition more common in your family? Do several family members have more than one condition? How many family members have all of these conditions?*

Investigating Blood Sugar

In this simulation, students investigate how Type 2 diabetes develops over time in response to lifestyle choices.

Setup

1. Gather materials.

2. Use paper and a marker to make labels for the four cups: *Food*; *Digestive System*; *Bloodstream*; and *Fat, Muscle, and Liver Cells*. Tape one label to each cup.

3. Label the plastic fork and the plastic spoon *Insulin*.

Procedure

1. Ask for five student volunteers to play the following roles: food, digestive system, bloodstream, insulin, and cells. Have the volunteers stand in that order. Make sure the person playing food has all the sand.

2. Model eating a healthy snack, such as a piece of fruit. The person who has the role of food carefully pours about 2 teaspoons of sand into the digestive-system cup. The person playing the digestive system pours the sand into the bloodstream. The person playing the role of insulin uses the spoon to scoop the sand from the bloodstream cup into the fat, muscle, and liver cell cup.

3. Next model a snack that is high in sugar, such as a large soda and a king-sized candy bar. The person who has the role of food pours about half a cup of sand into the digestive system. The digestive system pours the sand into the bloodstream. The student who has the role of the insulin uses the spoon to scoop the sand from the bloodstream into the fat, muscle, and liver cells.

4. Tell students to imagine that they are eating many high-sugar, high-calorie snacks every day for many years of their lives. The person who represents the food pours about half a cup of sand into the digestive system. The digestive system pours the sand into the bloodstream. The insulin (still using the spoon) moves the sand into the cells. While this is going on, "food" pours more sand into the digestive system, who passes the sand into the bloodstream. As the cell cup gets full, pour the sand back into the food cup so food can continue to pass it along.

5. Model the high-sugar, high-calorie snack scenario again. However, this time the system no longer works as it should. This time the student who is playing the role of insulin uses a fork instead of a spoon. The student playing the role of food adds sand to the digestive system just as fast as before.

Questions

1. *What does the sand represent in this simulation?*

2. *What happened when you modeled eating a healthy snack? How difficult was it to remove the sand? How long did it take?*

3. *What happened when you modeled eating a snack high in sugar? How difficult was it to remove all the sand? How long did it take?*

4. *What happened when you modeled eating high-sugar, high-calorie snacks every day for many years? How difficult was it to remove all the sand? How long did it take?*

UNIT 5

Maintaining Competence

Telling Others

AIM

To use what we have learned about making food and physical-activity choices and how they affect our bodies.

SCIENTIFIC PROCESSES

• gather data, apply

OBJECTIVES

Students will be able to:

• state scientific evidence for each of the *C3* food and activity goals;

• connect how the food and activity environments affect their health;

• communicate to others the scientific evidence that they have learned that supports the *C3* goals.

OVERVIEW

Throughout this module, students have been investigating how food and physical-activity choices affect their health. In this first lesson of Unit 5, students begin to explore the Unit Question, *How can I maintain my skills as a competent eater and mover?* Students discuss different ways that they can share what they have learned with others, and they begin to work on projects that will be displayed in Lesson 19. The lesson begins with students sharing their triumphs and challenges in meeting their food and physical-activity goals. This is followed by a review of the Lesson 16 homework reading. Use the homework questions to guide student discussion. Next, students begin to develop projects. They work in small groups, with at least one group working on each of the *C3* food and activity goals. The lesson closes with an assignment to write a newspaper op-ed piece that describes their *C3* food or activity goal and why it's important to try to reach this goal. For homework, students read and take notes on the final Calvin and Carol reading.

MATERIALS

For the teacher:
• Homework questions for Lessons 17 and 18 (p. 250)
• *Take Action to Make Change* lesson resource

For the class:
• Chart paper
• Construction paper
• Markers

For each student:
• *The C3 Journey* (pp. 251–274)
• *Step and Write* activity sheet (p. 277)

• (Optional) *24-Hour Activity Log* activity sheet (p. 279)
• **Reviewing the Scientific Evidence** student reading (p. 242)
• Notes from Lesson 16 homework
• (Optional) *Homework Notes* activity sheet (p. 275)
• LiFE Log

PROCEDURE

Before You Begin:

- Review the *Take Action to Make Change* lesson resource.

- Remind students to bring in their notes from the **Sharing Information** homework assignment, **The C3 Tracker,** and the *Step and Write* activity sheet (or *24-Hour Activity Log* activity sheet) so you can monitor their efforts to meet their *C3* goals. Have the homework questions available for discussion.

- Review the **Reviewing the Scientific Evidence** student reading and homework questions. Make a copy of the reading for each student. If you plan to distribute copies of the *Homework Notes* activity sheet, make enough to distribute one to each student. Alternatively, students can take notes in their LiFE Logs.

- If you have not already done so, post the Module Question and Unit 5 Question at the front of the classroom.

MODULE QUESTION

How can we use scientific evidence to help us maintain energy balance?

UNIT QUESTION

How can I maintain my skills as a competent eater and mover?

1. Discuss The C3 Tracker and Activity Log

Have students take out their copies of *The C3 Journey* and turn to **The C3 Tracker** and the *Step and Write* activity sheet (or *24-Hour Activity Log* activity sheet). Check to make sure that they are making entries on the tracker and the activity log. If they are not, you may

wish to give students a few minutes to work on them. However, encourage students to make their entries at the time they are attempting to reach their goals. Engage the class in a discussion of how the work is going. Invite volunteers to share their experiences. Acknowledge students' successes. Brainstorm as a class different ways to overcome challenges. If students need a reminder as to why the *C3* food and activity goals are important, refer to pages 255–260 of *The C3 Journey*. Draw this discussion to a close.

2. Review Module and Unit Questions

Remind students of the Module and Unit questions and tell them that this is the first lesson in Unit 5. In this lesson they will be exploring ways to help them continue to make healthy food and activity choices.

3. Discuss Homework

Have students take out their notes from the **Sharing Information** homework assignment. Engage them in a discussion of the reading. Use the homework questions to guide the discussion. Spend some time discussing public-service ads (PSAs) and the strategies that Mr. Morgan suggested for Calvin and Carol. Check for student understanding of target audience and the importance of aligning a campaign's communication strategy to the target audience.

4. Discuss Maintaining Skills

Use the Unit Question, *How can I maintain my skills as a competent eater and mover?* to guide this discussion. *What skills have you learned to help you make healthy food choices?* (I've learned how to estimate serving size. I've learned the importance of eating fruits and vegetables. I've learned to reduce the number of times I eat fast food and to make healthier food choices when I eat at a fast-food place. I've learned to drink more water and not as many sweetened beverages.) *Why is this important?* (It's important to be in energy balance. It's important to reduce the risk factors for chronic disease.) *Are there any actions you might take to help you continue to make healthy food and activity choices?* (We could try to change the food and activity environments so it's easier to meet our goals. We can ask for healthier snacks at school and more opportunities for physical activity.) *Did you find it challenging if your friends were not trying to meet the C3 goals and you were? How might you deal with this stumbling block?* (We could tell our friends what we have learned and see if they want to make changes, too.) Have students turn to **Reflections** in *The C3 Journey* (p. 274) and write a few sentences about what they would like to share with family and friends. Invite them to share what they wrote.

5. Plan "Take Action" Projects

Explain to students that they are going to use what they have learned in this module to come up with action plans for changing their food and physical-activity environments or for developing PSAs to communicate what they have learned to their peers. Use the **Sharing Information** reading to remind students what they have learned about public-service ads. The ***Take Action to Make Change*** lesson resource offers sample projects. Developing projects like these can help increase the availability of healthy food and activity choices in your local community. Encourage students to think creatively about what actions might help them make healthy choices the "easy" choices in your community.

Have students work in small groups. You may either assign projects or allow students time to develop their own. Make sure that at least several groups work on campaigns to educate others about the *C3* food and activity goals. Remind students to think about their project's goal. Some sample goals: 1) increase the availability of healthy snacks at school; 2) increase opportunities for physical activity; 3) teach others what I have learned about making healthy food and activity choices. Tell students that they will share their projects with others. In addition to the celebration in Lesson 19, you may wish to display the projects in the school hallways or in the cafeteria. Consider using this project as a formal assessment. Develop a set of criteria that you will use to evaluate the work, such as completeness, explanation of science concepts, and overall presentation. Review these criteria with students.

6. Develop Plan

Once students have chosen a project and established their project's goals, they can develop and implement a plan to meet them. Students should think hard about the kinds of actions that will be required to meet their goals. Make sure they develop a specific plan that will help them meet their goals. Remind them that it's important to remember that they may not see a significant change overnight. It will take time to build up support for their plan. You may want to encourage them to start small.

7. Implement Plan

Encourage students to look back over all they have learned in this module. Remind them to look at the research projects they began in Lesson 5 when they investigated their food and physical-activity environment. Challenge them to use this information as they develop their action plans. Remind them that throughout this module they have been gathering data and discussing scientific evidence that supports making healthy food and activity choices. Tell students to use this data to support their action plan. Encourage students to think about both the content of the message and the medium for delivering it. Tell them that the finished projects will be used in Lesson 19.

8. Review Homework Question

Distribute one copy of the **Reviewing the Scientific Evidence** student reading to each student. Post the homework questions for the reading on the board. Have students copy them onto the *Homework Notes* activity sheet or into their LiFE Logs. Remind them to bring their notes to the next class.

9. LiFE Logs

Ask students to write a newspaper op-ed piece, at least five paragraphs long, that describes their *C3* food goal or physical-activity goal and why it's important to try to reach this goal. Remind them to cite evidence from their readings and research to demonstrate what they have learned about making healthy food and activity choices.

Take Action to Make Change

Now that students have created and are tracking individual action plans for change, this lesson expands the work. Students choose to develop either a PSA or a project to increase the availability of healthy food and activity choices in their community. Encourage them to think creatively about what could help make healthy choices the "easy" choices in your community. Below are some project ideas to spur your students' thinking.

1. Walk to School

Tell adults you want to increase the amount of physical activity in your daily life. Talk to them about helping you develop a walk-to-school program in your community. Work together to create safe routes that you can take to school. Make walking to school part of your daily routine. Keep step counts of your walks to school. You can use a map to plot how far you collectively walk and post this map in your school (2,000 steps = 1 mile). Check out the resources on the National Center for Safe Routes to School Web site (*www.saferoutesinfo.org*).

2. Speak Up for Physical Education

If you don't have physical education every day, talk to your teacher about setting up a meeting with your school administrators. Explain why you think physical education is important for every student. Make a poster to share what you know with others.

3. Ask Your Local Stores to Stock Healthy Snacks

Educate your parents about the importance of healthy snacks. Ask them to help you partner with local stores to expand the availability of healthier foods in your school's neighborhood. Make posters to educate students at your school about making healthy snack choices when they buy snacks. See what others are doing. Check out the Healthy Bodegas Initiative on the Internet (*www.nyc.gov/html/doh/html/cdp/cdp_pan_hbi.shtml*).

4. Grow Your Own Healthy Snacks — Start a School Garden

If your school doesn't have a garden, talk to your teacher about starting one. Research fruits and vegetables you can grow in your region. Working in the garden will keep you physically active, and you can grow healthy snacks. Check out the resources in the National Gardening Association's Gardening with Kids online store (*www.gardeningwithkids.org*).

5. Ask for Healthy Snacks and Beverages in School Vending Machines

If your school has vending machines, find out who stocks them. Ask for a meeting to discuss offering healthy snacks and beverages. Explain why it's important to drink more water and fewer sweetened beverages. Share what you have learned about eating fewer processed snacks. Prepare a presentation.

6. Educate Parents and Students about the *C3* Goals — Make a Public-Service Ad (PSA)

Make PSAs that will help your target audience — your parents and other students — understand the importance of the *C3* food and activity goals. Include at least three examples of scientific evidence with each PSA. Think of ways to get your audience's attention.

7. Start a Campaign to "Unplug" — Reduce Recreational Screen Time

Do some research. Have a group of students keep track of the amount of time they spend watching television and playing video games each day. Prepare public-service ads that promote "unplugging" and moving your body.

8. Campaign for After-School Physical-Activity Programs

Get your parents involved! Prepare a presentation for the parent association at your school. Tell them about the importance of getting at least 60 minutes of physical activity per day. Present them with ideas for after-school physical-activity programs. Think about reasons it might be hard to set up these programs and be prepared to offer solutions.

9. Educate Students about Eating Less Frequently at Fast-Food Places and Making Healthier Choices When They Do

Survey the students at your school. Find out which fast-food places are their favorites. Use the Internet to research nutritional information for these fast-food places. Create fact sheets that students can use to make healthier choices when they do eat out. Make copies of the *How Much?* card and hand them out to students.

10. Sell Fruits and Vegetables at Your School Store

Write a letter to the parent association at your school. Ask for a meeting. Tell them you want to encourage students to eat more fruits and vegetables. Discuss setting up a cart in the school store that sells raw fruits and vegetables, like whole carrots, bananas, apples, and berries.

Bringing It All Together

AIM

To reflect on and synthesize what students have learned in this module.

SCIENTIFIC PROCESSES

- **construct knowledge, put into action**

OBJECTIVES

Students will be able to:

- **articulate their reasons for their behavior change;**

- **express in writing an answer to the Module Question;**

- **evaluate how their answer to the Module Question has changed;**

- **describe strategies to maintain their goal behaviors into the future.**

OVERVIEW

In this lesson, students continue to work on the PSAs and action plans they began in Lesson 17. The lesson begins with students sharing their triumphs and challenges in meeting their food and physical-activity goals. This is followed by a review of the Lesson 17 homework reading. Use the homework questions to guide student discussion. Next, students plan a healthy food celebration, including a menu of healthful foods to serve. Students' action projects and PSAs will be put on display so guests can view the work. Some classes we have worked with have expanded this celebration and turned it into a health fair that educates and informs the school community or the community at large. For homework, students think about how to continue working toward their food and activity goals and record their strategies in their LiFE Logs.

MATERIALS

For the teacher:
- Homework questions for Lesson 18 (p. 250)
- *Healthy Snacks Supply List* lesson resource
- *Healthy Snacks Recipes* lesson recipe
- (Optional) *Planning a Sharing-the-Health Fair* lesson resource (p. 182)
- 6 sheets of chart paper
- Markers
- Tape

For each student:
- *The C3 Journey* (pp. 251–274)
- **Reviewing the Scientific Evidence** student reading (p. 242)
- *Step and Write* activity sheet (p. 277)
- (Optional) *24-Hour Activity Log* activity sheet (p. 279)
- Action-plan project or PSA started in Lesson 17
- *Making a Personal Pledge* activity sheet
- LiFE Log

PROCEDURE

Before You Begin:

- Remind students to bring in their notes from their **Reviewing the Scientific Evidence** homework assignment, their *Step and Write* activity sheets (or the *24-Hour Activity Log* activity sheet), and their action-plan projects or PSAs. Have the homework questions available for discussion.

- Write one *C3* goal on each of the sheets of chart paper. Draw a line down the middle of each sheet. Label one column "Why-to" (reasons the goals are important) and the other "How-to" (ways to implement the goal in their lives). Tape these sheets to the classroom walls.

- If you are going to invite parents to the celebration in Lesson 19, or have students bring in healthy snacks to share, make these plans now so families have time to prepare. You may wish to review the *Planning a Sharing-the-Health Fair* lesson resource.

- If you have not done so already, post the Module Question and Unit 5 Question at the front of the classroom.

MODULE QUESTION

How can we use scientific evidence to help us maintain energy balance?

UNIT QUESTION

How can I maintain my skills as a competent eater and mover?

1. Discuss The *C3* Tracker and Activity Log

Have students take out their copies of *The* **C3** *Journey* and turn to **The C3 Tracker** (p. 268) and the *Step and Write* activity sheet (or the *24-Hour Activity Log* activity sheet). Check to make sure that they are making entries on the tracker and the activity log. If they are not, you may wish to give students a few minutes to work on them. However, encourage students to make their entries at the time they are attempting to reach their goals. Engage the class in a discussion of how the work is going. Invite volunteers to share their experiences. Acknowledge students' successes. Brainstorm as a class different ways to overcome challenges. If students need a reminder as to why the *C3* food and activity goals are important, refer to pages 255–260 of *The* **C3** *Journey*. Draw this discussion to a close.

2. Review the Module Question and All Unit Questions

Explain to students that this is the last unit in the module, and it is an opportunity to reflect on and synthesize what they have learned. Review the Unit questions for Units 1 through 4 one at a time. For each question have a few students share how they have expanded or changed their answer to the Unit Question as a result of the lessons. Have students turn to **Reflections** in *The* **C3** *Journey* (p. 274). Invite them to share their answer to the Module Question. Challenge them to think about how the Unit Questions help them expand their answers to the Module Question.

3. Discuss Homework

Have students take out their notes from the **Reviewing the Scientific Evidence** homework assignment. Engage them in a discussion of the reading. Use the homework questions to guide the discussion.

4. Synthesize Scientific Evidence

Have students turn to **Scientific Evidence that Supports My Goals** in *The* C3 *Journey* (p. 273). Engage them in a whole-class discussion of the scientific evidence that supports the *C3* food and activity goals. Elicit comments from the class about what influences our food choices and about the scientific evidence for why it is important to make healthy food and activity choices to have your body be able to do what you want it to do.

Point out to the students the chart-paper sheets with the *C3* goals on them posted throughout the classroom. Invite the students to circulate around the room to record scientific evidence, personal experiences, and ideas for how to implement the goals and why each goal is important. They can put their entries under "Why-to" or "How-to." Save these sheets to display at the celebration.

APPLYING TO LIFE

5. Plan a Healthy Food and Activity Celebration

You may wish to review the *Planning a Sharing-the-Health Fair* lesson resource (p. 182). Decide who you are going to invite to the final celebration. Plan what attendees will do and learn during the celebration. Make invitations to send to your guests. Have students brainstorm ideas for healthy foods to serve. Encourage them to base the menu on fruits and vegetables and other healthy foods. Be sure to let your students plan the menu. Use the *Healthy Snacks Recipes* for ideas. Ask for student volunteers to form an activity committee. Help them plan music, dancing, and other activities for the celebration.

6. Work on Projects

Check in with each group of students. Meet briefly with them to check their progress with their action plans or PSAs. Brainstorm with students a list of possible presentation styles to use at the celebration. Remind them to think of what they want to communicate, and how, to their target audience.

7. LiFE Logs

Have students write an answer to the Module Question in their LiFE Logs. Encourage them to write as complete an answer to the Module Question as they can. Remind them to look at and think about the Unit Questions and to incorporate what they learned in each unit into their answer.

8. Make a Personal Pledge

Distribute a copy of the *Making a Personal Pledge* activity sheet to each student. As homework, have students look over the progress they have made so far on **The** *C3* **Tracker** and their *Step and Write* records. After reviewing this work, tell students to use the *Making a Personal Pledge* activity sheet to make a plan for maintaining their goals in their daily lives.

Healthy Snacks Supply List

SALAD

Ingredients

- 1 head lettuce: romaine or other dark green lettuce
- 1 bag mixed salad greens
- 6 carrots
- 1 bunch celery
- 2 bunches broccoli
- 1 pint cherry tomatoes or 7 larger tomatoes
- 8 ounces ready-to-eat sunflower seeds

Supplies

- 1 sharp knife for chopping
- 1 vegetable peeler
- 1 cutting board
- 1 spoon for serving salad dressing
- 2 spoons to toss and serve salad
- 1 whisk
- 1 bowl to mix salad dressing
- 1 or 2 large bowls to hold salad
- 1 colander to rinse vegetables
- Enough bowls to give 1 to every group of 4–6 students

SALAD DRESSING

Ingredients

- 3/4 cup olive oil
- 3/4 cup red wine vinegar
- 4 tablespoons honey
- 3 tablespoons Dijon mustard
- 2 shallots
- 2 cloves garlic
- Salt and pepper

Supplies

- 1 bowl
- 1 sharp knife
- 1 cutting board
- 3/4 cup measure
- Tablespoon
- Whisk

VEGETABLES WITH HERB DIP

Ingredients

- 16 ounces low-fat plain yogurt
- 1/2 packet of dry salad-dressing mix (such as ranch, Italian herb, or onion)
- Fresh vegetables appropriate for dipping (carrots, celery, peppers, zucchini, cucumbers, and radishes all work well)
- (Optional) chopped scallions or grated vegetables such as carrots or radishes

Supplies

- 1 bowl for dip
- 1 spoon for mixing and serving dip
- 1 sharp knife for cutting vegetables
- 1 vegetable peeler
- 1 cutting board
- 1 large plate for serving vegetables
- Enough dip bowls to give 1 to each group of 4–6 students

FRESH FRUIT KABOBS

Ingredients

- 5 apples
- 5 bananas
- 2 cups red seedless grapes
- 2 cups green seedless grapes
- 3 cups pineapple chunks
- 5 cups nonfat vanilla yogurt
- Lemon juice

Supplies

- 1 sharp knife for cutting fruit
- 1 cutting board
- 1 or 2 large plates to hold fruit
- 2–4 spoons
- Enough bowls to give 1 to every group of 4–6 students
- 1 wooden skewer (if making kabobs)

FRUIT AND YOGURT PARFAITS

Ingredients

- 5 cups nonfat vanilla yogurt
- 5 cups whole-grain cereal
- 5 cups blueberries
- 5 cups strawberries

Supplies

- 1 sharp knife for cutting strawberries
- 1 cutting board
- 4 bowls to hold ingredients
- 4 serving spoons

CALIFORNIA VEGETABLE ROLLS

Ingredients

- 20 6-inch whole-wheat tortillas/wraps
- 1-pound bag fresh spinach leaves
- 4 carrots
- 8 ounces reduced-fat cream cheese
- 2 cups shredded reduced-fat cheddar cheese
- Ground black pepper
- (Optional) salsa

Supplies

For each group of 4–6 students
- 1 sharp knife
- 1 cutting board
- 4 bowls
- 1 plastic knife
- (Optional) 1 serving spoon for salsa

For each student
- 2 paper plates
- 1 plastic knife
- 1 plastic fork
- 1 plastic spoon
- 1 napkin
- 1 cup (preferably clear)

Healthy Snacks Recipes

SALAD

Makes 25 small portions

Ingredients

- 1 head lettuce, romaine or other dark green lettuce
- 1 bag mixed salad greens
- 6 carrots
- 1 bunch celery
- 2 bunches broccoli
- 1 pint cherry tomatoes or 7 larger tomatoes
- 8 ounces ready-to-eat sunflower seeds

Preparation Before Class

1. Wash the lettuce and mixed salad greens.
2. Wash the carrots. Peel them and slice them into thin strips.
3. Wash the celery.
4. Wash and (optional) blanch the broccoli. To blanch, place head of broccoli in boiling water for 1 to 2 minutes. Rinse and refrigerate. (Blanching the broccoli makes it easier to cut.)
5. Wash the tomatoes.

Directions

1. Use your hands to tear the lettuce into bite-sized pieces. Place the lettuce and mixed greens in the salad bowl.
2. Cut the carrots, celery, broccoli, and tomatoes into bite-sized pieces and place in the salad bowl.
3. Sprinkle salad with sunflower seeds.
4. Gently toss the salad until it looks mixed. Be careful not to overmix, which may damage the vegetables.
5. Prepare the salad dressing.
6. Serve salad on plates. Add dressing.

SALAD DRESSING

Yields 2 cups

Ingredients

- 3/4 cup olive oil
- 3/4 cup red wine vinegar
- 4 tablespoons honey
- 3 tablespoons Dijon mustard
- 2 shallots
- 2 cloves garlic
- Salt and pepper

Directions

1. Mince the shallots.
2. Mince the garlic.
3. Place olive oil, vinegar, honey, mustard, minced shallots, and minced garlic into a bowl. Whisk until thoroughly mixed.
4. Add salt and pepper to taste.

VEGETABLES WITH HERB DIP

Serves 20

This dip tastes best if it is refrigerated for at least 8 hours before eating.

Ingredients

16 ounces low-fat plain yogurt

1/2 packet of dry salad-dressing mix (such as ranch, Italian herb, or onion)

Fresh vegetables appropriate for dipping (carrots, celery, peppers, zucchini, cucumbers and radishes all work well)

(Optional) chopped scallions or grated vegetables such as carrots or radishes

Preparation Before Class

1. Mix the yogurt with the dry salad-dressing mix.
2. (Optional) Add scallions or grated vegetables to the dip.
3. Wash vegetables.
4. Peel carrots and slice into thin strips.

Directions

1. Cut vegetables into easy-to-dip pieces.
2. Divide dip among group bowls.
3. Serve vegetables on a plate with dip.

FRESH FRUIT KABOBS

Serves 20

Ingredients

5 apples

5 bananas

2 cups red seedless grapes

2 cups green seedless grapes

3 cups pineapple chunks

5 cups nonfat vanilla yogurt

Lemon juice

Preparation Before Class

1. Wash grapes.
2. Wash and core apple. Cut into slices. If not eating immediately, coat with lemon juice.
3. Place yogurt in bowl with spoon for serving.

Directions

1. Remove grapes from vine and divide into bowls, one bowl per group.
2. Peel bananas, cut into chunks, and divide into same bowls.
3. Divide chunks of pineapple into same bowls.
4. Cut slices of apples into squares and divide into same bowls.
5. Have each student slide desired fruit on a skewer.
6. Serve kabob with yogurt for dipping.

FRUIT AND YOGURT PARFAITS

Serves 20

Ingredients

5 cups nonfat vanilla yogurt

5 cups whole-grain cereal

5 cups blueberries

5 cups strawberries

Preparation Before Class

1. Wash strawberries, cut into thin slices, and place in first serving bowl.

2. Wash blueberries and place in second serving bowl.

3. Place yogurt in third serving bowl.

4. Place cereal in fourth serving bowl.

Directions

1. Layer berries, yogurt, and cereal in individual cups.

2. Serve with spoon.

CALIFORNIA VEGETABLE ROLLS

Serves 20

Ingredients

20 6-inch whole-wheat tortillas/wraps

1-pound bag fresh spinach leaves

4 carrots

8 ounces reduced-fat cream cheese

2 cups shredded reduced-fat cheddar cheese

Ground black pepper

(Optional) salsa

Preparation Before Class

1. Wash spinach thoroughly and allow to dry; divide into bowls, one bowl per group.

2. Wash, peel, and shred carrots with a grater; divide into bowls, one per group.

3. Divide cream cheese into bowls, one per group.

4. Divide cheddar cheese into bowls, one per group, and stir a pinch of black pepper into each bowl.

Directions

1. Give each student one tortilla/wrap.

2. Have students spread a thin layer of cream cheese onto wrap using plastic knife.

3. Place a layer of spinach to cover cream cheese.

4. Sprinkle carrots on top of spinach.

5. Sprinkle cheddar cheese on top of carrots.

6. Roll the tortilla as tightly as possible.

7. Either have the students slice the roll into 4 or 5 slices using a sturdy plastic knife or assist them with a sharp knife.

8. (Optional) Serve with salsa.

Name	Date

Making a Personal Pledge

Think about one strategy that has been helping you to be successful at reaching one of the *C3* food and activity goals. In this activity, you make a personal pledge to maintain (keep doing) this behavior. Make the pledge something that you feel confident you can do now and into the future. Be sure it is something you feel like you really have a choice about. Read the examples below, then write your pledge.

Examples:

MARIE'S C3 ACTIVITY GOAL: Walk more, including stairs — aim for at least 10,000 steps per day.

Marie realized that one of the ways she increased her daily steps was to walk up stairs whenever there were four or fewer flights. Here is Marie's personal pledge:

> Whenever I have a choice between an elevator and stairs, I will choose the stairs if it is four or fewer flights, unless I am really sick or carrying something on wheels or something very heavy.

ED'S C3 FOOD GOAL: Eat more fruits and vegetables — aim for at least 4 cups a day.

Ed realized that he was able to eat more fruit because he and his friends decided after they investigated their food environment that they wanted to buy fruit in the deli after school instead of candy or chips. Ed has been doing this at least twice a week. Here is Ed's personal pledge:

> At least two days each week when I go to the deli after school I will buy an apple, banana, pear, or other fruit instead of candy or chips, even if my friends are having other snacks.

Make a Personal Pledge

Write your *C3* food or activity goal here: _____

_____

_____

Record your pledge. Remember to make your pledge something you are already doing and something you feel confident that you can keep doing.

My personal pledge: _____

_____

_____

Sharing the Health

AIM

To share student work and food with others.

SCIENTIFIC PROCESSES

- **apply, communicate**

OBJECTIVES

Students will be able to:

- **discuss why their personal pledge is important and how they will make sure they stick to it;**

- **communicate scientific understandings and experiences with others.**

OVERVIEW

This final lesson is a chance for students to celebrate what they have created and accomplished in *C3* while sharing healthy food together. Before you begin the celebration, set aside some time for the class to discuss the personal pledges they made as homework in Lesson 18. Next, students prepare for the celebration. It can be as big or as small as you and your class choose to make it. It can take on a variety of different forms. You can expand the event to include members of your school community or even hold a more formal community fair — a great way to get the whole school or community involved and healthy. If possible, choose a time and place that ensures that parents and other community members can attend. You may also want to create flyers to advertise the event. At the event, students put their action plans and PSAs on display to share what they have learned with their guests. The class also shares healthy snacks and discusses how food and activity choices affect our bodies. Be sure to give students a role in presenting their work to others.

MATERIALS

For the class:
- *Planning a Sharing-the-Health Fair* lesson resource
- Food and supplies listed in the *Healthy Snacks Supply List* lesson resource (pp. 173–175)
- Completed action plans or PSAs from Lesson 17

For each student:
- Completed *Making a Personal Pledge* activity sheet (p. 179)

PROCEDURE

Before You Begin:

- Display students' projects.

- Remind students to bring in their completed *Making a Personal Pledge* activity sheets from the Lesson 18 homework.

- Review the *Planning a Sharing-the-Health Fair* lesson resource. Prepare the healthy snacks or ask students to bring in the food as planned in Lesson 18.

- If you have not already done so, post the Module Question and Unit 5 Question at the front of the classroom.

MODULE QUESTION

How can we use scientific evidence to help us maintain energy balance?

UNIT QUESTION

How can I maintain my skills as a competent eater and mover?

1. Review Module and Unit Questions

Remind students of the Module Question and Unit Question. Tell them that this is the last lesson of the module. It is going to be a celebration of all that they have learned and accomplished as well as a chance to enjoy delicious and healthy food together.

2. Review Personal Pledges

Divide the students into small groups. Within each group, have members share their pledges. Tell students to discuss the pledges and share any ideas or suggestions for how to maintain them. After the groups have shared their pledges, invite students to share them with the whole class. Encourage them to talk to one another and their families about their pledges. Point out that it can be hard to maintain healthful habits. Emphasize that sharing their goals and pledges with others can be very helpful.

3. Display Student Work

Have students display their projects around the room. You may wish to have one student leader per group discuss the team's project. If you have time, have students practice their presentations several times before the celebration. Ask student groups to critique one another's projects. Remind them to offer only constructive criticism.

4. Share Food

Set up the healthy snacks. Let each student sample a small amount of each food, and remind them that it is okay to try things they might not like, but not okay to make negative comments about foods that someone else might be trying to enjoy. As you are putting out the food, touch upon the idea that it takes time to plan for and prepare food that is nutritious and delicious. Point out that while it might be easier to grab fast food, homemade snacks often taste better.

Celebrate!

Planning a Sharing-the-Health Fair

In Lesson 18, we encouraged you to hold an event or celebration, which is a great way for students to be able to share what they have learned. You can start small, holding it in your classroom and inviting grade-level peers, or hold a school-wide expo and invite the entire student body and parents. Either way, your students will be the experts who educate and inform others on why to and how to make better food and activity choices. Once you make the decision to hold an event, the next step is to pick a date and decide on a location. Will it be during the school day, after school, or on a weekend?

Identify leaders in your class and assign them to help you organize. Plan to have a publicity committee and a program committee that will oversee the presentations and any exhibits you might wish to include. Don't forget a cleanup committee. Make it clear that they are not the only ones who will be cleaning up, but they will be the ones to develop a cleanup plan. Your role will be event coordinator. Have each committee leader work with a team so the entire class is involved. Hold regular meetings with committee leaders to make sure the work is progressing smoothly.

Have the publicity committee come up with a name for the celebration and create a banner to display at the entrance of the room. You may wish to have the committee think of several names and submit them to a class vote. Consider inviting your colleagues to share their expertise with different event committees. Invite the language-arts teacher to oversee the publicity. Ask the technology teacher to help students create graphs, diagrams, and maps of your local food environment on the computer.

Here's a checklist that you can use to help you get started. As you begin to develop the specifics of your event, you'll want to add to this list.

- Pick a date, time, and location and get school approval.

- Set up committees.

- Draft a program that includes students' action projects and PSAs.

- Send out early announcements about the event.

- Sign up volunteers, including someone who can take pictures the day of the fair and people to help prepare healthy snacks.

- Gather the following supplies for the "be prepared for anything kit": pens and pencils; felt-tipped markers — large, small, different colors; extension cords; paper clips, rubber bands, tacks, pins; stapler and extra staples; scotch, masking, and duct tape; hammer, nails, pliers, and screwdriver; poster board; paper; batteries; emergency kit with first aid supplies; trash bags; paper towels; tissues; and camera for the volunteer photographer.

- Purchase supplies to make healthy snack recipes (pp. 173–175)

Once the event is over, make sure you set aside time to discuss the experience with students. Encourage them to share both what they got out of the experience and what they think attendees got from the experience. Be sure to congratulate students on a job well done.

INVESTIGATING OUR CHOICES : DYNAMIC EQUILIBRIUM : FROM DATA TO HEALTH GOALS : EFFECTS OF OUR CHOICES : **MAINTAINING COMPETENCE**

Calvin & Carol Take Charge

Student Name: _____

Class/Teacher: _____

Contents

LESSON 1:
Becoming Researchers

On a sunny morning, 13-year-old Calvin Green timidly shuffled through the door at the LiFE Center. His mother was a few steps behind. Before he'd even settled into his waiting-room chair, the door opened again and in walked Carol Cooper. She surveyed the room, noticed Calvin, and took a seat on the opposite side. Her mother joined her after parking the car.

A few long moments later, the door leading into the office opened.

"Good morning! I am Ms. Lopez," called a cheery lady. "Calvin and Carol? We've been expecting you. Right this way, please."

The three of them sat together at a round table in Ms. Lopez's office. "Let me introduce myself," she said. "I am Evita Lopez, research dietitian here at the Linking Food and the Environment, or LiFE Center. It is my job to study our clients' diets, and help them to identify how they can improve their health by making healthy food and activity choices."

"Yo, I am like mad active, Ms. Lopez. I'm always out shooting hoops in the park," said Calvin.

"Yeah, me too! I've been dancing from the age of 7. And besides, I'm way too young to worry about my health," added Carol, almost at the same time.

"Slow down! Slow down. Let's start at the very beginning," said Ms. Lopez reassuringly. Calvin and Carol stared back at her with doubtful looks.

She began again, "I've been reviewing the medical charts that your doctors sent to us. It seems that your energy balance could use some tweaking. You see, on your growth charts I have observed that you are each gaining more weight than is healthy for your age and height. Also, for both of you, your **blood sugar** and **blood pressure** are a little high."

"But what does that have to do with my health?" asked Carol.

"Well, weight gain (especially in your **stomach** area), increased blood sugar, and **high**

blood pressure can increase your risk for **Type 2 diabetes** and cardiovascular disease. Many teenagers and young adults are being diagnosed with these diseases, especially Type 2 diabetes. And once you have Type 2 diabetes, there are lots of health risks and complications. So at the LiFE Center, our main goal is to prevent people from ever getting it at all, especially young people like you. Keeping your energy in balance is the first place to start."

"Energy balance — what do you mean?" asked Carol.

"Good question, Carol. *Energy balance* means that we keep the amount of energy coming into our bodies through the foods we eat equal to the amount going out through our physical activities. Here at the LiFE Center we are testing a hypothesis. We think if clients know *why* and *how* to make healthy food and activity choices, they will be able to maintain their energy balance. That is, we want to know if an understanding of biology, the environment, and personal behaviors can have an impact on a person's weight and health. We'd like you to help us test our hypothesis. To get started, I want to discuss energy balance with you — how it functions to keep us healthy, and what we can do to keep it, well, balanced. To begin to think about energy balance, let's talk about how physically active you have been lately."

Calvin's eyes were fixed on a spot on the ceiling, while Carol was studying a freckle on her arm.

"Calvin? How about you?" inquired Ms. Lopez.

"Well, I used to shoot hoops every day after school. But I've been too tired to do that lately. I just have a snack at home and rest up instead. I watch TV, or sometimes my brother and I play video games."

"Okay, thanks, Calvin. How about you, Carol?"

"Um, well, the dance club after school used to be my favorite thing to do, but now I skip it sometimes. I'm tired and sometimes I have to babysit for my little brother and sister. Anyway, I'd rather chat with my friends. There's so much to keep up with!"

"I bet there is. Thanks, Carol. We have just been talking about the energy-out part of the energy-balance equation. That is the energy that our bodies use to keep us moving, like dancing or playing basketball. Our bodies also use energy to make our hearts keep beating and to digest our food. What do you think the energy-in half of the equation refers to?"

"Energy in?" asked Carol.

"Yes, where does the energy come from?" probed Ms. Lopez.

"Food!" Calvin said.

"That's right — we put energy into our bodies with food."

"So how do we study that?" asked Carol.

"Another good question," said Ms. Lopez. "That is my job here at the LiFE Center. We're learning all about ways to investigate our energy balance."

"That seems like a lot of work for one lady. How do you do all that?" asked Calvin.

"With a lot of help," said Ms. Lopez. "At the LiFE Center, we have professionals in all different areas of health and behavior sciences to get this job done. I like my area best — the food! So now, Calvin and Carol, we need your help. Will you both join us in testing our hypothesis?"

They both thought for a second, and then nodded their heads.

"Great! Here are two LiFE notebooks for you to record what you find out along the way. We'll get started next time!"

LESSON 2:
Snack Foods Everywhere

The next time Carol returned to the LiFE Center, she met with Ms. Lopez one-on-one.

"Good afternoon, Carol! How are you today?"

"I'm okay, Ms. Lopez. My girlfriend said that she wanted to take over as the lead dancer, 'cuz I've been skipping out lately. But I said, no WAY, I have been dancing since the age of 7 and I am not about to let Jessie Wilcox take over. I am way more experienced than she is."

"Well, glad I asked," said Ms. Lopez. "Do you remember what we talked about last week?"

"You said that Calvin and I were sent here by our doctors because you can help us avoid getting Type 2 diabetes," said Carol.

"That's right, Carol, very good. And what concept did we discuss to help us evaluate the energy in and energy out of our bodies?"

"Um, energy balance?"

"You've got it. To understand our own energy balance, the first thing to do is to find out what influences our food and activity choices. At the LiFE Center, we interview clients to learn more about what they eat and how much physical activity they get. Next,

we compare their personal **data** with our food and activity goals. Then we work with our clients to help them select personal goals and develop an action plan. We help our clients understand that they can make choices about what they eat and do. They can use their skills and understanding to make the choices that are needed to reach a goal. Finally, we encourage our clients to make changes that will help their bodies do what they want them to do," explained Ms. Lopez.

"So you're saying that I have some choices?" asked Carol.

"Indeed you do. It's important for us to know what you're eating so we can tell if you're eating too much, too little, or just the right amount to have the energy for your body to do what you want. During your time at the LiFE Center, we'll collect data about how much energy you take in and how much energy you use. For today, we'll just look at energy in — what you eat. Tell me about your eating habits," said Ms. Lopez.

"I'll tell you about my favorite food. After school I'm always so hungry," said Carol.

"Why are you so hungry after school?" asked Ms. Lopez.

"I've practically not eaten since breakfast. I get school lunch but I don't eat much of it because I don't like it. I just eat the French fries."

"I see. So what do you eat before dance practice?"

"Oh, anything I can find. I get chips or candy from the vending machine at school."

"Okay. You're saying that you get a snack from what is available around you since you're so hungry after school. What about when you go home instead of staying for dance club?" asked Ms. Lopez.

"It depends. If my mom picks me up, sometimes I buy a snack at the mini-mart when she buys gas. If I take the bus, sometimes I stop and buy a candy bar on my way home from the bus stop. If I go straight home, I grab some chips and dip and then call my friends to chat about the drama of our school day."

"I see. When you go home after school there are places to buy snack foods, or they are available at home."

"Yeah, well, I like those snacks."

"What I want to point out here is that snack foods are all around us," said Ms. Lopez. "They are at school, at the gas-station food market, at the convenience store you can walk to in your neighborhood, and they are certainly numerous at the supermarket."

"I guess you're right," said Carol. "I never thought about it that way."

"What about dinner?" asked Ms. Lopez.

"My mom is in charge of that. She's a pretty good cook, when she has time. Her spaghetti is seriously delicious."

"Great. And when she doesn't cook, what do you eat for dinner?"

"We go out, or order takeout. My favorite is chicken tenders and French fries," said Carol.

"Oh, I see," said Ms. Lopez. "That's the second time I've heard you mention French fries. Do you know what I haven't heard you mention yet?"

"What?" asked Carol.

"Fresh fruits and vegetables," Ms. Lopez replied.

"Oh — I like those too!" Carol said quickly.

"You do? Why do you think potatoes, served as French fries, are the only vegetable you've mentioned so far?"

"Well, it just hasn't come up. I've been thinking of what I usually just grab in a hurry. I eat fruit when my mom cuts up a melon or something. And we have vegetables at dinner."

"This is my point, Carol. In our everyday environment, fresh fruits and vegetables aren't as easy to find as processed snacks such as chips, candy, cookies, or other sweets, or fried foods, like French fries. Even though they are easy to find, those foods are not as good for our bodies as fruits and vegetables."

"I know fruits and vegetables are good for me; I eat one every day," said Carol.

"And do you know how many **servings** of fruits and vegetables we should aim for in one day?" asked Ms. Lopez.

"Two?" questioned Carol.

"Try again."

"Three?" she asked.

"Four cups, and a cup is about the size of your fist," said Ms. Lopez. "Of course it is good for our health to have a variety of fruits and vegetables, too. I think we've covered enough for today. What have you learned?"

"That unhealthy snacks are all around us! It takes work to get the right amount of healthy food in a day."

"That's right. But I'm here to help you figure it out. See you next week!" called Ms. Lopez. But Carol was already out the door. She ran out to her mother's car and started telling her all about what she'd learned.

LESSON 3:
Sweet Tastes

"Yo, Ms. Lopez!" called Calvin as he walked into her office at the LiFE Center.

"Well hello, Calvin! You seem to be in a good mood today."

"I am! I have some news for you. I think you're going to like it."

"I can't wait to hear it," she said encouragingly.

"You know how you were talking about energy we get from food?" Calvin asked.

"Yes," she replied.

"And how too much belly fat can cause diabetes?" Calvin went on.

"Yes," said Ms. Lopez eagerly.

"Well, I decided to try not to

drink as much soda after school," he said proudly.

"Terrific. And how is that going?" inquired Ms. Lopez.

"Okay, I guess. The other day after shooting hoops, I drank a sports drink instead of a soda," he explained.

"What made you choose a sports drink?" she asked.

"It's healthier. And it tastes so good!" he exclaimed.

"And what makes it healthier?" inquired Ms. Lopez.

"It's what athletes drink, so it's got to be good for you," he explained.

"Well, Calvin, let's do some research." Ms. Lopez reached into a cabinet and pulled out a 20-ounce soda bottle. "**Carbohydrates** in

sodas are all from sugar. How many grams of sugar does this soda contain?"

"Twenty-six," Calvin declared, looking at the label.

"Not so fast," cautioned Ms. Lopez.

"What? It says 26 right there!" he exclaimed.

"Yes, and look at this line up here. Could you read that for me?" she asked.

"Servings per container: 2.5," Calvin read. "What does that mean?"

"It means that there are 26 grams of sugar per serving of soda, and 2.5 servings in this bottle. That means there are — "

"Sixty-five grams of sugar in that bottle! Wait, is that a lot?" asked Calvin.

"You'd have to eat 65 jelly beans to get that much sugar," said Ms. Lopez.

"What?" exclaimed Calvin. "Stop! You mean to tell me that I've been drinking that much sugar every day?"

"I'm afraid so," answered Ms. Lopez.

"And I often drink two or three sodas every day." Calvin sighed and rested his head in his hands. Suddenly he sat up and said, "You know what, Ms. Lopez? I don't think people would drink as much soda if they realized how sugary it was. It can't be good for you."

"You're right, Calvin, it's not. Now, you said you started drinking a sports drink after school instead of soda?" she asked.

Calvin nodded proudly.

"Well, look what I have here," she said as she pulled out a 20-ounce sports-drink bottle from the cabinet. "Could you tell me how much sugar is in this drink?"

"Fifteen grams per serving. The bottle has 2.5 servings again, so that's 37.5 grams of sugar in the bottle."

"That's about 38 jelly beans," said Ms. Lopez.

"Oh brother," said Calvin. "Now what am I supposed to drink? I always got sodas after school or when we ate out. They taste so good and they're easy to find. They're everywhere!"

"That's a good point, Calvin. People like sweet tastes. We are born with a liking for foods that are high in sugar."

"So it's my biology that makes me like sugar?" asked Calvin.

"That's right, our bodies are made that way. Did you know that our tongues can detect four basic tastes: sweet, salty, sour, and bitter? The average adult has about 10,000 taste buds that detect these tastes. Infants and children have even more taste buds, which makes them more sensitive to tastes. As children grow older, their craving for sweets usually decreases. They even begin to like bitter-tasting foods like broccoli and coffee," explained Ms. Lopez.

"But if my biology makes me like sugar, how can I change that?" asked Calvin, puzzled.

"Let's think this through. Do you believe that you have a choice about what you eat and drink?" asked Ms. Lopez.

"Yes," responded Calvin.

"When we learn what too much sugar does to our bodies, do you think it might encourage us to make different choices? Do you think you can take control of what you eat and drink and make a change?" asked Ms. Lopez.

"You've got that right," Calvin said.

"Can you think of something else to drink when you get thirsty? Something you can get anywhere? Something that doesn't cost a penny and is biologically necessary for your body?" she asked.

"I guess you mean water. Thanks, Ms. Lopez. Catch you later!"

She watched as he darted down the hall, paused to drink from the water fountain, and met his mother outside.

LESSON 4:
Fat Tastes Good

"Hi, Carol."

"Hi, Ms. Lopez."

"Do you remember what we talked about last time, Carol?"

"Yes, that it takes work to eat a healthy diet when unhealthy food is all around us."

"That's right. Do you remember which food group we gave special attention to last time?"

"Fruits and vegetables."

"Right. And how many servings of fruits and vegetables do our bodies need each day to stay healthy?"

"Four cups," said Carol.

"Yes, the recommendation is to eat at least four cups of fruits and vegetables a day. You want lots of variety, too. Remember, a cup is about the size of your fist. Now, what's your favorite fruit or vegetable?"

"Oh, I know that for sure. French fries. They are just so good, Ms. Lopez," said Carol, beaming. Her eyes were bright and wide as she continued. "I could eat them every day. I practically do at school."

"Well, you're right that they are made from potatoes, which are vegetables. What is it about French fries that you like?" questioned Ms. Lopez.

"Oh, what *don't* I like about them? They are so nice and crunchy on the outside, and squishy on the inside — well, except when they are soggy at school. But they smell good even when they're soggy."

"Ah, I see. And does the smell entice you to eat them?" asked Ms. Lopez.

"Does it ever. As soon as I smell them when I'm standing in the cafeteria line I just know that that's what I want to eat for lunch."

"What do you think makes them smell so good?" asked Ms. Lopez.

"Probably cooking makes them smell good," said Carol.

"And how are they cooked?"

Carol thought for a moment before answering, "They're fried?"

"Right. They're called French fries for a reason, right?"

"I guess so."

"So, Carol, do you see why French fries may not be the best vegetable to be one of your choices every day?"

"Because they are fried?"

"That's right," replied Ms. Lopez. "Frying adds a lot of fat to food. And that does not promote energy balance."

"Fat tastes good."

"It does taste good. Our bodies are programmed to like the taste of fat. Think about eating a plain slice of bread, or some plain steamed vegetables."

"Okay. Those things taste all right, I guess. But they don't have fat."

"Right. Now think about spreading some butter on that bread, or drizzling some oil over those vegetables," said Ms. Lopez.

"I think that would taste better," agreed Carol.

"Yes, when I sit here thinking about eating a nice crusty slice of bread with some sweet, soft butter, my mouth starts to water. That's one way I know that I like those foods. My body responds when I think about them," explained Ms. Lopez.

"That's what happens with me and the French fries at lunch!" Carol chimed in.

"That makes sense. That's your body telling you what it likes. People naturally like fat. But too much fat every day isn't good for our health."

"So I naturally like potatoes made with fat? That's like my body working against me."

"Well, liking fat helps us get enough energy from our food. And our bodies need fat, so it's not all bad. But when fat is in so many of our foods, or we eat fatty foods every day, it can lead to eating more fat than is healthy for us, and it can lead to positive energy balance."

"Hold on a second, Ms. Lopez, I'm confused," exclaimed Carol. "It sounds like you're saying too much fat isn't good for us, but then you say it leads to positive energy balance. Isn't 'positive' a good thing?"

"Excellent observation," remarked Ms. Lopez. "While 'positive' often means something good, in this case it means you are taking in more food energy than your body is using. You are not maintaining energy balance."

"It's a lot to remember. Do all of your clients get as confused as I am? Or do you just tell them to stop eating fat and sugar?"

"No, we don't tell our clients to just stop, Carol. Every person is unique. That's one reason that we work with our clients individually and collect data on their food and activity choices. Based on what we learn, we help them select personal goals that can fit into their lives and will lead them toward energy balance."

"Ms. Lopez, the first time I was here, you told me my doctor was concerned about how much weight I had gained. Are you going to put me on a diet so I lose weight?"

"No, I will not put you on a diet," answered Ms. Lopez. "Let's back up for a second. I am

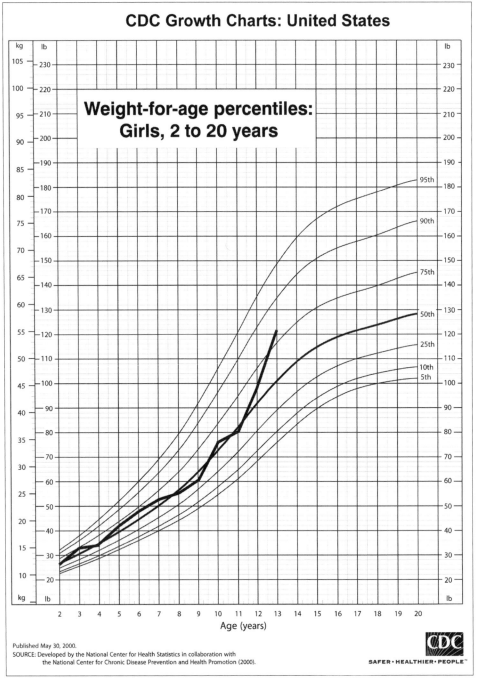

child's weight compares with other children. So, the 50th percentile means that a child's weight is right in the middle compared with other children of the same age."

"Oh, so that is why I get weighed when I go to the doctor every year, so my new weight can be added to this chart. Now I get it." Carol paused for a second and then continued, "My friend Susan's doctor was concerned that she was too skinny. I bet she was down there at the bottom, about at this 5th-percentile line," said Carol.

"Yes, doctors get concerned when children don't gain enough weight and when they gain too much. Either way shows that the child is not in energy balance," continued Ms. Lopez. "This is your growth chart, which your doctor sent me. It shows your weight every year from the time you were 2-years-old until now, at age 13. As you can see, your weight was close to the 50th percentile from 2 to 11 years. Then at age 12 your weight was almost at the 75th

going to show you your growth chart, but first I want to explain to you how growth charts work. About 40 years ago, researchers collected data on many children. This data gave doctors scientific evidence about the appropriate amount of weight for children to gain as they grow up. See all these curved lines? A child's weight usually follows one of these lines. They are percentiles — that is, they show how one

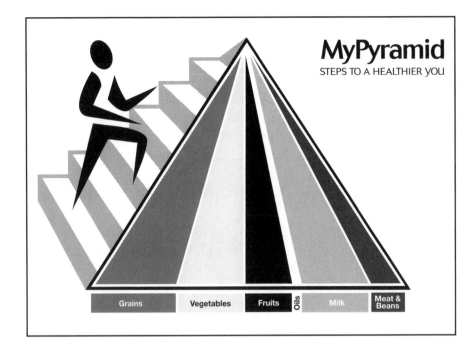

MyPyramid
STEPS TO A HEALTHIER YOU

Grains | Vegetables | Fruits | Oils | Milk | Meat & Beans

percentile, and here at 13 you are above the 75th percentile. The concern is that you are off the curve you were following. Some of my clients follow the 25th percentile their entire childhood and others the 85th percentile. Different children follow different lines. What the doctor looks for is a change."

"Oh, no one ever showed this to me before. So, how much do I have to weigh to get back to the 50th percentile?" Carol said.

"Just a second, let me get back to your question about putting you on a diet. We work with the children who come here to help them make changes that work for them as individuals. We will not tell you anything that you *have* to do. We help you figure out what changes will work for you. Often people go on a diet and then go off it."

"I know, my dad is always trying different diets and then when he gets tired of it he goes back to how he always ate," Carol said.

"That's common. That's why our approach is to not have people diet. In addition, we don't

want you to lose weight. Since you are still growing, what we want is for you to slow down the rate at which you have been gaining weight. That will help bring you back to the 50th percentile, the curve that seems to be the right energy balance for you. We will do this by helping you set personal goals."

"What kind of personal goals?" asked Carol.

"Take a look at this. Have you learned about MyPyramid at school? MyPyramid is the national food-guidance system developed by the U.S. Department of Agriculture. It provides Americans with guidelines on how to make healthy food choices and be active every day. At the LiFE Center, we developed six food and physical-activity goals based on the government recommendations. Here are our goals:

- **Eat more fruits and vegetables** — aim for at least 4 cups a day.

- **Drink more water** — aim for 64 ounces a day (that's eight 8-ounce glasses).

- **Walk more, including stairs** — aim for at least 10,000 steps per day.

- **Drink fewer sweetened beverages** — aim for no more than 8 ounces a day.

- **Eat less frequently at fast-food places** — aim for no more than three times a week, choose healthier foods, and ask for smaller portions.

- **Eat fewer processed snacks** — aim for no more than one small or medium snack each day.

"Scientific evidence supports these six goals and recommendations," continued Ms. Lopez. "Let's talk about the goals. We have an exercise goal of walking for at least 10,000 steps per day, and that includes walking up stairs. Here we recommend aiming for at least 64 ounces of water per day. That's 8 cups. And we recommend drinking no more than 8 ounces of sweetened beverages per day. A fourth goal is to eat no more than three times per week at fast-food chains and to make healthier choices and have smaller sizes if you are there. The next goal is to eat fewer processed snacks."

"What do you mean by 'fewer processed snacks'?" asked Carol.

"Aim for no more than one processed snack per day," explained Ms. Lopez. "By 'processed' we mean food that has been changed in some way after it was grown or raised on a farm."

"So an apple is unprocessed, but applesauce or applesauce cake is processed?" asked Carol.

"That's right. Let me tell you a little more about processed foods. It's important information to know, especially because so many popular snack foods, like candy, chips, cookies, and other baked goods, are what we mean at the LiFE Center when we say 'processed snacks'. The ones we are talking about are highly processed, that is, they have been changed a lot. They usually have a lot of fat and sugar added to them."

"But those are my favorite snacks! Now what can I eat?" Carol complained.

"Well, that leads us to the sixth goal: eat more fruits and vegetables. As I mentioned before, we recommend that you aim for at least 4 cups per day. Fruits and vegetables make great snacks."

"Let me guess, snacking on French fries every day isn't a good idea? But they have them for sale every day in school," said Carol.

"It's not just at school, is it? Think of all the places you can buy French fries. Or any other fried chips or snacks. They are easy to find and don't cost much money."

"And they taste good," Carol added with a sigh.

"They do," remarked Ms. Lopez. "In fact, would you like to help me gather some data about students' attitudes toward French fries? Here's what you need to do. First, gather some friends together. Then ask them to listen while you describe what it's like to walk down the street and smell French fries. You did such a great job describing it to me! Then, ask your friends to answer some questions and write their responses on these forms. You can bring the forms back to me when we meet next time."

"Sure — it will be easier to do than to give up French fries," said Carol.

"Sounds good. One more thing, Carol. French fries aren't the only fried potato snack. Remember those chips you mentioned before? Did you know that 1 ounce of potato chips, about 10 chips, has 2 teaspoons of fat? Next time you have a bag of chips, check how many ounces there are and then do the math and figure out how much fat is in the bag. You may be in for a shock!

"So," continued Ms. Lopez, "can you think of other sources of fruits and vegetables that aren't fried?"

"Only like a thousand," said Carol. "See you next time, Ms. Lopez!"

"See you, Carol," Ms. Lopez replied, but it was too late. Carol was already out the door, eager to tell her sister about what she'd learned that day.

LESSON 5:
Food and Activity Environments

The waiting room in the LiFE Center was busier than usual today. Calvin was already there, lost in a book. Carol had to take a seat next to a girl who looked about her age.

"Hi, I'm Carol. What brings you to the LiFE Center?" she said.

"Hi. My name is Rosanna. This is my first time here. My doctor said to come so I could learn to help my body be in energy balance," Rosanna said a bit timidly.

"Hey, that's why I am here, too. I want to get my body back into energy balance so that I feel like dancing again. You look really skinny to me. I would have guessed your balance was just fine."

"Yeah, I kind of said the same thing to my doctor. She told me that the fat in my **blood** is a little high and that you can't tell what's going on inside a person's body just by their weight. She thought it might be good for me to check it out here at the LiFE Center."

"Calvin and Carol," called Ms. Lopez.

"That's me," said Carol. "I hope you like it here. It's been fun for me so far," she whispered to Rosanna. She got up and hurried toward Calvin, who was already talking to Ms. Lopez.

"Hey, Ms. Lopez, we got your message to bring our walking shoes today. What's up?" asked Calvin. "What are all these maps? Are we going on a trip?"

"I'm glad you got the message," replied Ms. Lopez. "Yes, we're going on a trip of sorts — a field trip. I thought you might like to help us collect data about the food and activity environment near your school."

"**Food environment,** activity environment, great!" shouted Calvin. "Can we go to the skate park and have a picnic?"

"Not this time, Calvin," responded Ms. Lopez. "Today we're investigating where you get food on your way to school, at school, and on your way home from school. We want to learn about all the places where you could stop in and buy something to eat. We want to know about the places where you do buy food and the places where you could buy food. We'll be looking at the food-store environment, like grocery stores, supermarkets, convenience stores, snack bars, farmers' markets, and bodegas or corner markets. We also want to know about the restaurant-food environment, like fast-food and full-service restaurants, and, finally, we want to know about the school food environment, including cafeterias, vending machines, and snack shops. We are interested in **environmental factors** that influence the food and activity choices that you make."

Carol had been thinking, and she spoke up. "I get it, Ms. Lopez. At first when you said 'environment,' I thought you meant places in nature, like the forest, or a park, or the ocean. But now I see you mean *anyplace* when you say 'environment.' Is that right?"

"You make an interesting point, Carol. People often think 'natural environment' when they hear the word 'environment.' Let's see what the dictionary has to say." Ms. Lopez took a dictionary down from her bookshelf and handed it to Carol.

Carol flipped through the pages until she got to 'environment.' "It says 'surroundings; or, the surroundings, conditions, or forces that influence or modify.' It seems like environment can be more than places, but I can't imagine what else it could be," she said. She looked puzzled.

"Perhaps I can help you," said Ms. Lopez. "Remember, I said we are interested in environmental factors. Some of these might be places, but some

of them might be information, or family traditions, or even what food is available at different times of the year. These are the types of things that are meant by 'conditions' and 'forces' in the definition. Stop and think for a minute. Have you ever bought something because you saw an advertisement that made you think it would taste delicious or make you stronger?"

"For sure," exclaimed Calvin. "That's why I started drinking sports drinks. I wanted to be able to shoot hoops like the NBA players they show in the ads. I got my mom to buy these shoes 'cuz my favorite player wears them.

How else do you know what to buy?"

Carol rolled her eyes and said, "That's exactly why I DON'T buy those sports drinks. Who wants to look like a basketball player? I drink smoothies because my best friends do. On the weekend, we get together at the mall, buy our smoothies, and sit and chat while we drink them. It's our chance to catch up on all the news."

"I can see that you two are going to provide our researchers with lots of data about the environmental factors that influence your food choices! We also want to know what influences your activity choices. Calvin, you live in the city. Where can you go to get physical activity?"

"That's easy, Ms. L.," said Calvin. "We live on the eighth floor of our building. My mom is always telling me to take the stairs. When I do, I get plenty of exercise. Sometimes I walk home from school, but I never can walk TO school. I always wake up too late. Some days, my friends and I stay after school and shoot hoops. On the weekends, if the street is closed off, we play street hockey."

"Sounds like you have lots of opportunities to be physically active, Calvin," responded Ms. Lopez. "That's great! What about you, Carol? I know you live farther away and you can't walk to school. Where do you go when you want to get exercise?"

"We can jog or skate on the sidewalk near our house, or ride our bikes, but if we want to go to a park, we need to ride a bus or drive there in a car. Of course, I have my dance club. Then, in the summer, we visit my grandma and help her in her garden. She says pulling weeds is great exercise. It may be good exercise, but it's not as much fun as swimming in the lake. I almost forgot,

sometimes we visit our cousins at the beach. When we're there we swim, walk on the beach, and even play volleyball. That's lots of fun!" exclaimed Carol.

"Excellent," said Ms. Lopez. "The physical activity environments you just described include stairs, streets that are closed off, open spaces like beaches and parks, gardens, the school gymnasium, and sidewalks. This is a great start. Now I think we're ready to begin our field trip.

"Let's review our research questions: Where do students at your school buy food? How far do they travel to get food? Where do students at your school engage in physical activity? How far do they travel to do this activity? Calvin, since you live here in the city, let's explore your environment. Here's a map that includes your home and your school. Take a look at it and think about a typical school day. We'll begin our field trip by walking to all the food stores, restaurants, or school vending machines that you some-times visit in a day and locating them on this map. We'll do the same thing for where you go when you exercise. Then we'll look at all the places you don't go, but could go, and mark those on the map. Don't forget to make a map key so we can remember what we've labeled. Ready?"

Ms. Lopez handed them two small notebooks. "These are for your field notes," she said. "I have one, too. We'll record the names of the shops or restaurants, street names, what kind of food is sold, and the precise street address. We'll also see if anything grabs our attention, like ads in the windows, or the smell of the food, and we'll record that in our notebooks, as well. All of this data will help us think about what influences our food and activity choices."

Calvin and Carol retied their shoes, grabbed

the maps and some colored pencils, and were ready to go.

LESSON 6:
Modeling Energy Balance

"Hi, Ms. Lopez!" shouted Calvin and Carol in unison.

"Well hello! If it isn't my two research partners," chirped Ms. Lopez. She was standing in a laboratory, engaged in conversation with a young man. "There is someone I want to introduce to both of you. This is Christian Summers. He's a systems scientist we work with here at the LiFE Center."

"Systems scientist — what is that?" asked Carol.

"I'm glad you asked. First of all, Carol, Calvin, so glad to meet you! A systems scientist studies how groups of things work together as a whole. I'm interested in living systems. For example, the human body is made up of different biological systems. These systems interact and are dependent upon one another. My current research involves the impact that human-body systems have on your well-being. Can you think of a time when one of your body systems was upset? Did it affect your well-being?"

"My **digestive system,**" responded Calvin. "I had a stomach flu. I was sick for two days. My well-being was upset,

for sure."

"That's right," said Christian. "You probably felt terrible and your **stomach** may have ached. Something in your digestive system was malfunctioning. You may have felt like you had no energy, and you were right. Your digestive system couldn't get the energy from food to your muscular and **circulatory systems.**"

"I think I get how the systems interact, but I'm still not exactly sure what you do here at the LiFE Center," said Carol.

"As I said, I'm studying human-body systems, how they interact, and how the human body interacts with the environment. Part of my job here is to create models and simulations to represent the way a system works," explained Christian.

"Why would you want to do that?" inquired Carol.

"Think about the human-body. It's incredibly complex. By making models we can create a simplified version of the human body that lets us study specific parts and interactions without getting distracted by all the other parts and interactions. We can imitate how the human body works. The models we create here in the lab can help us visualize and observe scientific processes. We can learn about the human body in ways we might not be otherwise able to do," said Christian. "I was wondering if you might want to help me with a simulation today."

"Sure. What kind of simulation?" asked Calvin.

"First, why don't you tell me about what you've learned so far with Ms. Lopez," suggested Christian.

"I learned about how my body naturally likes the taste of sweet things and how this makes me want to eat sweet foods," said Calvin.

"Also that some foods that are sold everywhere aren't really good for us," added Carol.

"Yeah, like sodas, sports drinks, candy, and cookies," said Calvin.

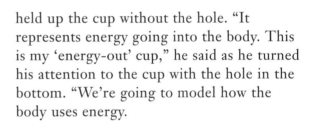

"Okay, great. I noticed that everything you have said affects the way our bodies maintain energy balance. You learned about energy balance with Ms. Lopez, right?" Christian asked.

Calvin and Carol nodded in agreement.

"Ms. Lopez said that keeping our energy balanced can help prevent Type 2 diabetes and other diseases," said Carol.

"That's right," said Christian. "Let's look at this simulation to see what we can find out about energy balance. Now, with a simulation, we can compress time. Think about how long it takes to digest food and get the energy from the food to other parts of the body. With this simulation, we can make a process that takes hours in real time take place in just a few minutes." He reached into a cabinet in the lab and pulled out a big plastic dishpan full of water, and two cups, one with a hole in the bottom.

"This is my 'energy-in' cup," he said as he

held up the cup without the hole. "It represents energy going into the body. This is my 'energy-out' cup," he said as he turned his attention to the cup with the hole in the bottom. "We're going to model how the body uses energy.

"Now watch as I pour the water from the energy-in cup into the energy-out cup. What do you see?" asked Christian as he scooped up some water and poured it from one cup to the other. As the water came out the hole, he poured more water into the cup.

"It's coming out of the bottom of the cup with a hole in it," said Calvin.

"And what do you see happening to the level of water in the energy-out cup?" asked Christian.

"It doesn't change, even though the water comes in and goes out," said Carol.

"Good job. Now let's kick things up a bit. Keep your eye on the level of the water when I pour it from the energy-in cup really slowly.

What happens?"

"The level of the water goes down," Carol said.

"Right. And why did this happen?" asked Christian.

"The water was going out of the energy-out cup faster than the energy-in cup could fill it up. So the level dropped."

"You've got it. We are in negative energy balance because more energy is being used than is coming in. And what do you think happens to our bodies when the energy is being used faster than what we give it?"

"We feel tired because we don't have enough energy," said Calvin.

"Right, Calvin. What can we do to correct this situation?"

"We have to give our bodies more energy in," he said.

"And what is 'energy in' to our bodies?" probed Christian.

"Food!" shouted Carol.

"That's it. Now we're going to do the simulation again. This time, I'm going to make the energy in more than the energy out," Christian explained as he scooped up water and began to pour it more quickly from the energy-in cup to the energy-out cup.

"What is happening when I increase the energy in?" asked Christian.

"The water level rises," Carol answered. "The energy in is faster, but the energy out is the same, so there is more and more water in the cup."

"Right. In this situation, we are giving the body more energy from food and our activity is staying the same. We are in positive energy balance. The body stores this extra 'energy in' in the form of body fat."

"So what do you do to get it back in balance?" asked Calvin.

"That's a good question. Do you have any ideas?" asked Christian.

"This time, more water was coming from the energy-in cup. What if more water went out of the energy-out cup?" asked Calvin.

"That sure would do the trick," said Christian. "In our bodies, that means if we increase our energy in from food, we need to also increase our energy out from activity to keep our energy balanced. What is another option?" he asked.

"Just decrease energy in," said Carol.

"Ah, you nailed it, Carol. When people reduce their energy intake from food, it can become easier to achieve energy balance. Do you two have any more questions about my nifty model here?"

"Yes," said Carol. "You said the water represents total energy, but last time I was here I learned about fat in food. We also want to balance how much fat we take in, right?"

"Yes. We also want to keep our fat, sugar, **vitamins**, and other **nutrients** in balance, too. That's why Ms. Lopez doesn't just talk to you about the total amount of food you eat, but also about what food you eat," answered Christian.

"I have been thinking about this girl Rosanna. I met her in the waiting room last time I was here. Even though she was skinny, the fat in her blood was high, so her body was out of balance."

"You're making the connections, Carol. Good thinking," said Christian. "Glad we got to work with a model and simulations today! See you later!" he shouted, spilling water in the hallway as he rushed away.

LESSON 7:
The Digestive System

"Hey, Ms. Lopez, what's going on this week?"

"Hi, Calvin! Well, last time you and I met one-on-one, we talked about the amount of sugar in sodas and sports drinks."

"I remember," said Calvin.

"Part of what I do here at the LiFE Center is to help people understand what is happening inside their body when the doctor sends them in. Your doctor told me that your blood glucose was a little too high. Do you know what **glucose** is?" asked Ms. Lopez.

Calvin shook his head.

Ms. Lopez continued, "It's a sugar. Blood glucose is the main sugar that our bodies make from food. After we digest carbohydrates, they are broken down into glucose and go from our **small intestine** to our blood."

"Wait, you're telling me my food gets into my blood?" asked Calvin, a little shocked.

"That's right. When you eat food, it's broken down into nutrients that are absorbed into your **bloodstream**. There are six groups of nutrients: carbohydrates, fats, proteins, vitamins, **minerals,** and water. Let's review what happens when you eat a cracker." Ms. Lopez pointed to a chart on her wall. "Remember, it all starts with your first bite of food. Imagine you've just taken a bite of cracker. What's the first thing that happens?"

Calvin thinks for a second. "My teeth crush the cracker into tiny pieces. I chew and chew, and then I swallow."

"That's part of the first step," replied Ms. Lopez, "but there's something else going on. Think about how soggy that cracker gets. Your **saliva** glands spray saliva and make the inside of your mouth very wet. While your teeth are grinding the cracker, it's getting mixed with your saliva. Before you know it, you have a wet, mushy ball of food that you swallow. Let's look at this diagram of the digestive system and trace the cracker as it

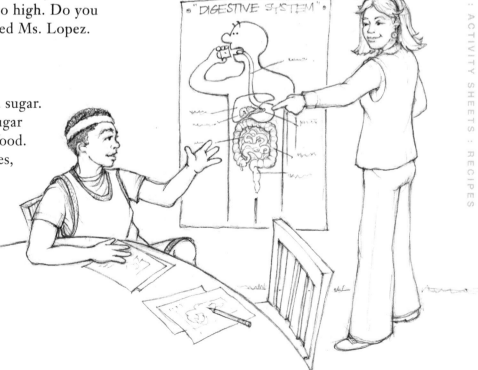

moves through the system."

"Whoa, Ms. Lopez, wait! You keep saying 'system,' and this diagram has lots of parts that look like they are connected. But when I think about eating, I just think of putting food into my mouth to fill up my stomach so I'm not hungry! Now you're telling me it has to go through all of *this* to get to my stomach! How's that work?"

"Well, if you look at this diagram, you'll see that the digestive system is made up of the digestive tract — the parts that you noticed. These parts are the organs that help the body break down large **molecules** of food into smaller molecules that the body absorbs."

Ms. Lopez stopped, noticing that Calvin looked puzzled.

"Okay, Calvin," she said. "We'll follow that cracker step-by-step through the digestive tract. Find the **esophagus.**"

Calvin pointed to the esophagus. "It looks like a tube."

"It does! The swallowed cracker is pushed into the esophagus, which connects the throat with the stomach," said Ms. Lopez, pointing to the place where the esophagus and the stomach meet. "There is a muscle here that closes the entrance to the stomach. When food, like the cracker, gets close to this muscle, it relaxes and lets the food pass through to the stomach."

"What happens to the mushy cracker once it's in my stomach?" asked Calvin.

"Remember the saliva that made that cracker mushy? Well, saliva is one kind of digestive juice. Saliva contains an enzyme that begins to break down the **starch** in your cracker into smaller molecules. Don't forget that

enzymes are substances that speed up **chemical reactions.** The stomach has digestive juices, too. These juices produce stomach acid and an enzyme that digests protein. When food enters the stomach, it gets mixed up with digestive juices. Muscle action in the lower part of the stomach does the mixing. Finally, the stomach empties its contents into the small intestine." Ms. Lopez paused.

"How long does this take?" asked Calvin.

"It depends," replied Ms. Lopez.

"Carbohydrates, like the cracker, are in your stomach the least amount of time. Proteins stay longer, and fats stay the longest." She pointed at the small intestine. "Here," she continued, "the food is broken down even more. In the small intestine, the mixture of food and digestive juice combines with juices of two other digestive organs, the pancreas and the liver." She pointed to both organs on the diagram. "These digestive juices break down the food into even smaller molecules."

"Ms. Lopez," Calvin exclaimed, "it's like the digestive system is a big chemistry lab! Enzymes, **acids**, chemical reactions…I never thought about eating a cracker this way!"

"You're right, Calvin, we generally don't think about what happens to the food we eat after we enjoy how it tastes. But it's important to understand how **digestion** works for our energy-balance research.

"Okay," she continued, "let's pick up where we left off in the small intestine. The digested nutrients are absorbed through the intestine walls." She turned to Calvin. "Are you still with me? Does this seem possible?"

Calvin shook his head. "No way, Ms. Lopez. Are you saying that small chunks of food go

THE DIGESTIVE SYSTEM

Imagine being able to look inside the human body. If you took a look at the digestive system you would see the organs. These are the parts of that system that help the body break down food so it can be absorbed. Now, imagine this: stretch out the entire digestive tract — it's about 30 feet long. The small intestine alone is about 20 feet long! Read the captions below to see how the digestive system works.

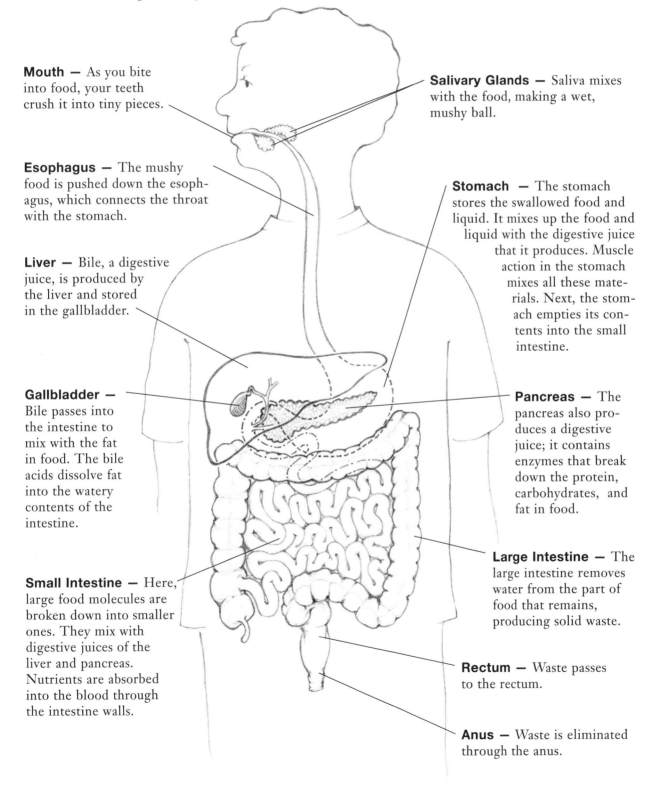

Mouth — As you bite into food, your teeth crush it into tiny pieces.

Esophagus — The mushy food is pushed down the esophagus, which connects the throat with the stomach.

Liver — Bile, a digestive juice, is produced by the liver and stored in the gallbladder.

Gallbladder — Bile passes into the intestine to mix with the fat in food. The bile acids dissolve fat into the watery contents of the intestine.

Small Intestine — Here, large food molecules are broken down into smaller ones. They mix with digestive juices of the liver and pancreas. Nutrients are absorbed into the blood through the intestine walls.

Salivary Glands — Saliva mixes with the food, making a wet, mushy ball.

Stomach — The stomach stores the swallowed food and liquid. It mixes up the food and liquid with the digestive juice that it produces. Muscle action in the stomach mixes all these materials. Next, the stomach empties its contents into the small intestine.

Pancreas — The pancreas also produces a digestive juice; it contains enzymes that break down the protein, carbohydrates, and fat in food.

Large Intestine — The large intestine removes water from the part of food that remains, producing solid waste.

Rectum — Waste passes to the rectum.

Anus — Waste is eliminated through the anus.

through the intestine wall? No way."

"Well, not really chunks. Remember, the cracker isn't solid little pieces anymore. It has been digested. The enzymes in the digestive juices I mentioned started some chemical reactions in your digestive system. It started with the saliva. Enzymes in the saliva broke down the carbohydrates in the cracker into smaller and smaller molecules. Eventually these were broken down into glucose, which can be absorbed into the blood and travel through the circulatory system. The part of the cracker that your body can't use, called the waste, is pushed into the large intestine. Here water is taken out and recycled back into your body. What's left is about a third the size of what first arrived in your intestines! The last part of the digestive process, called **elimination,** begins. The waste arrives at your rectum, waiting for you to get rid of it through your anus. But I think we'll stop here for now, Calvin. I'll let you digest what we've just discussed," said Ms. Lopez with a smile.

"Digest what I learned," groaned Calvin. "I get it, Ms. Lopez."

"Here's a copy of the digestive-system diagram for you to study and a simulation that you can try out with your friends. Since we can't directly observe the digestive system in action, Christian developed an activity that simulates, or mimics, the digestion process. Try it out and let us know what you think."

"Sure thing," said Calvin. "Thanks! See you next time."

....

"Hi, Ms. Lopez! I studied that diagram and tried out the digestive simulation with my class. It was *way* cool. I got to be the stomach! I think I kind of understand how

digestion works, but I still have some questions about blood glucose."

"No problem, Calvin," replied Ms. Lopez. "What would you like to discuss?"

"I'm a little confused about how the sugar in soda gets into my blood and makes the sugar in my blood too high. Can we go over that again?"

"Sure. Remember, your digestive system breaks down food into the smallest parts it can. Then those small parts enter your blood and travel around your body. That's how all the **cells** in the body get nutrients from food," Ms. Lopez explained.

"So the sugar in my blood is too high because I drank too much sugar that day? Maybe I should go back now and get tested again, 'cuz I haven't had that many sodas recently," Calvin suggested.

"Well, that's not exactly how it works. There are more steps involved. When the sugar in soda along with other carbohydrates from your food gets digested and absorbed into your bloodstream as glucose, your pancreas picks up on it."

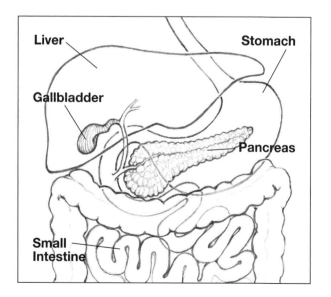

"My what?" asked Calvin.

"Your pancreas. Remember, it's a long, skinny organ next to your stomach. See, right here," said Ms. Lopez, pointing to a diagram of the pancreas. "One of its jobs is to help the cells throughout your body use glucose."

"How does my pancreas do that?" asked Calvin.

"When blood-glucose levels rise, the pancreas makes **insulin**. The insulin goes into the blood," began Ms. Lopez.

"Okay, the pancreas makes insulin," said Calvin. "Then what?"

"The insulin in the blood goes to all parts of the body, and the cells respond to the insulin," explained Ms. Lopez. "It is like getting a knock on the door for cells to let in the glucose. When the cells hear it, they open up the door."

"Wow. I never knew that something had to tell my cells to use my food," said Calvin.

"Yes, it's pretty neat how the body gets things done," said Ms. Lopez. "So when things go normally, the sugar reaches the blood, the pancreas secretes insulin, and the cells take up the sugar. The sugar levels in the blood

fall back to normal levels a few hours after you eat a meal."

"I have a feeling this is when you're going to tell me how I'm not normal," said Calvin, sighing.

"It's true. One reason your doctor wanted you to visit us, Calvin, is that your blood test showed us that your blood sugar was high — that is, it was abnormal. Do you remember what time of day you got that blood test?" asked Ms. Lopez.

"It was before breakfast. Did that mean I had too much sugar with dinner the night before?"

"Not exactly. It means that over time, your cells have stopped answering the knock on the door. Think about it. What would you do if you were at home and the pizza delivery man started delivering pizza every hour instead of once a day? Would you still answer the door for him every hour?" asked Ms. Lopez.

"I doubt it. That would be way too much pizza."

"Right. When cells have a lot of sugar, but they keep getting signals that more sugar is outside, they respond less and less. And then where is the sugar left?" asked Ms. Lopez.

"In the blood," replied Calvin.

"You've got it," confirmed Ms. Lopez. "But this is not something that happens after one sugar-heavy day. The process of insulin resistance — that is, insulin having a hard time doing its job of getting sugar from the blood into the cells — develops over years of a high-sugar diet."

"Oh. That's a lot of sodas," said Calvin.

"It sure is."

"Well, now that the level is up, can I bring it back down again?" asked Calvin with raised eyebrows.

"Yes! This is the good news I have for you today," she said.

Calvin let out a sigh of relief.

Ms. Lopez continued, "First, eating and drinking less added sugar helps us keep our blood sugar at healthy levels. And second, exercise lowers blood sugar."

"Okay, Ms. Lopez. Thanks, I have to go!"

"Thanks, Calvin!" But it was too late. He was on his way out the door, headed for the basketball court.

LESSON 8:
Energy in Food

Ms. Lopez opened the door to her office and found Calvin with his head resting on her desk. His eyes were closed. Carol sat nearby, wearing earbuds and listening to music on her MP3 player. Her eyes were closed, too.

"Good afternoon," said Ms. Lopez.

Neither one responded.

Ms. Lopez said a little louder, "Good afternoon!"

Calvin and Carol sat up.

"Good afternoon, Ms. Lopez," said Calvin, giving a big yawn.

"Hi, Ms. Lopez," said Carol. "I didn't hear you come in."

"You two seem tired today," observed Ms. Lopez. "What's going on?"

"I don't have any energy," said Calvin.

"Me, neither," said Carol.

"Most days you two have so much energy that I sometimes can't keep up with you. I wonder what's different. Any ideas?" asked Ms. Lopez.

Calvin thought for a minute. "Well, this week has been crazy busy. I've been getting up *way* late and haven't had time to eat breakfast. My mom made me promise to eat it at school, but I didn't like what they served, so I didn't eat anything."

"Me, neither," added Carol. "But I did eat lunch. Well, I ate fries, lots of fries."

"I see," said Ms. Lopez. "Do you remember when we discussed digestion, Calvin?"

"Sure," said Calvin. "I learned that the food we eat gets broken down into smaller molecules that are absorbed into the blood and travel through the circulatory system."

"Right," agreed Carol. "I did the same simulation that you gave to Calvin with my class, too. We learned that the circulatory system carries the nutrients in food to the cells in our bodies, and the cells use them for things our body need."

"My body needs energy," sighed Calvin. "I don't think my cells are working."

"Ms. Lopez, I know we always say that food has energy, but how can we observe this? And what do our cells do with the energy, anyway?" asked Carol.

"Aahh," exclaimed Ms. Lopez, "would you like to look for some evidence that there is chemical energy in food? Yes? Okay, but before I begin, are you allergic to peanuts?"

"Peanuts? No, I love peanuts," said Carol.

"Not a problem," echoed Calvin.

"Well then, step over here to my lab," said Ms. Lopez. "Here are some safety goggles for you to wear, lab coats for you and one for me, and we need to tie back our hair. Okay. First, we gather our materials: a potato, a paper clip, several peanuts, some matches, a beaker, a beaker stand, water, a beaker holder, a thermometer, and a thermometer holder."

"A potato, very high tech, Ms. L.," joked Calvin.

"We unfold the paper clip. Stick one end into the potato, like so. Fold the other end into a V-shaped basket and place the peanut into the basket," continued Ms. Lopez. "Next, set up the beaker like so, pour 50 milliliters of water into the beaker, adjust the thermometer, and finally, place the peanut setup under the beaker. Now, take out your LiFE notebooks and write down what we just did. It might help you later if you draw a sketch of what the setup looks like."

The two young scientists looked over the setup and made their notes.

"Okay, ready to make your observations? What's the temperature of the water?" asked Ms Lopez. Calvin and Carol peered at the thermometer. "What does the peanut look like now?" she continued. "What do you predict will happen when I hold a lighted match under the peanut? Remember to write your predictions in your notebooks. Ready?" Ms. Lopez lit a match and held it under the peanut.

"Nothing's happening," observed Calvin.

"Be patient," said Ms. Lopez. "Sometimes it takes several matches before you'll notice a change." She lit two more matches and the peanut started to burn.

"Wow, Ms. L., the peanut's on fire!" exclaimed Calvin. "Let me use my watch to time how long it burns. Look at the fire! It has so many colors…. Okay, we are at 1 minute 30 seconds and it is still going strong."

"Let's take a look at the thermometer. Do you notice any change in the temperature of the water?" asked Ms. Lopez.

"Whoa. There's a huge change," exclaimed Carol. "The temperature went from 18 degrees Celsius to 37 — that's 19 degrees!"

"I am still timing. Wait! The fire is slowing down," said Calvin. "Now it's out." He looked at his watch. "The peanut burned for a total of 2 minutes and 37 seconds."

"The temperature on the thermometer is now 51 degrees, so that little peanut raised the temperature of the water 33 degrees? That is really cool, but what exactly does it mean?" asked Carol.

"You've learned that food gives you energy. By burning a peanut, we gathered evidence that a peanut has stored chemical energy. We used heat from the matches to convert, or change, the chemical energy in the peanut into heat energy that would warm up the water. Now, we can figure out how much energy is in the peanut by how much the water is heated. We measure the amount of energy in units called '**calories**.' I'm sure you've heard that word before," said Ms. Lopez.

Calvin and Carol nodded.

"The word 'calorie' comes from the Latin word '*calor*,' which means heat. A calorie is the amount of heat energy needed to raise the temperature of 1 gram of water by 1 degree Celsius. So, if we know how many degrees the water was heated up, we can calculate how many calories the peanut has.

Scientists do this to determine how many calories different foods have. A food that has more chemical or stored energy will have more energy to convert to heat. It will raise the temperature of the water more when the food is burned."

"Slow down, Ms. L.," begged Calvin. "I can't write fast enough! Latin, chemistry, burning peanuts, calculating the number of calories in food. How can I remember all of this?"

"Don't worry about the details. What scientists do in the lab to accurately calculate the calories in food is a bit more complicated than what we just did. What you have observed from burning the peanut is that it does have stored chemical energy and we can measure that energy in calories," replied Ms. Lopez. "We can test other kinds of food, too, and make more observations. Does this help you understand why we say food has stored chemical energy, Carol?"

Carol nodded.

"Okay, then," said Ms. Lopez, "let's get back to the cells. How do cells take the stored chemical energy from digested food and turn it into the kind of energy that lets our bodies do all the things they need to do? Think about that burning peanut. But remember, if you had eaten that peanut, it wouldn't look like a peanut anymore by the time it got to your cells."

"Right," chimed in Calvin. "It's been broken down into nutrients and absorbed into the blood. Is there stored energy in the nutrients?"

"That's it, you've got it!" exclaimed Ms. Lopez. "Inside our cells, some of the digested nutrients are broken down to release the stored energy.

This process is called **metabolism,** which is a term that describes all the chemical reactions that an organism, like you, needs to survive. We'll discuss that next time."

· ·

"Hi, Ms. L.," exclaimed Calvin. He stopped in his tracks. "What the — Ms. L., it looks like an alien landed in your office! What's that?"

"Hi, Calvin," said Ms. Lopez, chuckling. "This is an artist's model of an animal cell. I borrowed it for our session today. We're going to continue our investigation of food and energy. Let's start with what you had for lunch."

"I had a burger, fries, and some milk," replied Calvin.

"Okay, now the question is, how does that

food become part of your body? Any ideas?"

"Well, I spilled catsup on my shirt and my friends told me I had a milk mustache, but I'm guessing that's not what you mean," teased Calvin. "I have a feeling you mean what happens after the food molecules are absorbed through the small intestine, right?"

"Precisely. We've discussed how food is broken down into smaller molecules. Now we're going to investigate how they meet your body's needs — how those molecules keep you alive. How can your body use that food you ate for lunch to grow and provide your body with energy? Remember what we learned so far — the food we eat is broken down and energy is released."

Calvin nodded. "I remember."

"Now, Calvin, sit very still. Don't move a muscle," ordered Ms. Lopez. "There, do you feel anything? Is anything moving?"

"No, you told me not to move," he said, looking perplexed.

"You may not be moving on the outside, Calvin, but inside there is nonstop activity. Blood is rushing through your circulatory system. **Oxygen** and **carbon dioxide** are moving in and out of your respiratory system. Your liver is processing the nutrients from your digestive tract, and then, inside your body's cells — well, it's just amazing! Let's take a look at this model. Now think about this: scientists estimate that there may be as many as 100 trillion cells in the human body! Of course, the artist did not make this model the actual size of a cell. It's larger so we can look at the different parts that make up an animal cell. But just imagine, inside our cells hundreds of chemical reactions are taking place every minute."

Cells have essential roles in the human body. For example, they're in your blood. They make up organs and tissues. They are constantly working to keep your body healthy and operating smoothly. Think about their role in digestion. Cells transport food into the blood, where it travels to every part of the body. Find the mitochondria. They convert energy from the food you eat into ATP and discard what's left as carbon dioxide and water.

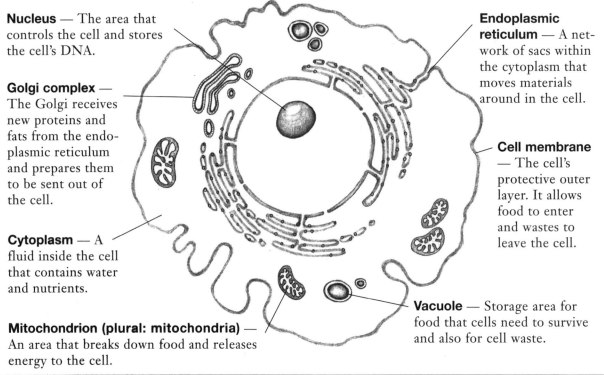

Nucleus — The area that controls the cell and stores the cell's DNA.

Golgi complex — The Golgi receives new proteins and fats from the endoplasmic reticulum and prepares them to be sent out of the cell.

Cytoplasm — A fluid inside the cell that contains water and nutrients.

Mitochondrion (plural: mitochondria) — An area that breaks down food and releases energy to the cell.

Endoplasmic reticulum — A network of sacs within the cytoplasm that moves materials around in the cell.

Cell membrane — The cell's protective outer layer. It allows food to enter and wastes to leave the cell.

Vacuole — Storage area for food that cells need to survive and also for cell waste.

"Well, this model helps me visualize what a cell looks like, but what do you mean by chemical reactions?" asked Calvin.

"Metabolism — remember from our last session?" Ms. Lopez was clearly excited and didn't wait for an answer. "It describes all of the chemical reactions that happen inside a cell. The metabolic reactions include converting nutrients, such as fats, proteins, and carbohydrates, into energy, and making other molecules that are used to maintain your body. Think about it! All that activity, but you can't feel it. Our bodies are pretty amazing!

"Now, look at this cell, Calvin. These different parts are called organelles, and each one has a different function.

The nucleus controls what goes on in the cell. And this organelle, do you know what it does?"

"You mean this part that kind of looks like a sausage?" asked Calvin.

"That's the one," said Ms. Lopez. "That's called the **mitochondrion.** Some people describe it as a cell's power station or factory. The mitochondrion releases the energy from

CELLULAR RESPIRATION:

glucose + oxygen —> carbon dioxide + water + energy

The equation:

$$C_6H_{12}O_6 + 6O_2 \longrightarrow 6CO_2 + 6H_2O + energy$$

STUDENT READINGS

nutrients. The process of releasing energy from the food molecules is called **cellular respiration.**

"Respiration? That sounds like breathing," noted Calvin.

"Good observation. See the O_2 in the equation? The 'O' is the symbol for oxygen. We'll get to that in a minute.

"Remember when we burned the peanut? This process is similar, but in the cell, the energy is released slowly rather than all at once, as it was in the burning peanut. The cells release the energy through a series of chemical reactions that are controlled by enzymes. The cells break down or 'burn' the nutrients they receive from our bloodstream. The stored chemical energy is changed into a form of energy that lets our bodies do everything they need to do, including move around. The energy released from food is also used to heat our bodies. Instead of using actual fire to do this, though, our cells use lots of chemical reactions. In order for those chemical reactions to happen, our cells need oxygen. This is why we must breathe oxygen into our lungs and have our circulatory system pump that oxygen to every cell in our bodies. And every time those chemical reactions happen, our cells give off carbon dioxide as waste."

Calvin stared intently at the cell. "Look, Ms. L., it says here on the label that human cells vary in size, but you can get about 10,000 average-sized human cells on the head of a pin! That's awesome. All those chemical reactions taking place in these minuscule parts of our bodies and we can't even feel them!"

"And releasing energy from food isn't all that cells do," Ms. Lopez added. "Another major job of metabolism is to build the things our bodies need. Have you ever heard the saying 'You are what you eat'? Well, that is absolutely true. After our digestive systems break our food down into nutrients and our **blood vessels** deliver them to our cells, our cells take some of those nutrients and use them to build the things that our bodies need to help them grow. This includes building body parts, like our bones, our skin, our eyes, our blood, and our heart and other muscles. We also need nutrients for all of our body functions such as helping our eyes to focus, our blood to **clot**, our lungs to breathe, and our heart to beat.

"Now," Ms. Lopez continued, "you may have heard people use the terms 'fast' or 'slow' metabolism."

"Sure have," interrupted Calvin. "My cousin is very skinny and my aunt says he's that way because he has a fast metabolism. She said I've got a slow one 'cuz I'm heavier than my cousin."

"Lots of people would agree with your aunt, Calvin. They believe that a heavier person is slow to burn the energy in food and stores more of it as fat for later use and that the opposite is true for thinner people. They think a thinner person burns food energy faster, which prevents weight gain. However, that's not what research tells us. It is true that people may have genetic differences in the rate that they use the energy from food. But this is a very small part of what determines their weight. The biggest factor that determines our weight is the balance between how much we eat and how much we move around — how much physical activity we get."

Ms. Lopez paused. "I seem to have done all the talking today. What do you think about all this?"

"Well, Ms. L.," Calvin said, then hesitated. "Does this mean when I drink lots of soda or eat lots of fries that I am giving my cells more energy than they need?"

"That's right, Calvin," replied Ms. Lopez. "And that extra energy is stored as fat."

"I think I'd better go shoot some hoops, Ms. L.," Calvin replied as he picked up his backpack. "I ate an awful lot of fries with my burger. See you next time."

LESSON 9:
Visualizing Change

"I bet you're Calvin and Carol," a cheerful man said to the pair as they entered a new office at the LiFE Center. "Please come in! I am Ken Morgan, art therapist and communication specialist. I've been expecting you."

As Calvin and Carol walked into Mr. Morgan's office, they noticed that it looked different from other rooms at the LiFE Center. One wall was painted an earthy orange, and another was plummy purple. He had lamps shining soft light and decorative fabrics hanging on the walls. The far wall was full of shelves stocked with all sorts of items that captured their attention.

One shelf had a large drum, some sponges, a bucket, and some paintbrushes. The next was stocked full of paper of all colors and sizes,

watercolor paints, markers, and colored chalk. And all across the shelves, spilling over onto the walls and on Mr. Morgan's desk, were framed pictures. Large ones, small ones. They were all images of boys and girls engaged in activities.

"You can see my collection of supplies there. As an art therapist, I make art with the young people who come in here, and help them express themselves. Using art, people can imagine and visualize change. It helps them understand themselves and lets them focus on how they want to change. Allow me to show you some of the past works other young people have made here."

Mr. Morgan turned to a frame on the wall portraying a boy holding a baseball bat standing with a smaller boy who had a baseball and glove in his hand.

"This was Matthew, who wanted to teach his brother to play baseball with him. Over there," Mr. Morgan said as he pointed across the room, "is Sophia, who wanted to be a gardener. Here you can see Augusto, who wanted to be a computer-game programmer. This is Elizabeth, who wanted to be a great basketball player."

Calvin and Carol gazed at each of the four portraits.

"Do you know what these works all have in common?" inquired Mr. Morgan.

"They're all of kids doing the things they like to do," offered Carol.

"Yeah, things you do because you like them. There is no one making you do them," added Calvin.

"That's right. We all have activities we enjoy doing in our free time, and doing them on a regular basis helps us achieve two things.

First, it helps us feel good about ourselves when we stick with something and develop our skills. Second, these activities help us keep our energy balance. I hear you have been discussing energy balance with some other folks here at the LiFE Center," said Mr. Morgan.

"We have. Christian showed us how the amount of energy you put in or take out makes a difference in energy balance," said Carol.

"Yeah, sometimes when too much energy came in too fast, it didn't have time to go out, so the water overflowed out of the cup," Calvin added.

"Ah, that is a great exercise. You two understand what energy balance means for your body, then. Do you understand how the activities we do can affect our own energy balance?" asked Mr. Morgan.

"What do you mean?" asked Carol.

"Well, the things we do every day, over and over, day after day, have an impact on our energy balance. Practicing the activities we enjoy most in life, especially physical activities, helps us keep our energy balance steady."

"You mean practicing basketball is more than just about my skills?" asked Calvin.

"Right. Whether we're experts or not in the things we do is not the point. It is just a matter of doing them, and enjoying them. Would you like to make a self-portrait today?" asked Mr. Morgan.

"I would!" said Carol.

"Sure," added Calvin.

"Splendid!" said Mr. Morgan. "Here is how it works. You may choose from any of these materials to work with. The only guidelines I have for you are that it must be a self-portrait,

and it should portray you doing something you aspire to do well. Does that sound possible?"

They nodded their heads as they started toward the shelves packed with supplies. Twenty minutes later, they were each deep into their creations. Carol was gliding her paintbrush over her paper with watercolors, while Calvin was working with modeling clay. When they had finished, they each showed Mr. Morgan what they had created.

Carol beamed as Mr. Morgan examined her watercolor painting of herself wearing a beautiful dance costume and jumping in midair.

"Ah, Carol, I see that being a dancer is very important to you," observed Mr. Morgan. "Tell me about it."

Carol Dancing!!

Choice, Control & Change
©2010 Teachers College Columbia University

"I've always loved dance," said Carol. "I haven't been dancing as much lately, but that's something that I'd like to change. I've been learning that I can make choices, and one of my choices is to keep dancing and get really good. I've learned from Ms. Lopez that that means I need to make choices about what I eat, too, so I have the energy to dance."

"Very good," Mr. Morgan exclaimed. "Now, Calvin, tell me about your work."

Calvin grinned as he shared his sculpture of himself high on his toes, preparing to take a shot at the basketball hoop. "It's the last few seconds of a game, the buzzer is about to go off, and I shoot the ball…swish, and we win by two points! Of course, like Carol, I need to work on my energy balance. But I think I can do it and get back into shape. I've already made a change in what I drink and I'm going to make a change in my activity. To have more time for basketball, I am going to reduce the amount of time I play video games."

Just then, Ms. Lopez stuck her head in the door of Mr. Morgan's office.

"Hello! Looks like you've been busy with Mr. Morgan today. I just wanted to drop these off with you before you leave. They are food logs, for you to report each and every morsel of food you eat, including drinks. Please fill them out for next time. Do your best, and don't forget to bring them back. Thanks!" she called as Calvin and Carol tucked the food logs into their bags and ran out to show their parents their artistic creations.

LESSON 10:
Bite, Write, Learn

"Hi, Ms. Lopez!" shouted Calvin and Carol when they entered her office.

"Well hello, Carol, hello, Calvin. Good to see you this week. I gave you an assignment to keep a food log last week. How did it go?" asked Ms. Lopez.

"That was way hard!" insisted Calvin.

"Ah, you found it challenging? What part was difficult?"

"Remembering to write down what I ate before I ate it," said Calvin.

"Remembering that I was even supposed to write it down," said Carol.

"So one challenge was remembering to keep the food log," said Ms. Lopez.

"Right. And then, when I remembered, it wasn't so clear what I should write," said Calvin.

"Give me an example of when you didn't know what to write, Calvin," said Ms. Lopez.

"I grabbed some chips after school and I didn't know what to write in the 'How Much' column," said Calvin.

"Okay, portion size can be tricky," said Ms. Lopez. "How about you, Carol, what was hard for you?"

"I had some green beans with my dinner and fruit salad after dinner and I couldn't figure out how much for those, either," said Carol.

"So, again, the 'How Much' column was the hard part," said Ms. Lopez.

"It's not just hard, Ms. Lopez, it's practically impossible!" insisted Carol.

"Wow, it sounds like quite a struggle," said Ms. Lopez. "I have something I think might help." She took two cards out of her desk and

PROCESSED-SNACKS SERVING SIZE

Using this 3"x5" card:
- Smaller than this card = small
- Same size as this card = medium
- Larger than this card = large

Using calories:
- Less than 150 calories = small
- 150–300 calories = medium
- More than 300 calories = large

FAST-FOOD SERVING SIZE

Use the sizes listed on the menu. If you want to know specific amounts of calories, fat, sugar, sodium, or other nutrients in fast foods, ask for nutrition information when purchasing the food, or look up the information online.

FRUITS AND VEGETABLES SERVING SIZE

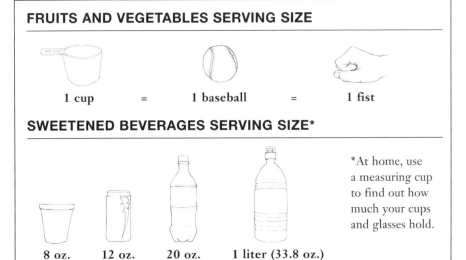

1 cup   =   1 baseball   =   1 fist

SWEETENED BEVERAGES SERVING SIZE*

8 oz.   12 oz.   20 oz.   1 liter (33.8 oz.)

*At home, use a measuring cup to find out how much your cups and glasses hold.

"I see," said Calvin. "In the food column, I would write that I had a bag of chips. In the stores I go to there are bags that are really tiny, medium, and large. The really tiny bags are smaller than this card, so that would be a small, the medium are about the size of the card, and the large bags are bigger than the card, so a large. I had a medium bag, so I would write a medium processed snack. Oh, and I could do the same thing with those chocolate-chip cookies my mom makes. Two of her cookies would be a medium. Using this to estimate portion size sure makes it easier for me to judge how much I have eaten. I'm going to carry it around until I get the hang of it,"

gave one to each of them. "These are your *How Much?* cards. Carry them with you when you do your food log this week to help you determine the portion size of foods you are eating."

"How do we do that?" asked Calvin.

"Take a look at the processed-snacks section of this card. It says that for processed snacks like chips, candy, cookies, and other baked goods, you can use this 3"x5" rectangle, the size of an index card, to estimate portion size. Smaller than the card is a small, about the same size is a medium, and bigger is a large," replied Ms. Lopez.

said Calvin.

"Yes, that makes sense for snack food, but what about my fruits and vegetables? They were all spread out on my plate," said Carol. "How do I use the card?"

"Good question, Carol. How big was the pile of green beans on your plate?" asked Ms. Lopez.

Carol studied the serving size examples on the card. "I think it was like a whole baseball," she concluded.

"Okay, then, what quantity of green beans is

that, according to the card?" asked Ms. Lopez.

"One cup," said Carol.

"Right. Try to do the same for the fruit salad."

"Hmm. Probably a baseball and a half," said Carol.

"Does that help explain things?" asked Ms. Lopez.

They both nodded their heads.

"I got it," said Calvin. "For snack foods we can use small, medium, or large based on the rectangle, and for fruits and vegetables we can use cups, baseballs, or our fists for the portion size."

"Good. I want you to pay particular attention to the foods that are part of the food and physical-activity goals — that is, fruits, vegetables, processed snacks, sweetened beverages, water, and fast food.

CALVIN'S FOOD LOG	
Breakfast	**How Much?**
Packaged cinnamon bun	medium size
Banana	1 cup
Water	12 ounces
Lunch	**How Much?**
Chicken nuggets	6 nuggets
Green beans	1/2 cup
Bread roll	1 small
Grape soda	20-ounce bottle
Snack	**How Much?**
Potato chips	medium bag
Lemon-lime soda	20-ounce bottle
Dinner	**How Much?**
Hamburger patty	two 4-ounce patties
Cheese	1 ounce
Lettuce and tomato	1/2 cup
Bun	1 bun
French fries	medium
Cola	16 ounces (medium)

"I have already been looking at my beverage containers to see how many ounces of sports drink I have been drinking," Calvin chimed in.

"Excellent. Ounces is a great way to put down portion size for sweetened beverages," said Ms. Lopez. "Now, drinking water out of a glass can be a little harder, since glasses can vary in size. You may want to use measuring cups to find out how many ounces are in the different-sized glasses you have at home."

"At home I always drink water from the same kind of glass. I'm going to use a measuring cup to figure out how many ounces it holds. Then it will be easy for me to know how

many ounces I'm drinking," said Carol.

"Sounds like you are both getting this. Do you have any other questions?" asked Ms. Lopez. "No? Okay then, let's try to add more details to what you recorded. Calvin, let's use your food log as a model."

"Let's see. For breakfast I was in a hurry. I slept late and had to grab something to eat on my way to school. I ate a cinnamon bun and a banana. The bun was about the same size as the 3"x5" card, so I think that was a medium processed snack. If I squished the banana into a ball, it would be about the size of baseball, so it was 1 cup. Then, when I got

Choice, Control & Change
©2010 Teachers College Columbia University

to school, I drank about one and a half cups of water. The cup was 8 ounces; that is 12 total ounces."

"Good job, Calvin," said Ms. Lopez. "How about lunch. What did you eat for lunch?"

"Lunch was in the school cafeteria. We had chicken nuggets, which I love. I ate six of them, but I don't know how much that would be."

"Well, 3 ounces of meat is about the size of a deck of cards," said Ms. Lopez.

"Let's see, three of them are about the size of a deck of cards, so twice that, since I ate six, would be 6 ounces. Plus a few green beans, I think about half a cup, plus a roll with some butter and a grape soda I had picked up on the way to school. The roll was small and the soda was a 20-ounce bottle. And then I was so hungry after school that I had a snack. I ate the bag of potato chips I told you about before, so a medium-sized processed snack, and I drank a 20-ounce bottle of lemon-lime soda. I know I said I'd drink less soda, and I'm trying, but sometimes I forget."

"That's okay, Calvin. This data is going to help us see which foods you need to eat more or less of," explained Ms. Lopez. "Now let's see what you ate the rest of the day."

"We ate out last night to celebrate my cousin's birthday," said Calvin. "It was great! I had a double cheeseburger with lettuce and tomato on a hamburger bun, plus a medium order of French fries and a medium cola."

"Okay," said Ms. Lopez, "let's see. A medium cola is a 16-ounce soda and the double cheese-burger was two 4 ounce hamburger patties plus a 1 ounce slice of cheese. Calvin, you ate 2.5 cups of fruit and vegetables for the day. When you add up the amount of fat and

sugar, you get 22 teaspoons, or 110 grams, of fat and 50 teaspoons, or 200 grams, of sugar. The recommendation for a 2,000-calorie diet is no more than 13 teaspoons, or 65 grams, of fat and 12.5 teaspoons, or 50 grams, of sugar," observed Ms. Lopez. "Any questions?"

"What does all this matter anyway?" asked Carol.

"Do you all remember on the day when I first met you, I told you I had a hypothesis and I wanted you to help me test it?"

"I do — it was about energy balance," said Calvin with a wide grin.

"That's right. And how did I want to study energy balance?" Ms. Lopez asked.

"With evidence?" said Carol.

"Yes, with scientific evidence," said Ms. Lopez, as she held up a blank food log. "These records help us to gather data on ourselves, so that we can analyze it and learn more about ourselves. Then, the results can be compared with the recommendations for a healthy diet. We can see by this analysis whether we need to adjust our eating habits to maintain our energy balance. Does that make sense?"

"Sure does," Carol exclaimed.

Ms. Lopez looked at her watch. "I'm afraid we've run out of time today. Now, let's see if you can apply what you learned today as you continue to keep your food logs. We're learning a lot from the data you're collecting."

"Thanks!" said Calvin, as they both walked out of the office.

LESSON 11:
Steps

Calvin came running into Ms. Lopez's office on the day of their next meeting. Ms. Lopez greeted him with, "Hello, Calvin! That's a lot of steps you're taking."

Calvin looked at her with a puzzled expression, catching his breath. Just then, Carol walked in behind him.

"Hi, Ms. Lopez! Are we meeting someone new today?" she asked.

"Good afternoon, Carol. As a matter of fact, we are. Let's go upstairs and meet Ms. Lee."

Calvin and Carol walked toward the elevator down the hall, but Ms. Lopez called them in the other direction.

"Let's go this way, to the stairs. We'll add more steps that way," she said.

Calvin and Carol looked at each other, then followed Ms. Lopez to the stairwell.

"Fifty-one, fifty-two, fifty-three…" counted Ms. Lopez.

"What's she doing?" Carol quietly asked Calvin.

"You got me," answered Calvin.

They reached the floor with Ms. Lee's office and started down the hallway. Ms. Lopez was still counting.

"Ninety-seven, ninety-eight, ninety-nine, one hundred!" she finished.

"Ms. Lopez, do you always count out loud when you walk to other offices?" asked Carol, puzzled.

Ms. Lopez did not seem to notice her question. She was busy peeking at something clipped to her waistband.

"One hundred two. Not bad!" Ms. Lopez exclaimed as she removed the object. "What's that, Carol? I'm sorry, I didn't hear your question. I was concentrating on **calibrating** my **pedometer**."

"Your what?" asked Calvin.

"My pedometer. You're about to learn more about them. Let me introduce you to Ms. Maya Lee, who will get you started."

The three of them walked through the door into Ms. Lee's work space. It was much larger than an office. In fact, it looked like a small gym, with exercise machines, weights, mats, and electronic equipment. Then, out from behind a desk walked a fit woman in workout clothes.

"Ms. Lee, these are the two researchers-in-training I was telling you about. Calvin and Carol, meet Ms. Lee," said Ms. Lopez.

"Calvin and Carol? Welcome to the exercise lab here at the LiFE Center! I am the exercise physiologist here. I study how exercise affects people's health. Would you all like to come in and have a look around?" Calvin and Carol nodded and followed Ms. Lee as she pointed out the different types of equipment she used in her work.

"Here is a treadmill that I have my clients run on to test their level of **fitness**," said Ms. Lee. "Here are some skinfold calipers I use to measure a person's body-fat percentage. These are all tools I use to collect data on my clients. This information helps me to evaluate a snapshot of my client's physical fitness. Then I analyze it to make conclusions about his or her health."

"What kind of conclusions?" asked Carol.

"Oh, all sorts. We have gathered strong evidence in the field of exercise physiology that being active benefits your heart, lungs, bones, muscles, blood sugar, brain...just about every part of your body. Physical activity is also a key to energy balance. Our bodies were made to be active. But the benefits of exercise aren't just long-term. They are right here and now. I want you to think about your favorite activity — one that gets your heart pumping, and maybe gets you a little sweaty. Do you have it?"

"Yes, basketball!" said Calvin.

"Dancing!" added Carol.

"Good. Now, think of how you feel when you are finished. What is that like?" asked Ms. Lee.

"It's like my muscles wake up. I can be really tired before I play ball, but when I am finished, my body feels worn out but also energized," said Calvin.

"Ah, so you are tuned in to the energizing effects of physical activity. Excellent! How about you, Carol?" asked Ms. Lee.

"When I'm dancing after school, I just feel better. I think better in class. I even actually sleep better!" exclaimed Carol.

"Yes, that is what happens!" Ms. Lee responded.

"But last year when school ended and I wasn't dancing as much, I noticed I was tired more of the time. Wouldn't I be more tired from all that dancing?"

"Not necessarily. Regular activity boosts our energy level during the day and helps us rest at night. It also keeps us from getting sick as often, it supports good moods, and it helps us maintain energy balance," said Ms. Lee. "From what I'm hearing, you both are very active young people."

"Well, I used to be," said Calvin. "But I just haven't felt like it lately."

"Why is that, Calvin?" asked Ms. Lee.

"I've been going home to play my brother on his video-game system. He's up three games to two, and I have to even out the score," explained Calvin.

"Oh, I see. What about you, Carol?"

"Well, this year I can't dance as much. I have to babysit for my little brother and sister. And now my dance clothes don't fit and I just didn't feel like going anymore," said Carol.

"Did you think about getting clothes that did fit?" asked Ms. Lee.

"Yes. But the other kids who dance all the time are getting better than I am, so I just haven't felt like going," said Carol.

"Then is it fair to say that you both have been less active this year than you were in the past?" asked Ms. Lee.

They nodded.

"Well, you've come to the right place. Your doctors sent you to the LiFE Center because they were concerned about your test results from your physical this year. Do you remember the benefits of exercise I told you about before?"

"Healthy heart and lungs," said Carol.

"Maintaining energy balance," said Calvin.

"Yes, good!" exclaimed Ms. Lee. "What else?"

"More energy," added Calvin.

"Healthy bones and brain," said Carol.

"All true, good!" said Ms. Lee. "I'll add controlling blood sugar to the list. And my favorite, good mood!"

"Is that why you're so happy?" asked Calvin.

"I have no doubt that is part of it, Calvin," replied Ms. Lee. "You both said that you are less active than before. As an exercise physiologist, I know that the concerns your doctors had with your health can be addressed through increasing your physical activity."

"I had a feeling you were going to say that," said Carol.

"Right you are, Carol! Now, I have a tool that can be used to motivate you to increase your physical activity," said Ms. Lee, and she pulled two small items from her desk drawer and handed one to Calvin and one to Carol.

"Hey, that's what Ms. Lopez was wearing before!" said Calvin. "And counting to herself," he added, with raised eyebrows.

"Yes, she was. She was helping me calibrate her pedometer. Do you know what it means to calibrate something?" asked Ms. Lee.

They shook their heads.

"It means the comparison of a device, like a pedometer, to a known standard. You compare the measurement your pedometer is making with your own count. You want to make sure it is counting accurately."

"Counting what, Ms. Lee?" asked Carol.

"Counting the steps we take. A pedometer, when worn properly, counts the number of steps we take. So wearing one day after day can tell us over time something about our physical-activity level. How many steps do you think you take in a day?"

"Four hundred?" guessed Carol.

"Seven hundred!" guessed Calvin.

"The average person takes between 5,000 and 7,000 steps per day," Ms. Lee said. Calvin and Carol stared back. "But I want to challenge you two to each take 10,000 steps per day. Are you up for the challenge?"

"Yeah!" they both said.

LESSON 12:
Choosing a Goal

Calvin and Carol walked into Dr. George Kostas's office and noticed at once how tidy it was. A few books lined the shelves, and some art hung on the walls, but generally the contents of the room were sparse.

Dr. Kostas wasted no time in getting down to business. "Good morning, Calvin and Carol! I'm Dr. Kostas, behavioral scientist here at the LiFE Center. Do you know what a behavioral scientist does?"

"You study people's behavior?" asked Calvin.

"Exactly, Calvin," said Dr. Kostas. "Part of what I do here at the LiFE Center is to study people's behavior around food and the food choices they make. I also work with people to change their behavior. I know you have been keeping food logs..."

"Yes, it is so hard!" Carol interjected.

"Keeping a food log takes new skills and attention to detail," Dr. Kostas said. "Ms. Lopez and I discussed your medical records and then she gave me your food logs. You two put a lot of effort into your record-keeping. That's a job well done. Let's take a look at them, shall we?"

He pulled out their food logs, and paused to look them over, nodding.

"Now, based on my examination of your food logs, I think we can gather some important details about your food and beverage choices. First, tell me your thoughts about the foods you chose last week," said Dr. Kostas.

Calvin said, "I used to drink sodas a lot after school, but then Ms. Lopez showed me how much sugar they have, and I've been trying to drink less. I tried switching to sports drinks since I was playing basketball, but those have sugar, too."

"They sure do," said Dr. Kostas. "What did you see in your food log, then?"

"Well, it seems like I drink soda a lot less. The first day I had three sodas, but then over the next two days, I only had one," said Calvin.

"What other drinks did you have?" asked Dr. Kostas.

"I had some fruit punch — with 'fruit' in the name I figure it has to be healthy."

"Well, 100% juice does have vitamins in it, but fruit punch is not usually fruit juice, and fruit punch and fruit juice usually have about as much sugar as soda."

Calvin was shocked. "You mean that even though I am already trying to cut out soda and sports drinks, I have to cut out one more thing?" he demanded.

"Not cut it out. But have smaller amounts less often. That is why our food goal is no more than 8 ounces a day for sweetened beverages. That is a small cup a day or a 20-ounce bottle every two or three days." Dr. Kostas paused, turned his attention to Carol, and said, "What did you think about your food log?"

"It seems like I ate out a lot more than I realized," replied Carol.

"Oh? How often are you eating out?" asked Dr. Kostas.

"Well, last week I had practice for a dance performance two nights and then the performance another night. When my mom picked me up, I was so hungry that I begged her to stop at a fast-food place. Then, after the performance, we all went out to celebrate, so I ate out again. Then, of course, there were the snacks. I was in a hurry, so I grabbed something quick from the vending machines where we were rehearsing. My mom packed some fresh fruit for me, but I forgot it!"

"Okay, Carol. How do you think eating out for many of your meals and snacks affects your food choices?"

"Dr. Kostas, I never really thought about it that way, you know? I just buy what I like when I go out," said Carol.

"That is important for us to realize, then. You may not be making food choices according to what is healthy for your body, and generally people eat more calories when they eat out compared to when they eat at home. I hear you saying that you are buying foods that are available to you, and that appeal to your tastes."

Carol nodded in agreement, her eyebrows raised.

"What I've learned as a behavioral scientist is that you are not alone in your food choices," said Dr. Kostas. "Many of us make our food choices based on foods that are readily available, brightly packaged, heavily advertised, and appealing to our tastes. Let's take a look at what is emphasized in your diet when you eat the foods you like when you eat out. Let's see. Here, you've written that one day you had a fried chicken sandwich for dinner and candy and cookies throughout the day as snacks. Now, what do these foods all contain a lot of?"

"The snacks have a lot of sugar," said Calvin.

"Yes, that's true," replied Dr. Kostas.

"The chicken sandwich really tasted so good," said Carol.

"Okay, other than taste, what do they do after they are in your body?"

"You mean are they healthy?" asked Carol.

"Along those lines, yes. What do they contribute to your overall diet?"

"I guess probably a lot of fat and sugar, and I remember from those demonstrations what too much fat and sugar do in our body," she said.

"Many of these foods are also high in salt, which contains **sodium**," added Dr. Kostas. "Consuming too much sodium can increase blood pressure and risk of **heart disease**."

Carol sighed, "So eating whatever is easy to find and tastes good can add up to too much fat, sugar, and now salt, too?"

"I'm afraid so. Food choices that are readily available provide us with more fat, sugar, and salt than is healthy for our bodies. Now, what food group do you think gets left out when we are just eating what is readily found in our environment?" asked Dr. Kostas.

"I bet you want me to say fruits and vegetables," said Carol, smirking.

"I do. It's important to realize that when we

eat smaller amounts of sweetened beverages, processed snacks, and fast food and we consume the recommended 4 cups of fruits and vegetables, we are eating in a way that will help us stay healthy."

"Hold up, Dr. K. I just realized something!" exclaimed Carol.

"What's that?"

"You said when we came in here that you looked at our medical records, but also our food logs. Are you saying that you can understand why our doctors sent us here just by looking at what we eat? Are you serious?"

"I am, Carol. Your food logs are only a week's worth of eating, but they represent your food choices over a long period of time. And eating habits over time affect our health. That is why I wanted to look at your food diaries. From your medical records, I could speculate that these were your habits, but your food logs help me know for sure. And, what we just discussed about Carol's food records touches on three of our food goals: to eat no more than one small or medium processed snack a day, to eat at fast-food places no more than three times a week — and to choose healthier foods like grilled chicken and smaller portions when you do go to fast-food places — and to get at least 4 cups of fruits and vegetables, to get all of those vitamins without the fat and sugar.

"Now, the work for you two is to decide how you want to go about shifting your habits toward health. You can do it. It starts with the choices you make about foods and beverages. I'm here to help you. Why don't you think about that, and we'll talk about it when I see you next time."

Deep in thought, Calvin and Carol said good-bye to Dr. Kostas and slowly walked out the door.

. . . .

The next time Calvin and Carol saw Dr. Kostas, they walked in more confidently than they had left the last time.

"Hello, my researchers-in-training! You two appear ready to get down to business this morning," commented Dr. Kostas.

They nodded back at him attentively.

"Today I want to talk to you about action plans. What do you think that means?" he asked.

"I think that would be like a play we talk about in basketball, Dr. K.," offered Calvin. "It's when you plan ahead of time with your teammates how you're going to play the ball to score some points."

"Excellent comparison, Calvin. And why are plays useful in basketball?" he asked.

"Because you know what you're going to do before you start playing, and it helps you go ahead and do it."

"Marvelous," shot back Dr. Kostas. "Today we're going to work on personal action plans, sort of like a basketball play to use in life off the court. It will outline how you plan to meet your goals. Sometimes I call it a how-to."

"Who's going to write these plays, er, plans?" asked Carol.

"You are," said Dr. Kostas. "And to get you going in your action plan, you're going to select a personal goal."

"What kind of a goal?" asked Calvin.

"It will be a goal focused on your eating and drinking behaviors. Setting goals and tracking your progress with them has been shown to help people start up new behaviors. It helps them stay on track. In the case of goals focused on better eating and drinking choices, these behaviors can lead us to better health over time. Think you're up for the challenge?" asked Dr. Kostas.

Calvin and Carol looked at each other, then looked back at Dr. Kostas and nodded.

"Excellent. Shall we begin? Do either of you remember any of the LiFE Center's food goals that Ms. Lopez and I mentioned before?"

"Eating more fruits and vegetables, like you said last time, Dr. K.," offered Carol.

"A great start," remarked Dr. Kostas as he marked the goal on a sheet of paper. "What else?"

"Drinking less soda and sports drinks and juice stuff," said Calvin.

"Indeed! Fewer sweetened beverages," he said, and he added the second goal under the first.

Carol spoke again. "How about eating fewer cupcakes and candy, like they sell at the mini-market?"

"Great choice. I'd add chips and salty snacks to that category. Fewer processed snacks that often come in packages at mini-markets and other stores," Dr. Kostas said as he sketched the goal on the list.

"Mini-markets aren't the only places you can get that stuff. Fast-food places are all over my neighborhood," said Calvin. "And fast foods have a lot of fat and salt, like you said last time, Dr. K."

"Absolutely. Fast-food places make food that tastes good to a wide range of people, and yes, Calvin, it's very high in fat and salt. Good one," he said. He added "Less fast food" to the list.

Calvin and Carol both paused in thought for a moment, stumped.

Dr. Kostas broke the silence. "So far we have three things to reduce and one thing to increase. We need two more things to increase to even it out."

Calvin said, "Well, if drinking less sweet stuff is a goal, maybe drinking more things that aren't sweet should be on the list, too."

"It should. How about water?" Dr. Kostas offered. Calvin nodded in approval and Dr. Kostas added it to the list. "And another?"

"I have something to add, but it's not something you eat or drink, Dr. K.," said Carol.

"What is it?" Dr. Kostas asked expectantly.

"You know Ms. Lee, the exercise physiologist?" asked Carol.

"I work with her closely, yes," said Dr. Kostas.

"She talked to us about how to use pedometers. We almost forgot to add the physical activity goal to the list."

"Terrific, Carol. That makes six goals! Stupendous work, you two. You remembered them all. I do have to say it is a great list of healthy behavioral goals."

They gazed over the list, quietly pleased with their achievement.

"Now, I had asked you to think about how you wanted to take action to improve your health last time. Do you see anything on this list that supports that?" he asked them.

"I see lots. How do I pick just one?" asked Calvin.

"Pick the goal that applies the most to you. And pick something you think is realistic for you to do," Dr. Kostas advised.

"Okay," said Calvin. "I think fewer sweetened beverages is the way for me to go. I've been thinking about that a lot already, and it seems like every time I try and do it, I run into something that holds me back. I'm going to really try to do it now."

"Wonderful, Calvin. How about you, Carol?"

"I was thinking about two of them, Dr. K. But I'm choosing one that is adding something instead of taking away. That seems the better way for me."

"Great, Carol. Which goal is that?"

"Something I've already discussed with Ms. Lopez… adding more fruits and vegetables," Carol replied.

"Very good. I think you might find that adding fruits and vegetables may reduce some of the other foods anyway," said Dr. Kostas.

Carol looked pleased.

Develop an Action Plan

STEP 5: Think about exactly what you will do to meet your goal. Add in details such as the time of day and what foods you will or will not eat. Write your notes below. For example, "I will drink water instead of soda each day after school."

STEP 6: Think about any roadblocks you might encounter. Write them below. These are the challenges you will face when making a try at your specific goal. For example, "All my friends drink soda after school. I really like the taste of soda."

STEP 7: Think about strategies you can develop to help you overcome any roadblocks. What things can you do to help yourself be successful at achieving your goal no matter what roadblocks you encounter? Write these strategies below. For example, "I will tell my friends that I think drinking water is very cool. I will make sure I can get really cold water because I think that tastes the best."

Dr. Kostas continued, "The next step to the action plan is to write down how you're going to achieve your plan — this is the how-to… how to do it. I have a special planning sheet to support you in pursuit of your healthy goals. Take these," he said as he handed them each a sheet of paper.

"There is space for you to write about things you can do to meet your goal. Think about what will support your new choices. Where will you go? What will you look for?"

Calvin and Carol thought and wrote on the first set of lines.

"Next, think about what might get in your way when you are trying to follow through with your new goals. What might you be up against? What kind of roadblocks might you run into?" asked Dr. Kostas.

"Oh, I can think of plenty for this one," remarked Carol. The two of them wrote for a few minutes, then looked up again.

"Finally," Dr. Kostas said, "think of a strategy to handle these roadblocks when they come up. What could you do to keep you on track with your chosen goal? And, to help you as you try to reach your goal, here's something I call *The C3 Tracker*. It will help you track your progress."

Calvin and Carol filled in this final portion of their action-planning sheet, and then packed up their belongings to leave.

"Good luck! Let me know how it goes," said Dr. Kostas.

"Okay, Dr. K.!" they called over their shoulders as they scurried down the hall to the stairwell.

LESSON 13:
Step Success

As Carol entered the LiFE Center waiting area, she saw Rosanna. "Hi, Rosanna, remember me? I'm Carol. I talked to you on your first day at the LiFE Center. How's it going?"

"Oh, I do remember you," replied Rosanna. "You were right, it is fun here. I am learning so much about myself and it is fun to be a researcher with the scientists here. I have been trying to cut down on French fries. Even though I do feel better, I have to admit, I miss my fries."

"Wow, I have been trying to cut down on fries, too. Sounds like we have something in common," Carol replied.

"I went back to my doctor and she said that the fat in my blood had already gone down a little. That made me feel good. It also helps me to keep on trying," commented Rosanna.

"Carol and Calvin, please report to the exercise lab to see Ms. Lee," announced the receptionist.

"Okay, I've got to go. Hope I get to see you again," Carol said. She was thinking about how what she was learning was really important for all kids, no matter what their shape, size, or interests, and how proud she was of her own accomplishments.

Calvin and Carol walked into Ms. Lee's office with huge smiles on their faces. "We did it! We met your challenge, Ms. Lee!" they exclaimed. "But it wasn't easy."

"Congratulations! I'm sure it wasn't easy, but let's see what kind of data you collected when you compared your different activities. Tell me what you did," answered Ms. Lee.

"Well, Ms. Lee, I did what you suggested," began Calvin. "I made a list of all the activities that I do each day. Then, I started to keep track of how many steps I did in each activity. I was curious about how many steps I did in each one."

"Me, too," added Carol. "I was really curious about how many steps I took during my dance routines. Since I can't walk to school and have to get a ride, I needed to find other ways to get the steps up to 10,000."

"Tell me how you compared the different activities," urged Ms. Lee.

"I put my pedometer on first thing in the morning and set it to zero," said Carol. "I

GETTING READY FOR SCHOOL		
	Steps	**Time**
Before	Pedometer reading: 0	Start time: 7:30 am
After	Pedometer reading: 2,280	End time: 8:30 am
Difference	2,280 steps	60 minutes

recorded zero and wrote down what time it was when I started. Then I went downstairs and ate breakfast, helped my mother in the kitchen, went back upstairs to brush my teeth and get ready for school. Just before I left the house to get my ride, I wrote down the number on my pedometer and the time. Here's the table that I set up."

I repeated this every time I changed an activity, so I did it for the time I was at school, after school with my dance club, then at home again in the evening when I walked the dog."

"That's great, Carol! What about you, Calvin?"

"I used the same process, but my activities were different. Since I can walk to school, I get more steps in the morning than Carol does, and instead of taking the elevator in my building, I have started to use the stairs."

"Good thinking, Calvin! What other activities did you include?"

"I decided to see how many steps I use when I play video games, and of course, I calculated the number of steps I take when I play basketball."

"Okay," said Ms. Lee, "Let's take these tables you made and do some calculations. Carol, how many steps did you take getting ready for school?"

"I took 2,280."

"How long did it take you?" asked Ms. Lee as she wrote the number of steps on the board.

minute getting ready for school."

"Not many steps," sighed Carol, "but I was sitting and eating breakfast part of the time!'

"Okay, Calvin, let's see how you did walking to school. How many steps did you record?"

"I took 1,820 steps and I did it in 35 minutes," said Calvin.

"That's 52 steps per minute. Now that you two know how to do the calculations, I'll let you figure out the rest of your activities on your own. Once you've calculated the steps per minute for each of your activities, you can put them in a table like this so you can compare them."

COMPARING ACTIVITIES

Activity per Minute	Steps
Getting ready for school	38
Dance squad	125
Walking the dog	52
Basketball practice	133
Walking to school	52

Just then Ms. Lopez walked in. "Calvin and Carol, you look busy! What have you been doing?"

$$\text{Steps per minute} = \frac{\text{\# of steps} \rightarrow \boxed{2{,}280} \text{ steps}}{\text{\# of minutes} \rightarrow \boxed{60} \text{ minutes}} = \boxed{38} \text{ steps/minute}$$

"It took 60 minutes."

Ms. Lee continued the calculation on the board. "Looks like you take 38 steps per

"We've been working on our energy balance," reported Calvin. "Ms. Lee challenged us to take 10,000 steps a day, and we did it! Now she's helping us compare activities. We are going to use this data to help us keep on meeting the 10,000-step challenge."

"That's great!" exclaimed Ms. Lopez. "Do you see what I'm seeing here? It's very interesting to note the different kinds of activities that you do. You live in the city, Calvin, so you can walk to school. Carol, I see that your walking is generally done when you're close to home, like taking your dog for a walk. Another point I'd like to make is that you are using personal data to make changes that are helping you achieve energy balance. That's great! Keep it up! Now, let's step into my office for a minute so we can check in with how you are doing with your food goals."

Carol and Calvin seemed to have extra pep in their steps as they walked toward Ms. Lopez's office.

"Can I go first, Ms. L.?" asked Calvin. Carol sat back as Calvin continued, "Those how-to take action tips you gave me really helped. I found the coldest water fountain at my school and every time I walk by I take a few sips. That keeps my thirst level down. I never thought I would be saying this, but sometimes water really tastes better than soda. It leaves a cool, clean feeling in my mouth. I've noticed that when I don't feel thirsty all the time it is easier to stop myself from drinking a soda after school."

"Calvin, that sounds great, I am so proud of you!" exclaimed Ms. Lopez. "Are there any times when you still do have a sweetened beverage after school?"

"Yeah, when I'm with my friends and they're having soda, I just have one, too. I am trying to work on that. My cousin told me that one of his teachers said to picture taking a shower with soda instead of water and to think about how sticky the outside of your body would feel. That image is kind of disgusting. Instead, what I do is imagine I can touch the inside of my body and it feels sticky after I have soda. I grossed my friends out when I told them this. But I think it convinced a few of them to start drinking less soda, too."

"Sounds like a great plan to me, Calvin," replied Ms. Lopez.

Carol chimed in, "I have been thinking so much about what we learned about our food environment and activity environment and I think what we are learning here is so important for all kids to understand. I think if all kids knew what we now know they would make different choices. Calvin, I think it is so great that you are helping your friends."

Carol moved to the edge of her seat and continued talking. "Okay, my turn. The first week I did really well and I had vegetables every night at dinner. When my mom didn't have time to make them, I cut up some raw carrots and cucumbers. The second week was harder; I went four nights without vegetables. One night I just had pasta, although I could have added some vegetables to that. Another night I had plain pizza. Next time, I'll add some broccoli and peppers."

"Good thinking, Carol. Do you have a plan for this week?" asked Ms. Lopez.

"When I eat out I will remember to order vegetables. I also asked my mom to buy some carrots, green beans, and peppers, since those are easy to cut up and eat raw, so I can add vegetables in no time at all."

"You are both doing so well. I know how hard it is to change. We will catch up more next time."

"Bye, Ms. Lopez," Calvin and Carol said, and they raced each other down the hallway.

LESSON 14:
Move, Move, Move

"Hello, Calvin and Carol!" called Ms. Lee as the pair stepped into the exercise lab.

"Morning, Ms. Lee," said Calvin. "You seem extra happy this morning."

"Well, Calvin, I have someone new for you to meet today! It is my pleasure to introduce you to the cardiologist at the LiFE Center, Dr. Carla Floyd."

"It's very nice to meet you both," said Dr. Floyd, shaking hands with Calvin and Carol. "Do you know what a cardiologist is?"

Calvin and Carol shook their heads. "I bet you will tell us," Calvin commented.

"It's a doctor who specializes in the heart and blood vessels. And that means that Ms. Lee and I have a lot to work together on."

"Why is that?" asked Carol.

"I'm so glad you asked, Carol. Have you ever thought about the effect that exercise, which is Ms. Lee's specialty, has on the heart?"

"Yes, exercise is good for your heart. We learned that already."

"Great. And do you know how it is good for your heart?"

"Not really," replied Carol.

Choice, Control & Change
©2010 Teachers College Columbia University

"What happens to your heart when you exercise? What can you feel it doing?" asked Dr. Floyd.

"It pumps hard when I run around the court," said Calvin.

"Right, the heart works harder when we're active. And what do you think happens over time when it does that?" Dr. Floyd asked.

"It gets stronger?" said Calvin.

"Right! The heart is a very strong muscle, and as it gets stronger it becomes more efficient at pumping blood around your body," said Dr. Floyd. "I understand from Ms. Lopez that you've learned about how blood carries digested nutrients from our food to all the cells in our body. These nutrients provide our bodies with energy and are used to build the molecules we need to grow and survive. Our blood also contains oxygen, which we breathe in through our lungs. Do you remember why our cells need oxygen?"

"For cellular respiration," replied Calvin. "That's the process that releases the energy stored in the food we eat."

"Well done, Calvin!" exclaimed Dr. Floyd. "Our heart pumps blood with oxygen to all our cells and takes away the carbon dioxide that is a by-product of cellular respiration. It's waste that our cells need to get rid of. Eventually, we expel it when we exhale."

"Ew," said Carol. "What else?"

"Activity also affects the **cholesterol** in your blood. There is good cholesterol, **HDL,** which you want to be high, and bad cholesterol, **LDL,** which you want to be low."

"H is for high, L is for low!" Carol interjected.

"That's right!" said Dr. Floyd. "Physical activity increases the HDL, and decreases the LDL cholesterol. It helps keep the levels where you want them to be, along with a healthy diet. And that's good for your heart."

"Why does it matter if there is cholesterol in your blood?" asked Calvin.

"Excellent question, Calvin," said Dr. Floyd. "High levels of LDL cholesterol in the blood create fatty deposits on the inside walls of the arteries. As these fatty deposits get thicker, the opening through which blood can flow gets smaller. And if a fatty streak inside your blood vessels gets so thick that it blocks the flow of blood entirely, your heart will end up with a big problem."

"Like what?" asked Calvin, wide-eyed.

"If the blood vessel bringing blood to your heart gets blocked, that's what we know as a heart attack," explained Dr. Floyd.

"Oh," said Carol. "I didn't know that's what happened."

"But physical activity is one very simple thing we can do to keep the cholesterol in our blood at healthy levels. Remember, exercise raises HDL, or good cholesterol, and lowers LDL, or bad cholesterol," added Dr. Floyd.

"Sounds like a good deal to me," said Carol.

"Hold on, Doc," said Calvin. "Sometimes when I'm running up and down the court, my insides feel really bad. And I can hardly breathe, my heart is pumping so hard. Isn't that bad for your heart?"

"In fact, Calvin, that just means you're working hard. When we exercise, our bodies need more energy, which means they need more oxygen and nutrients. Our heart has to pump faster to get the oxygen and nutrients to our cells. We also have to breathe faster during exercise so that our bodies can take in more oxygen and we can release, or breathe out, more carbon dioxide. Getting into shape isn't always easy, but it's good for your heart to get a workout every now and then. Some days on the court feel easier than others, don't they?" asked Dr. Floyd.

"I guess you're right. The more I play, the easier it gets," replied Calvin.

"And that's your heart getting stronger. That's good!" said Dr. Floyd. "Exercise that challenges us helps us improve our fitness. Do you know what I mean by fitness?"

"Well, I'm strong," replied Calvin. "We do sit-ups and push-ups in gym, and my backpack is really heavy. It's kind of like lifting weights to carry it."

"And I'm very flexible," added Carol. "I do lots of stretches and bends in dance."

"**Strength** and **flexibility** are two components of fitness," said Dr. Floyd. "The third is **endurance,** which is the ability to do something for a long period of time without getting tired. Some exercise experts say that raising our **heart rate** for 30 to 60 minutes at least four times a week can improve endurance. Dancing, climbing stairs, running, and swimming are great for raising your heart

rate. Because they require lots of oxygen, we call them **aerobic activities.**"

"That's a lot of time to spend exercising," remarked Carol. "I have lots of other things to do, so it's not easy to do all that exercise just so I can be fit."

"I understand. You've got very busy schedules. But what if I tell you that there are other benefits to fitness? Being fit improves our moods, helps us sleep better, and reduces the risk of Type 2 diabetes. Being fit also increases our energy out, which helps us maintain energy balance."

"You've convinced me," said Calvin. "Let's take the stairs today, Carol, and get our heart rates up."

"Thanks for meeting with me today, Calvin and Carol," said Dr. Floyd. "See you next time."

LESSON 15:
Healthy Hearts

Calvin and Carol knocked on Dr. Floyd's office door and walked in. "Hi, Dr. Floyd. Ms. Lee said you wanted to meet with us today. What's up?" asked Calvin.

"Where's Christian?" inquired Carol. "Ms. Lee said he'd be joining us, too. Are we going to work with models?"

"So many questions," laughed Dr. Floyd. "You certainly are curious — and yes, Christian will be joining us. He just had to go back to his lab and pick up some materials. Last time we met, we discussed why physical activity is important for our bodies. Today, we're going to investigate why healthy food choices are important."

Just then Christian pushed open the door. His hands were full of plastic tubing and a box of other materials. "Let me help you," said Calvin. He took the box and peered inside. "What's all this for? Is this play dough? Hmm, red food coloring, a bowl… Are we going to make something out of play dough?"

"Slow down, Calvin," chuckled Dr. Floyd. "Give Christian a chance to get set up here. Christian and I have been meeting and discussing how to design a simulation that will help you have some hands-on experience with the flow of blood through the human body."

"Awesome," said Calvin. "I'm ready!"

"I don't know," remarked Carol. "It sounds pretty messy. Where's my lab coat? Should we put on gloves and a mask if we're working with blood?"

"Here are your lab coats and safety glasses, but we're not working with real blood, Carol, it's fake blood," said Christian. "We're going to compare two models of blood vessels. One is very clogged with fat and cholesterol. As a result, you can see how the plaque has built up. The other model is a blood vessel that isn't clogged with plaque. Here's a printout that describes the setup for you, and here are your materials."

Christian handed them two pieces of plastic tubing 3 inches long and 3/4 inch wide. "This yellow play dough represents the plaque. Put one piece of tubing aside. It represents the blood vessel without plaque. Now, here's a

piece of play dough for each of you. Roll it out into a long, skinny piece, skinny enough that it can fit into the ends of the tube."

Calvin and Carol used their hands to roll out the play dough. "Now what do we do?" asked Carol.

"Stuff one roll into each end of this tube. Now push a pencil all the way through the middle of the play dough so there is a small opening that runs the length of the tube," instructed Christian. He checked their model. "Excellent, now we'll get the blood."

Dr. Floyd handed Christian a container with a red liquid in it.

"Yuck," exclaimed Carol. "How did you make that?"

"I started with some 'simple' blood — just water and food coloring. But I wanted to give it a consistency that's similar to real blood, so I added some cornstarch. What do you think?" asked Dr. Floyd.

"Looks like blood to me," said Calvin. "I'm convinced."

"Okay, then," said Christian. "Let's take the unclogged blood vessel and pour a cup of blood through it as fast as possible. Remember to record your observations in your notebook."

Calvin picked up the empty tube and Carol poured the "blood" through it into the bowl.

"Now can we try the clogged blood vessel?" asked Carol as they finished writing. "Can I hold it over the bowl this time?"

"Okay, then I'll pour the blood," added Calvin. "Whoa, what a difference! The blood flows a lot faster through the unclogged blood vessel than the clogged one!"

"Good observation, Calvin," commented Dr. Floyd. "Now, what do you think would happen if your heart had to pump blood through very clogged blood vessels? Do you think this would be a problem?"

"For sure it would be a problem, Dr. Floyd," Carol exclaimed. "The clogged vessels would make it harder to get the oxygen and nutrients that our bodies need."

"And blood still has to get to all parts of our body, even if the vessels are clogged. Probably the heart would have to pump harder to get the blood through," observed Calvin.

"You're both right," said Dr. Floyd. "When the heart pumps harder to push the blood through the clogged vessels, it causes increased pressure inside the blood vessels, which causes high **blood pressure**. If you'll look at this diagram of a heart, you'll see there are blood vessels that supply the heart with the oxygen and nutrients that it needs to keep beating. If the coronary artery, which is the major blood vessel that 'feeds' the heart,

The heart is located between the lungs. The right and left sides of the heart do different jobs. Both are important. The right atrium receives oxygen-poor blood from the body and the right ventricle pumps it to the lungs, where it gets oxygen and gets rid of waste—carbon dioxide. The left atrium receives oxygen-rich blood from the lungs, and the left ventricle pumps this blood into a network of vessels that provide every cell of the body with oxygen and nutrients. Blood also carries waste away from cells.

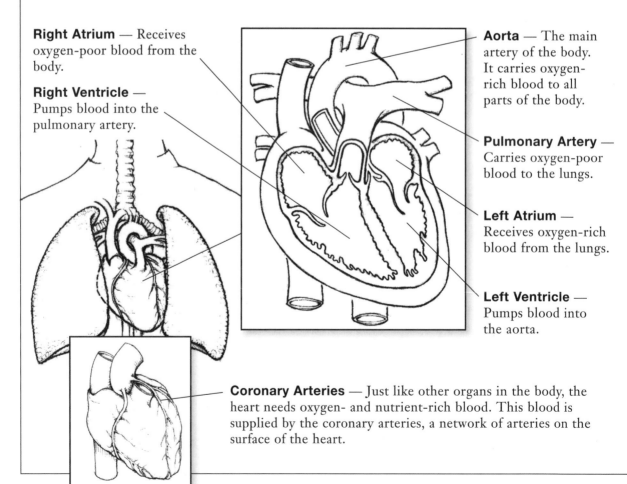

Right Atrium — Receives oxygen-poor blood from the body.

Right Ventricle — Pumps blood into the pulmonary artery.

Aorta — The main artery of the body. It carries oxygen-rich blood to all parts of the body.

Pulmonary Artery — Carries oxygen-poor blood to the lungs.

Left Atrium — Receives oxygen-rich blood from the lungs.

Left Ventricle — Pumps blood into the aorta.

Coronary Arteries — Just like other organs in the body, the heart needs oxygen- and nutrient-rich blood. This blood is supplied by the coronary arteries, a network of arteries on the surface of the heart.

gets completely clogged, it causes a heart attack."

"My grandfather had a heart attack, but I never understood what that meant. I remember when he got better, he had to be on a diet and stop eating fried foods. He was grumpy, but my grandmother told him he had to do it. Now I understand why," said Calvin.

"I'm glad your grandfather is okay," said Dr. Floyd. "Your observations about his diet lead into our next topic, eating for a healthy heart. Let's summarize what we've learned about fatty foods. Cholesterol is a soft, fatty substance that's found in your body's cells. Your body makes some cholesterol and gets some from food."

Calvin and Carol wrote furiously in their notebooks, trying to keep up with Dr. Floyd. Carol stopped and asked, "Do eggs have cholesterol?"

"Yes, eggs and other foods that come from animals, such as whole milk, eggs, meats, cheese, and butter all have cholesterol and **saturated fat**."

"Everything I love," sighed Calvin. "So, I'm guessing that foods with lots of cholesterol and saturated fats are not good for you, right? So what can we eat for a healthy heart?"

Ms. Lopez walked in just at that moment. "Why, Calvin, there are lots of foods that you can eat. You can eat foods that come from plants. They are naturally high in nutrients that our bodies need and they are low in fat. Can you name a few?"

"I can," said Carol. "I am eating more fruits and vegetables as my food goal. Many of the vegetables I'm eating, like green beans and

carrots, I'm harvesting from my grandmother's garden!"

"Excellent," noted Ms. Lopez. "What about you, Calvin, anything to add to the list?"

"My grandmother made my grandfather oatmeal for breakfast, and he ate whole-wheat bread. She also fixed dishes made from beans. Now that I think of it, all of those come from plants, too," observed Calvin.

"Right you are," exclaimed Ms. Lopez. "This seems like a perfect place to end this session. But before you go, let's head down to my office and take a look at how you're doing with your goals."

Calvin and Carol gathered up their backpacks. "Thanks, Dr. Floyd, thanks, Christian. The simulation worked great!"

LESSON 16:
Type 2 Diabetes

"Ms. Lopez," Calvin called out, "You said that today we'd meet with an endo… um, endocrinologist and Christian. But what's an endocrinologist?"

"Glad you asked, Calvin," said Ms. Lopez. "I'll let Dr. Shapiro tell you for himself. Calvin and Carol, let me introduce you to Dr. Eli Shapiro."

"Glad to meet you both. An endocrinologist is a doctor who is specially trained to study the endocrine system. The endocrine system is your body's system of glands, so endocrinologists diagnose and treat diseases that affect your glands." Dr. Shapiro looked at Calvin and Carol's blank faces. He paused for a moment and continued, "Glands are organs in the body that make **hormones**. Different kinds of hormones control metabolism, reproduction, growth, and development. The pancreas is an example of a gland."

"Okay, now I'm with you," said Calvin with a sigh of relief. "I remember we learned about the pancreas. It makes insulin, a hormone that helps move glucose from the blood into the cells, right?"

"That's right," replied Dr. Shapiro. "Now, I understand your doctor referred you to the LiFE Center because he was concerned you were at risk for Type 2 diabetes. What can you tell me about diabetes?"

"Well, I know that some of my family members have diabetes, but I don't really know how to describe it. I have learned that to decrease my risk of getting diabetes it was a good idea for me to reduce the amount of sugar that I was taking in. I am cutting back on the sweetened beverages. That's my food goal and I'm doing quite well," crowed Calvin. "I hardly drink sodas or other sugary beverages at all!"

"Congratulations, that's great!" said Dr. Shapiro. "Let me tell you a bit about diabetes. It's a condition that makes it difficult for the body to regulate blood-sugar levels and to have the body cells effectively use sugars in food. There are two main kinds. Type 1 diabetes is when the pancreas no longer produces insulin, the hormone that regulates blood sugar. Typically, Type 1 diabetes develops in childhood, it comes on suddenly, and the cause is not related to eating and activity choices. People with Type 1 diabetes take insulin by injection, several times a day. Some people with Type 1 diabetes wear an insulin pump. A very small percentage of the population of the United States has Type 1 diabetes."

"That sounds like a bad disease, but good news that not many people have it,"

remarked Calvin. "So I'm guessing that Type 2 diabetes is the other kind, right?"

"That's right. Type 2 diabetes is the kind that most people who get diabetes have. It used to be called adult-onset diabetes because people usually got it as they got older. Now, however, more and more children and young adults are developing Type 2 diabetes. The good news is that it can be prevented by making healthy choices," noted Dr. Shapiro.

"I'll bet I can guess. Eat more fruits and vegetables, drink fewer sweetened beverages, and get more exercise. I know what you're supposed to do, but I don't really understand how Type 2 diabetes works," remarked Calvin.

"When a person has Type 2 diabetes, his body is not able to process sugar in the bloodstream the way that it should. Normally, when we eat a meal or have a drink that is high in sugar, our digestive system breaks down that sugar and sends it into the bloodstream. Insulin helps bring the glucose from the blood into the cells of your body — specifically, the fat, muscle, and liver cells. Once the glucose is in the cells, they can break it down to provide our body with the energy it needs to carry out important functions. Our body is in a state of balance when we are able to properly remove the glucose from the blood for it to be used by the cells of the body and able to maintain our blood-glucose level — that is, not to have extra sugar build up in the blood over time. Let's take a break here and see what Christian has for us."

"Thanks, Dr. Shapiro," said Christian. "Today I thought we'd set up a five-person simulation that shows how Type 2 diabetes develops over time in response to environmental factors and lifestyle choices. Okay, Calvin, you're the food — stand here and hold this cup. Ms.

Lopez, you're next in line; you're the digestive system. Here's your cup. Carol, stand next to Ms. Lopez; you're the bloodstream. Here's your cup. Dr. Shapiro, you're next; you're the insulin. You get a spoon. I'm last — the fat, liver, and muscle cells."

The group lined up. Calvin measured out two spoonfuls of sand and dumped it into the digestive-system cup. Ms. Lopez poured the sand into the bloodstream cup. Dr. Shapiro used the spoon to move the sand to the fat-, liver-, and muscle-cells cup. "Okay, every-one," said Christian, "we just modeled eating a healthy snack, like a piece of fruit. Now let's see what happens with a snack that is high in sugar."

"Okay, let's say I just ate a giant candy bar," exclaimed Calvin as he dumped about half a cup of sand into the digestive-system cup. Ms. Lopez poured the sand into Carol's cup. Dr. Shapiro tried to scoop the sand into the fat-, muscle-, and liver-cells cup as quickly as possible. "That was harder," he remarked.

"Now," said Christian, "imagine you are eating many high-sugar, high-calorie snacks

every day for many years." Calvin dumped another half a cup of sand into the digestive-system cup. Ms. Lopez poured it into the bloodstream cup. Dr. Shapiro used the spoon to move sand into the cell cup.

While Dr. Shapiro was doing this, Calvin continued to dump sand into the digestive-system cup. "Stop," cried Dr. Shapiro, "I can't keep up!"

"Wait until you try this, Dr. Shapiro," said Christian. "Do it again, but this time I am going to take away the spoon and give you a fork to move the sand." Calvin's mouth gaped open as the group passed the sand from cup to cup.

Dr. Shapiro begged them to stop. "There's sand flying everywhere," he cried. "I just can't keep up. It's just like what happens when the insulin is not able to remove the glucose from the bloodstream and get it into the fat, muscle, and liver cells. Great simulation, Christian. You can see what happens when the amount of glucose in the blood increases. The body is out of balance

— it can't use all the calories or sugar you put into it — just like I couldn't keep up with you. People with Type 2 diabetes have to be careful to eat a diet that is not too high in calories or sugar, and to get enough exercise to keep their blood, bodies, and hearts as healthy as possible."

"That was an awesome simulation," remarked Calvin. "I think I really get it now. I'm going to work even harder at achieving my goal!"

"That's great, Calvin," said Ms. Lopez. "Let's take a couple of minutes before you go to see how you're doing. You, too, Carol." Calvin and Carol pulled out their notebooks and reviewed their progress with Ms. Lopez.

Carol starting talking excitedly while Ms. Lopez and Calvin sat back listening. "Last week I stuck to my plan and had vegetables every night at dinner. I realized something else. Before coming to the LiFE Center I did not really care about nutrition because I thought of it as all about what I could not eat. And you both know how much I love French fries. I feel like I am now discovering all the things I *can* eat — things that taste good and that I can feel good about eating. I am beginning to be a person who really wants to eat vegetables!"

"This is terrific, Carol," said Ms. Lopez.

"I have also been helping my grandmother more in her garden and plan to spend a lot of time in the garden once school gets out. My mom even said we could have a small garden at home if I promised to take care of it. I can grow tomatoes, cucumbers, and green beans, my new favorite foods!"

"Great, Carol. We have found that one of the ways to stick to a change is to begin to feel like it is a permanent part of who you are. It sounds like you are on your way. I look

forward to next time. Calvin, we'll catch up with you then as well."

"Bye, Ms. Lopez," Calvin and Carol said together as they pulled on their backpacks.

LESSON 17:
Sharing Information

"Calvin and Carol, how nice to see you again," said Mr. Morgan. "I hear you've been involved in all kinds of interesting research here. Ms. Lopez tells me that you're at the point where you'd like to share this information with other people your age, is that right?"

"It is," replied Carol. "We've learned so much and we think we can really help other kids. Some of our friends have asked us to tell them what we've learned."

"Right," added Calvin, "but there's so much information and we want to make sure we get it right."

"You've come to the right place," responded Mr. Morgan. "Part of my job is to help the researchers here at the center communicate scientific information effectively. One of the first questions I ask has to do with audience. Who is your audience?"

"Like we said, we want to communicate to kids our own age. We were thinking that maybe the best way is to just tell them what to do," said Calvin.

"Hmmmm," replied Mr. Morgan, "that is one approach. Let's go ask Dr. Kostas what he thinks. He's a great source when it comes to trying to figure out how to help people change their behavior."

The trio walked down the hall to Dr. Kostas's office and knocked on the door.

"Good afternoon, Mr. Morgan, I see you've got our young researchers with you. I've been hearing great things about your work, Calvin and Carol. You've really done a great job meeting your personal goals. What can I do for you today?"

"We want to get other kids to change their behavior, too," said Calvin, "and Mr. Morgan thought that we might want to run our idea by you. We want to tell kids what we've learned and tell them what they should do so they can have energy balance."

"Well, you could do that. However, in my research, I've found people seldom like to be told *what* to do. I've found they generally respond better if I tell them *why* to do something and then *how* to do it, rather than *what* to do. What do you think?"

Carol laughed. "I think that's the approach that Ms. Lopez and the rest of the LiFE team took with us," she said. "And it worked!"

"Good, it sounds like we've got a plan," replied Mr. Morgan. "Thank you, Dr. Kostas. Let's head back to my office and begin to sketch out some ideas." Mr. Morgan kept talking as the team headed down the hall. "Now that we have an approach, I have some more questions for you. What medium are you thinking of using…TV? Magazines? Web site? Any ideas?"

"Not really," replied Calvin. "We hadn't discussed anything other than telling our friends what to do. Now I'm not sure where to begin."

"No problem, that's what I'm here for," said Mr. Morgan. "I can help you. Have you ever seen an ad on television or in a magazine that tells you about the risks of smoking? Perhaps you've seen an ad on a bus or subway or train that has a message about keeping your body drug-free. This type of advertisement is called a public-service announcement, or PSA. A PSA is meant to inform the public about the risks or benefits associated with certain behaviors. I can help you get started. Your PSA can inform other kids about scientific reasons to change their behavior. Let's talk about what form your PSA will take."

"I need help, Mr. Morgan," pleaded Carol. "I don't even know what kinds of PSAs there are!"

"You can create a visual one, like a poster, or you can create one that you could read over a loudspeaker. Or you could do a skit or rap."

"I want to make a poster," said Carol. "Now what?"

"I'm thinking that I want to rap," said Calvin.

"Great! Now you need to think about the scientific information you want to communicate. You should include at least three pieces of information that you've learned during your work here at the LiFE Center. Next, think about what you learned about advertising. What strategy can you use to attract your audience's attention? Maybe you have a catchy slogan?" suggested Mr. Morgan.

"How about: 'Fruit is what to be eating to keep your heart beating'?" asked Calvin, tapping out a beat on the top of the desk.

Carol showed Mr. Morgan her list of scientific information that she thought other kids might want to know about. "I think I was the most surprised about our biological preference for fat and sugar. And I was surprised by how much the environment influenced my food choices."

"I found it was really helpful to keep track of my activity," added Calvin. "It shocked me when I found out how much time I spent playing video games with my brother. I still play, but not as much. That, plus getting up a little earlier so I can take a slightly longer route to school, helped me reach 10,000 steps per day. Of course, now that I drink more water and less soda, that helps, too."

"Here you go, Calvin and Carol," interjected Mr. Morgan. "I've pulled together some materials for you to get started on your PSA. Carol, here are some supplies: poster board, some markers, and some sketch paper so you can draft your poster first. Calvin, here's some paper so you can draft your rap. Come back when you're ready to present the projects. I'll help you make a video of yourself rapping, Calvin!"

"Thanks, Mr. Morgan!" they called out as they gathered up their supplies and headed down the hall.

LESSON 18:
Reviewing the Scientific Evidence

Ms. Lopez greeted Calvin and Carol as they walked into her office. "Hello there! This is one of the last times we'll be meeting. I've asked Dr. Kostas to join us. What we'd like to do is review the scientific evidence behind the LiFE Center food and activity goals. You remember that one of the first questions we asked was 'How can we use scientific evidence to help us maintain energy balance?' We thought you might like to go over what researchers in medical science have learned. You did such informative PSAs, perhaps you would like to use this information to make even more."

"Right," added Dr. Kostas. "You remember when we discussed your PSAs I told you that my research has shown that an effective way to get people to modify their behavior is to tell them why they should change it and how they can change it: I call it the why-to and how-to strategy."

Ms. Lopez pointed to the *Choice, Control & Change* food and activity goals poster hanging on her wall. "Let's get started with our first goal. Eat more fruits and vegetables — aim for at least 4 cups per day. Research suggests that eating more fruits and vegetables helps reduce blood pressure and prevent heart disease. For example, they can help decrease LDL cholesterol in our blood."

"I remember that you told us that it helps reduce the risk for Type 2 diabetes," added Calvin, looking over his notes. "It also helps with weight control, right?"

"That's correct, Calvin," said Ms. Lopez, beaming. "It also helps stimulate our brain chemicals and helps us feel like we can think more clearly."

Choice, Control & Change
Food and Activity Goals

Follow these goals to help your body do what you want it to do!

Do More

- **Eat more fruits and vegetables**
  — aim for at least 4 cups a day

- **Drink more water**
  — aim for 64 ounces a day

- **Walk more, including stairs**
  — aim for at least 10,000 steps a day

Do Less

- **Drink fewer sweetened beverages**
  — aim for no more than 8 ounces a day

- **Eat less frequently at fast-food places**
  — aim for no more than three times a week

- **Eat fewer processed snacks**
  — aim for no more than one small or medium snack each day

"I think I remember that it gives us shiny hair and can help us have a clear complexion," added Carol.

"Most impressive, Ms. Lopez," noted Dr. Kostas. "Our two researchers really seem to understand the scientific evidence. Many people, including adults, don't understand why fruits and vegetables are so good for us."

"I am really glad I chose this goal. My skin is clearer now and I think my concentration is better, too," exclaimed Carol.

"Eat at fast-food chains no more than three times per week," continued Ms. Lopez.

"I know this one," exclaimed Calvin. "This helps reduce the amount of fat, sugar, and salt that we take in."

"Very good, Calvin! Research has found that people who eat frequently at fast-food chains are more at risk of disease than people who eat fast food less frequently. For example, if you decrease the amount of fat, sugar, and salt that you take in, you reduce your risk of heart disease and Type 2 diabetes," said Ms. Lopez.

Carol looked at her notes and added, "If we take in lots of sugar on a regular basis, we gain weight. And if we get excess calories from the sugar, over time it can increase our blood insulin and sugar levels, which can lead to diabetes. Excess fat can make us gain weight and it can stick to the sides of our blood vessels, which can lead to heart disease. Whew...that's a lot."

"My research shows that commercials are one reason people like to eat at fast-food chains," said Dr. Kostas. "In my interviews I found that people liked the bright colors and happy environment that they saw in the commercials. The people in the ads looked like they were having fun and the people viewing them wanted to have fun, too."

"Last week we showed our research team the movie *Super Size Me*," Ms. Lopez told them. "In this movie, the filmmaker Morgan Spurlock eats and drinks nothing but what he could buy at a fast-food chain over a period of one month. The doctors and nutritionists who worked with him were astonished at the impact that this behavior had on his weight, blood cholesterol, and blood-sugar levels. And it was just for one month!"

"Even though I have added other fruits and vegetables, reducing the amount of French fries that I eat has been one of the hardest goals for me," admitted Carol. "I replace fries sometimes with other vegetables, but other times I still eat them. They smell so delicious I just can't resist, and I love the taste!"

"You are doing excellently; change takes time," commented Ms. Lopez. "Our next goal is drinking no more than 8 ounces of sweetened beverages per day. Since that was your goal, Calvin, why don't you tell us what scientific evidence you remember."

"Sure, Ms. Lopez. My dentist told me that sugar on your teeth is food for **bacteria** that cause **cavities.** By reducing   the amount of sugar that I take in, I can help reduce the amount of cavity-causing bacteria. It also helps decrease the risk of increased insulin levels. This means it decreases the risk for Type 2 diabetes and heart disease."

"Ms. Lee told us that some people find that drinking water does a better job of quenching your thirst," added Carol. "Sweet drinks make your mouth feel sticky and sometimes leave you feeling even more thirsty! She also told us that kids who drink sweetened beverages usually drink less milk. They replace the milk with the sweetened drinks. We need **calcium** to have strong bones."

"Very good. Now, our next goal is to eat no more than one small or medium processed snack per day. Do you remember what we mean by a processed snack?" asked Ms. Lopez.

Carol glanced at her notes. "I remember. We learned in *C3* that processed snacks are chips, candy, and baked goods like cookies or brownies. Foods like these have been processed, or changed, a lot."

"Can you explain why it is important to eat fewer processed snacks?" asked Ms. Lopez.

"I can," responded Calvin. "In my notes, it says that processed snacks can be high in fat, sugar, and salt. Sometimes they are high in fat and sugar, like cookies, brownies, or candy. Other processed snacks, like chips, can be high in fat and salt. That's what makes them taste oh, so good. We learned that when we studied taste, remember, Carol?"

"Fat, sugar, and sodium…these three things seem to be part of the scientific evidence for most of the goals so far," noted Carol.

"You are very observant, Carol," said Dr. Kostas. "Did you know that drinking one 20-ounce bottle of soda every day for a year gives you about 92,000 calories? And sweetened beverages only have sugar. They don't have vitamins, minerals, or other nutrients."

"I was at the history museum recently and they had an exhibit about soda in American life. It said that back in 1900, when soda was new, it came in 6-ounce bottles and people only had it once in a while. Now the average person drinks about 20 ounces a day. That's so much more," Carol added excitedly.

"Wow, Carol, that's quite an increase! This brings us to our next goal, to drink at least 64 ounces of water per day. That's eight 8-ounce glasses. Who can tell me why?" queried Ms. Lopez.

Calvin and Carol quickly flipped through the pages of their science notebooks. "I can," said Calvin. "We've been learning about the human-body systems, and every system in our body depends on water."

"It improves our skin," added Carol. "It also washes out chemicals that can harm our bodies. Here's an amazing fact: on average, most adults lose about 10 cups of fluid a day through sweating, exhaling, urinating, and bowel movements. We have to drink water so we can stay hydrated. If we get dehydrated, it can be hard to concentrate and we can get headaches, become irritable, and get tired."

"I got dehydrated last summer," observed Calvin. "It must have been at least 100 degrees outside and we were playing basketball in the middle of the day. I got so caught up in the game that I didn't remember to drink water. All of a sudden, I got dizzy and thought I'd pass out. I had a headache for the rest of the day. Coach tells us that we need to drink plenty of fluids before, during, and after exercise to replace what we are losing through our sweat. It helps reduce muscle cramps, too."

"Did you know that drinking water helps control weight? It keeps you from confusing hunger with thirst. It also helps prevent constipation," noted Ms. Lopez. "Now, on to the final goal: walk an average of 10,000 steps per day. Can you tell me what scientific evidence there is to support this goal?"

"We learned a lot about this from Ms. Lee," said Carol. "For example, I wrote in my notes that physical activity gets the blood moving more rapidly through the body. This helps our **immune system** clear out foreign stuff more quickly. Regular exercise can even keep you from getting sick. However, Ms. Lee said that it is not a good idea to do strenuous physical activity when you are very sick."

"Ms. Lee makes an excellent point," noted Ms. Lopez. "What else did you learn?"

"We learned that exercise increases **muscle mass**. Muscles make us stronger so we can do everything better. And they make us look toned!" added Calvin, showing off his biceps. "And don't forget the heart. It's a muscle and it gets stronger when you are active. This means your heart will pump more blood with each beat."

"It also helps with energy balance," remarked Carol. "Physical activity is energy out, so it helps us balance the energy in and controls our weight. I also see in my notes that physical activity increases HDL and can help reduce LDL."

"Exercise does promote a healthier blood-cholesterol ratio," agreed Ms. Lopez. "When you exercise regularly, your body uses fat as the source of energy. Physical activity also stimulates your body to use the hormone insulin, which clears sugar out of your blood. Getting regular physical exercise can help keep both your blood insulin and your blood sugar under control and decrease your risk of Type 2 diabetes."

Dr. Kostas clapped his hands vigorously. "Very impressive, Calvin and Carol — you've really learned a lot about the scientific evidence behind the LiFE Center's food and activity goals. Well done! Now let's talk about how you can take what you have learned and continue to have healthful eating and activity habits. Are you ready?"

Calvin and Carol nodded and grabbed their pencils to begin to take notes.

"You both picked goals and developed action plans. Now it's time for you to think about one strategy that has been helping you to be successful at your goal. Let's start with you, Carol."

"For my goal to eat more fruits and vegetables, I talked with my mom, and she said she would have more fruit in the house so when I got home from school I could have fruit for a snack instead of chips or some other processed snack. I've been eating fruit almost every day after school. When I stay after school for activities, I bring fruit with me. My mom packs it in a small plastic container that's just a little larger than the piece of fruit. The container protects it so it doesn't get squished in my school bag."

"That's marvelous! So, your strategy was to have more fruit available to you." Dr. Kostas took notes. "Now, Calvin, you're next."

"My goal was to reduce the amount of sweetened beverages that I drank each day. This was hard, 'cuz they really taste good, but I did it. I increased the amount of water I drank and reduced the amount of soda. Hey, that's almost doing two goals! Anyway, my basketball team got personal water bottles, so I started using my bottle every day. My grandmother showed me a trick. She had some fresh lemons and she squeezed one into my water bottle. Now the water tastes like lemon and I like it a lot more. She said cucumbers make water taste good, too. Does that mean I'm adding more fruits and vegetables to my diet, too? Pretty soon I'll be doing all six goals at once!"

"Excellent, Calvin. So your strategy is to carry water with you at all times. Now let's talk about your pledges," said Dr. Kostas.

"The pledge is to yourselves. Make it something that you feel confident you can do, now and into the future. Remember 'control'? Be sure your pledge is something that is in your control. In my research I've found that clients get very discouraged when they can't keep their pledges. Ms. Lopez and I want this pledge to make you feel good and confident! To begin, make your pledge something that you are already doing and that you feel confident you can continue to do."

"I'll start," said Calvin. "Every day I will fill my water bottle at home and bring it to school with me. Whenever I get thirsty, I'll reach for my water bottle. I'll remember to squeeze some lemon juice into the water to give it some flavor. Drinking all this water will help me improve my basketball game."

Carol took a deep breath and said, "I will make a list of the fruit that I love and ask my mom to buy it for me to have as a snack. On days when I have after-school activities, I'll remember to bring a piece of fruit with me and eat it, even if my friends are eating chips or candy. I'll keep an image in my mind of me dancing and looking great!"

Ms. Lopez and Dr. Kostas stood up and clapped. "Well done, Calvin and Carol," they said. "This marks the end of your work with us at the LiFE Center. Thank you for helping us test our hypothesis that if people know why and how to make healthy food and activity choices, they can maintain their energy balance."

Homework Questions

Lesson 2: Snack Foods Everywhere

• How do researchers at the LiFE Center learn about their clients' energy balance?

• What choices can LiFE Center clients make?

• What does Ms. Lopez mean by *energy in*?

• What influences Carol's food choices?

• What does Carol learn about fruits and vegetables?

Lesson 3: Sweet Tastes

• What change did Calvin make, and why did he make it?

• What does Calvin learn about sports drinks?

• Why does Calvin like foods that are high in sugar?

• What basic tastes can our tongues detect?

• Describe how our biological preferences for certain tastes influence what we choose to eat and drink.

Lesson 4: Fat Tastes Good

• What reason does Carol give for liking French fries?

• Why does Carol like fried foods?

• Does eating fat affect energy balance?

• What are some foods other than French fries that are high in fat?

• How is Carol going to help Ms. Lopez gather information about students' attitudes toward French fries?

Lesson 5: Food and Activity Environments

• What does Ms. Lopez mean when she uses the term *food environment*?

• What does Ms. Lopez mean when she uses the term *activity environment*?

• What environmental factors affect Calvin's and Carol's food choices?

• What activity-environment factors affect Calvin's and Carol's exercise choices?

• What information are Calvin, Carol, and Ms. Lopez going to gather when they take their field trip?

Lesson 6: Modeling Energy Balance

• What does Christian do as a systems scientist?

• How did Calvin's stomach flu affect his body systems?

• Why does Christian create models and simulations?

• What do Calvin and Carol learn from the energy-balance simulation?

• What do the terms *negative energy balance* and *positive energy balance* mean?

Lesson 7: The Digestive System

- What is the major role of the digestive system?
- Where does food go after you swallow it?
- What are the six groups of nutrients?
- How do the nutrients from our food get to every cell in our body?
- Why does Calvin say the digestive system is like a chemistry lab?

Lesson 7: [second reading]

- What is the pancreas?
- How does the pancreas help cells in the body use glucose?
- What happens in the body when your blood sugar is high?
- What is *insulin resistance*?
- What can Calvin do to lower his blood sugar?

Lesson 8: Energy in Food

- Why do Calvin and Carol think they don't have any energy?
- How does Ms. Lopez propose investigating whether or not peanuts have stored energy?
- Describe what Calvin and Carol observe when they burn the peanut.
- How is energy measured?
- What is a calorie?

Lesson 8: [second reading]

- Where does metabolism take place?
- What happens during cellular respiration?
- Why is the mitochondrion called the *power station of the cell*?
- What are two major jobs of metabolism?
- Why does Ms. Lopez say "You are what you eat" is true?

Lesson 9: Visualizing Change

- What does an art therapist do?
- How does Mr. Morgan help people express themselves?
- What choices does Carol discuss after she completes her self-portrait?
- What changes does Calvin want to make and why?
- What kinds of things do you like to do?

Lesson 10: Bite, Write, Learn

- How can you estimate portion sizes?
- How did Calvin estimate how many chips he ate?
- How did Carol estimate how many green beans and how much fruit salad she ate?
- What did Calvin learn by keeping a record of what he ate?
- What can Calvin and Carol do with the information they collect in their food logs?

Lesson 11: Steps

- What does an exercise physiologist do?
- What tools does Ms. Lee use to collect data on her clients?
- How does being active benefit the human body?
- Why are Calvin and Carol meeting with Ms. Lee?
- What does it mean to calibrate a pedometer and why is it important?

Lesson 12: Choosing a Goal

- What does a behavioral scientist do?
- Are all juices healthy beverage choices? Explain.
- How does Carol think eating out affects her food choices?
- What do Carol's food choices contribute to her overall diet?
- What does the information in food logs represent?

Lesson 12: [second reading]

- What are action plans?
- Why does Dr. Kostas call an action plan a how-to?
- Why does Dr. Kostas want Calvin and Carol to pick personal goals?
- What are some of the goals that Calvin and Carol discuss?
- What kinds of roadblocks might Calvin and Carol run into as they try to reach their goals? Think about what their goals are.

Lesson 13: Step Success

- What tool did Calvin and Carol use to help them keep track of their physical activity?
- What method did Carol use to compare the number of steps in different activities?
- What did Calvin do to increase the number of steps that he took each day?
- How do you calculate the number of steps per minute in different activities?
- How do Calvin and Carol use personal data to help them achieve energy balance?

Lesson 14: Move, Move, Move

- What happens when the heart pumps blood throughout the body?
- Describe the effect that exercise has on the heart.
- Why does it matter if there is cholesterol in your blood?
- What is fitness?
- What are some of the benefits of being fit?

Lesson 15: Healthy Hearts

- What does Dr. Floyd want Christian to simulate?
- What happens when the heart has to pump hard to push blood through clogged blood vessels?
- What happens if the coronary artery gets completely clogged?
- What is cholesterol?
- Why are healthy food choices important for a healthy heart?

Lesson 16: Type 2 Diabetes

- What is an endocrinologist?
- What is Calvin doing to decrease his risk of getting diabetes?
- What are the two main kinds of diabetes?
- What happens when a person has Type 2 diabetes?
- What food choices can a person with Type 2 diabetes make to be as healthy as possible?

Lesson 17: Sharing Information

- What is one of the first things to consider when you want to communicate information effectively?
- What approach does Dr. Kostas recommend to help people change their behavior?
- What is a public-service announcement (PSA)?
- What are some strategies that Mr. Morgan suggests for Calvin's and Carol's PSAs?
- What strategy does Calvin plan to use to attract his audience's attention?

Lesson 18: Reviewing the Scientific Evidence

- What are the LiFE Center's food and activity goals?
- Why are fruits and vegetables so good for us?
- Why is it important to limit the amount of fat, sugar, and salt that you take in?
- Why is it important to eat no more than one small or medium processed snack per day?
- Why is it important to drink at least 64 ounces of water per day?

The *C3* Journey

A Why-to and How-to Guide to Making Healthful Choices

Student Name: _____

Class/Teacher: _____

Contents

Overview

From the beginning of this module, you have been on a journey that will help you become competent at navigating the food-and-activity environment so you can take action and make choices that will improve your health and help your body perform better.

Where You Have Been

Let's review what you've learned so far. In Unit 1, **Investigating Our Choices,** you explored the question *What influences our food and activity choices?* You learned about human preferences for the taste of fat and sugar, and you studied your own food-and-activity environment. You met Calvin Green and Carol Cooper and learned about the challenges and triumphs that they encounter as they work with the LiFE Center researchers to make *choices*, take *control* of the events in their daily lives, and make *changes* in their food and physical-activity choices. In Unit 2, **Dynamic Equilibrium,** you learned about the human body and energy balance through investigating the question *How can we make sure that we get the right amount of energy to help our bodies do what we want them to do?* You explored what happens to food after it enters the body — from digestion, to the circulation of nutrients to cells, to metabolism.

Where You Are

In Unit 3, **From Data to Health Goals,** you have been gathering personal data as you investigate the question *How can we use personal data to help us make healthy food and activity choices?* In this unit, you have been examining your own eating and activity behavior. Now you are about to choose a *Choice, Control & Change* food goal. For the rest of this module, you will try to reach your food goal, as well as the *Choice, Control & Change* activity goal of increasing physical activity by walking 10,000 steps per day, using a pedometer that can count steps. If you don't have a pedometer, you can use a 24-hour physical-activity log to track your current level of activity and look for times during the day when you can add more physical activity. This booklet will guide you as you select a food goal. First, you will learn about the scientific evidence that supports these goals and read some tips that will help you reach your own goal. Once you have selected your goal, you will develop an action plan. Next, with your goal selected and your action plan in place, you will keep track of your progress with **The *C3* Tracker,** recording the triumphs and challenges you meet each day as you try to reach your food and activity goals.

Where You Are Going

In Unit 4, **Effects of Our Choices,** you will learn even more about the science behind the *Choice, Control & Change* goals. You will investigate the question *Why are healthy food and activity choices important for our bodies?* and learn about how healthy food-and-exercise habits can keep the heart healthy and decrease the risk of diet-related diseases such as Type 2 diabetes. In Unit 5, **Maintaining Competence,** you will develop the understandings and skills that are needed to maintain a healthy lifestyle as you explore the question *How can I maintain my skills as a competent eater and mover?*

By the time you finish the *C3* journey, not only will you be able to navigate the food-and-activity environment, you will also be able to share what you have learned.

Choice, Control & Change
Food and Activity Goals

Follow these goals to help your body do what you want it to do!

Do More

- **Eat more fruits and vegetables**
  — aim for at least 4 cups a day

- **Drink more water**
  — aim for 64 ounces a day

- **Walk more, including stairs**
  — aim for at least 10,000 steps a day

Do Less

- **Drink fewer sweetened beverages**
  — aim for no more than 8 ounces a day

- **Eat less frequently at fast-food places**
  — aim for no more than three times a week

- **Eat fewer processed snacks**
  — aim for no more than one small or medium snack each day

GOAL: Eat more fruits and vegetables — aim for at least 4 cups a day.

Why?

Here's the scientific evidence... and how it benefits you!

1. You can prevent heart disease.
Eat fruits and vegetables to help keep your heart and circulatory system healthy by decreasing LDL cholesterol in blood. Too much LDL cholesterol can clog blood vessels.

2. You can reduce blood pressure.
Antioxidants found in fruits and vegetables help prevent plaque from building up in your blood vessels. This keeps blood pressure at a normal, healthy level.

3. You can reduce the risk for Type 2 diabetes.
Fiber in fruits and vegetables can help slow the absorption of sugar. If you replace foods that are high in fat and sugar with fruits and vegetables, then you reduce the risk for developing Type 2 diabetes.

4. You can maintain energy balance.
Fruits and vegetables are filling and naturally low in calories. Eat them regularly to help stay in energy balance.

5. You can have clearer skin and shinier hair.
The nutrients in vegetables and fruits can help reduce acne breakouts and make your hair healthy and shiny.

6. You can regulate your bowel movements.
Fruits and vegetables provide roughage in our digestive system, and that helps move waste out.

How to take action...

• Get fruit in before your day really starts: add fruit to your breakfast.

• Pack some fruits and vegetables for lunch and snacks. Keep them in a container so they don't get crushed. Apples, carrots, celery, grapes, peppers, and blueberries are just a few examples that travel well.

• Add more vegetables — try the salad bar at school or in restaurants.

• Keep cut-up fruits and vegetables in the refrigerator so they are easily available when you come home hungry.

• Replace chips, candy, and other snacks with some of your favorite fruits and vegetables.

Did you know that dark green leafy vegetables, orange vegetables, and fruits are made up of nutrients that are particularly beneficial?

GOAL: Drink more water — aim for 64 ounces a day (that's eight 8-ounce glasses).

Why?

Here's the scientific evidence... and how it benefits you!

1. You can help your body function.
Every system in your body needs water to function. Water lubricates your joints and muscles, helps make saliva, helps keep your body at a healthy temperature, and helps prevent constipation.

2. You can flush harmful chemicals out of your body.
The kidneys, part of the excretory system, clean and filter blood to remove wastes and excess water. Cleaned blood leaves the kidneys and flows through the body, while urine, the collected wastes and excess water, is stored in the bladder.

3. You can reduce your risk of a heart attack.
Studies have found that healthy people who drank more than five glasses of water a day were less likely to die from a heart attack or heart disease than those who drank fewer than two glasses a day.

4. You can stay hydrated.
We get water from the food we eat and the beverages we drink. On average, most adults lose about 10 cups of fluid a day through sweat, exhalations, urine, and bowel movements. Even minor dehydration can cause impaired concentration, headaches, irritability, and fatigue.

5. You can reduce your risk of disease and infection.
Water can help prevent kidney stones and reduce your chances of getting bladder, kidney, and urinary-tract infections.

6. You can recover quickly from illnesses.
The traditional prescription to "drink plenty of fluids" when you're sick still holds strong. Water can help control a fever, replace lost fluids, and thin out mucus.

How to take action...

• Water tastes best when it is ice cold. Keep a pitcher in the refrigerator and look for a water fountain that has really cold water.

• What's a great way to quench your thirst? Drink water! Keep a water bottle with you so that you have it anytime you are thirsty.

• Make your own flavored water — add natural flavorings, like freshly squeezed lemon juice.

GOAL: Walk more, including stairs — aim for at least 10,000 steps per day.

Why?

Here's the scientific evidence . . . and how it benefits you!

1. You can make your heart stronger.

Research has shown that a stronger heart will pump more blood with each beat. Your heart is a muscle that you can make stronger by being physically active on a regular basis.

2. You can reduce the LDL cholesterol in your blood.

When you exercise regularly, your body uses fat as the source of energy. This can help reduce the LDL cholesterol in your blood, and it increases the HDL cholesterol. Improving your ratio of LDL to HDL prevents heart disease.

3. You can reduce risk for Type 2 diabetes.

Physical activity stimulates your body to use the hormone insulin to clear sugar out of the blood. Regular exercise can help keep both your blood insulin and your blood sugar in control and decrease your risk for Type 2 diabetes.

4. You can stay in energy balance.

Physical activity is energy out, which means it helps balance the energy in and helps keep you from gaining extra fat.

5. You can increase muscle mass and enhance endurance and flexibility.

Exercise makes your muscles stronger. Not only will you look toned, you'll also be able to play longer before you get tired and have an extended range of motion so you can reach that ball or do those splits more easily.

6. You can improve your concentration.

Exercise is good for the body and the mind. Get some physical activity so you can concentrate better on what you need to do.

7. You can stimulate your immune system.

Research has shown that blood moves more rapidly through your body when you exercise. While regular activity can keep you from getting sick, it's not a good idea to do strenuous physical activity when you are very sick.

How to take action . . .

• Walk or ride your bike, skateboard, or scooter whenever you can.

• Take the stairs instead of elevators or escalators.

• Play sports for fun or join a team.

• Dance.

• Cut back on the amount of time you spend watching television and playing video games. Aim for less than two hours a day.

GOAL: Drink fewer sweetened beverages — aim for no more than 8 ounces a day. That's about three 20-ounce containers or four to five 12-ounce cans per week. Less is even better.

Why?

Here's the scientific evidence… and how it benefits you!

1. You can reduce the risk of cavities.

Sugar on your teeth feeds the bacteria that cause cavities. When you drink sweetened beverages throughout the day, you are constantly feeding cavity-causing bacteria.

2. You can reduce the number of calories you take in.

Which will make you feel more full — 200 calories of sweetened beverages or 200 calories of solid food? Some scientific studies show that sweetened beverages don't make you feel full. Eat solid food — it stimulates the hormone that makes you feel full!

3. You can cut down your overall intake of sugar.

Sweetened beverages are a high source of sugar in the typical diet. Cut out those drinks and you will decrease your overall sugar intake.

4. You can quench your thirst.

Have you ever noticed that sweetened beverages don't quench your thirst the way water does? Some people say sweetened beverages make them feel thirstier and make their mouths feel sticky. Quench your thirst — switch from sweetened beverages to water.

5. You can improve your bone health.

Did you know that teens who drink lots of sweetened beverages often drink less milk and eat less of other calcium-rich foods? These foods are very important when you're growing because bones are gaining minerals, and strength, at that time. Pack in the minerals before you turn 30, because that's when your bones begin to lose mineral content and get weaker.

6. You can cut down on caffeine and artificial substances.

Did you know that some sodas contain caffeine? Many also contain artificial colors and flavors that could have long-term health effects.

How to take action …

- Carry a water bottle with you at all times — if you get thirsty, you'll be less likely to buy a sweetened beverage.

- Got milk? It's an excellent beverage choice. Drink it whenever you can.

- If you drink sweetened beverages every day of the week, make the choice to ban them for one day. Slowly increase the number of days without sweetened beverages.

- Downsize your serving of sweetened beverages. The recommended serving size is 8 ounces — that means a 20-ounce bottle is 2.5 servings.

- Make sweetened beverages a special treat. Drink them only at parties or on special occasions.

- Switch to seltzer. Try mixing it with 100% fruit juice. You get the same fizz but less sugar.

GOAL: Eat less frequently at fast-food places — aim for no more than three times a week, choose healthier options, and ask for smaller portions.

Why?

Here's the scientific evidence ... and how it benefits you!

1. You can stay in energy balance.
Research suggests that fast food tends to promote positive energy balance. Since many choices at fast-food places are high in fat and sugar, they can add lots of calories to your diet, and make it easy to be in positive energy balance. Eating less frequently at fast-food places and ordering small sizes when you do can help you maintain energy balance.

2. You can reduce your risk for diseases such as Type 2 diabetes and heart disease.
Eating small amounts of fat, sugar, and salt won't harm you, but eating too much of them will. Even teenagers and young adults are at risk for these diseases.

3. You can increase nutrient intake by eating less often at fast-food places.
Research has found that meals eaten at fast-food places tend to be lower in fruits and vegetables than meals eaten elsewhere. If you eat less often at fast-food places, you will probably increase your fruit and vegetable intake. This means you get the benefits of eating more fruits and vegetables. Check out the goal of eating more fruits and vegetables.

4. You can cut down on artificial substances.
Have you ever noticed how fast foods all taste alike — whether you eat them in Alaska, Michigan, Texas, or New York? How do they get that consistency from place to place? They add artificial flavors and preservatives. Right now, science doesn't know the long-term effects of eating these substances, but it's better to be safe than sorry.

How to take action ...

• Downsize your meal. Ask for a regular-sized hamburger instead of a large cheeseburger. If you order a sweetened beverage, make it a small.

• Skip the French fries. If you really want them, order a small fries or split a medium with a friend.

• Try something different. Instead of eating fried chicken or a burger, eat grilled or baked chicken.

• Be creative. Try a deli. You can order a sandwich with exactly what you want on it.

• Go online and check out the nutrition information from your favorite fast-food place. Find out how much sugar, fat, sodium, and other nutrients are in the foods they serve.

• Try thinking of fast-food restaurants as a once-in-a-while treat instead of a place you eat at frequently.

GOAL: Eat fewer processed snacks — aim for no more than one small or medium snack each day.

Why?

Here's the scientific evidence... and how it benefits you!

1. You can lower your overall calorie intake.
Processed snacks — especially large portions of them — are high in calories, making it hard to balance energy in with energy out.

2. You can promote clear skin and shiny hair.
A study conducted by Australian researchers suggests that there is a connection between diet and acne. If you lower your intake of fat and sugar and increase your intake of other nutrients, you can help reduce acne breakouts and make your hair healthy.

3. You can decrease your overall intake of fat, sugar, and sodium.
Some processed snacks, such as candies, are high in sugar; some, like chips, are high in fat and sodium, found in salt. And others, like cookies, brownies, cupcakes, and chocolate, are high in fat and sugar.

4. You can reduce your risk of diseases like Type 2 diabetes and heart disease.
What causes these diseases is complex, but eating a diet with moderate amounts of sugar, fat, and salt helps keep blood sugar, blood fat, and blood pressure at normal levels.

5. You can cut down on artificial substances.
Processed snacks often have artificial substances added, like colors, flavors, and preservatives. Scientists are not sure what long-term regular consumption of these substances does to our health. It's better to be safe than sorry.

How to take action...

• Try fruits, vegetables, or trail mix instead of processed snacks.

• Instead of buying snacks, bring a homemade snack.

• When you are having a processed snack, small-size it.

• Trade processed snacks, like candy and chips, for granola bars or fruit-based cookies. They are satisfying and have more nutrients than processed snacks. Plus, they have less sugar and less added fat.

• Switch from fried chips to baked chips.

Analyze Food Data

STEP 1: Compare the data on your food and beverage intake to the *C3* food goals. In the space below, write down the totals you measured on your ***24-Hour Food Intake*** activity sheets from Lesson 10. For fast foods, look at the number of times per week.

Total Amounts on Your 24-Hour Food Intake Activity Sheets

Fruits and Vegetables (cups)	Water (ounces)	Sweetened Beverages (ounces)	Fast Foods (times per week)	Processed Snacks (number per day)

STEP 2: Use the graph sheets on the following five pages to compare your food intake data to the *C3* food goals. In the space above "My Amount," draw a bar that represents the amount of your total intake. How does your current food intake compare to the *C3* goals? Over the next few weeks add more bars to track your progress in reaching your goal.

Choose a Food Goal

STEP 3: Review your graphs and think about your daily life. What *choices* do you make? Which food *choices* are in your *control*? What do you want to *change* so you can make progress in meeting one of the *C3* food goals? Review the goals below and select one. Circle it.

- Eat more fruits and vegetables — aim for at least 4 cups a day.

- Drink more water — aim for 64 ounces a day (that's eight 8-ounce glasses).

- Drink fewer sweetened beverages — aim for no more than 8 ounces a day (about three 20-ounce containers or four or five 12-ounce cans a week).

- Eat less frequently at fast-food places — aim for no more than three times a week, choose healthier foods, and ask for smaller portions.

- Eat fewer processed snacks — aim for no more than one small or medium snack each day.

STEP 4: Answer the following questions.

Why is it important for you to achieve this goal? _____

_____

_____

Continued on p. 267

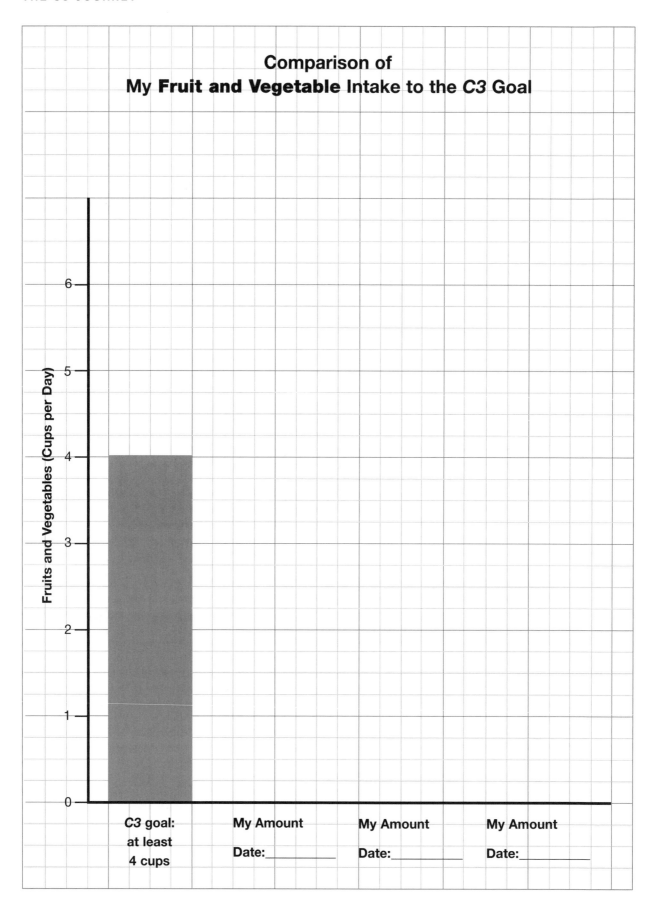

Comparison of
My **Fruit and Vegetable** Intake to the *C3* Goal

Fruits and Vegetables (Cups per Day)

6

5

4

3

2

1

0

C3 goal:
at least
4 cups

My Amount

Date:_____

My Amount

Date:_____

My Amount

Date:_____

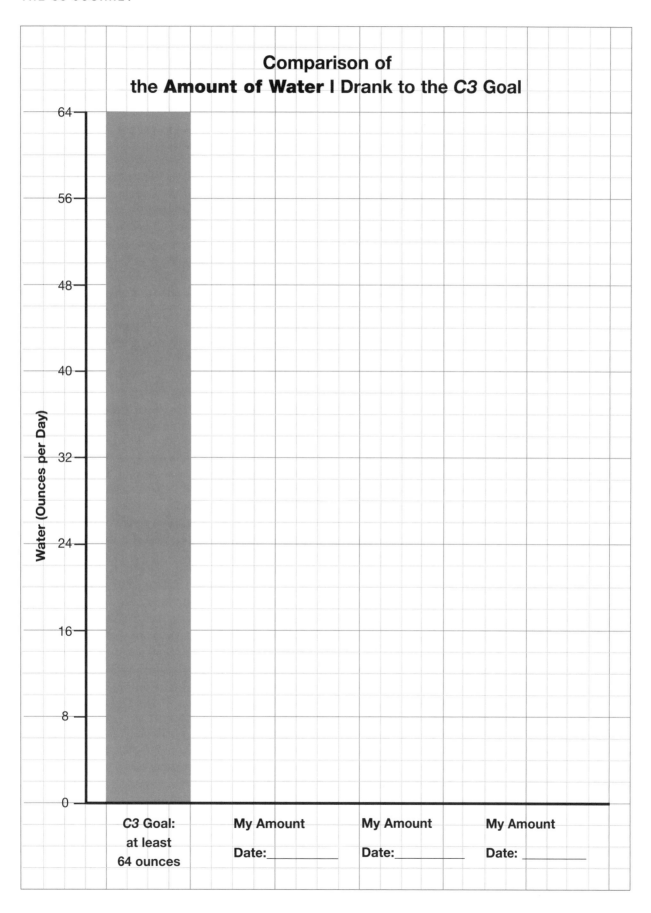

Comparison of
the **Amount of Water** I Drank to the *C3* Goal

Water (Ounces per Day)

64

56

48

40

32

24

16

8

0

C3 Goal:
at least
64 ounces

My Amount

Date:_____

My Amount

Date:_____

My Amount

Date: _____

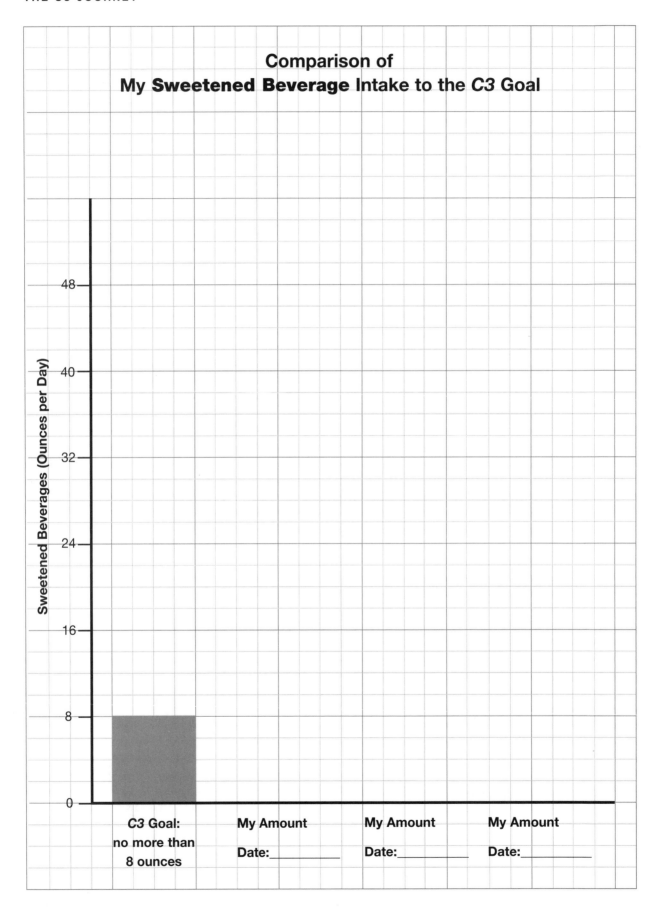

Comparison of
My **Sweetened Beverage** Intake to the *C3* Goal

Sweetened Beverages (Ounces per Day)

48 —

40 —

32 —

24 —

16 —

8 —

0 —

C3 **Goal:**
no more than
8 ounces

My Amount

Date:_____

My Amount

Date:_____

My Amount

Date:_____

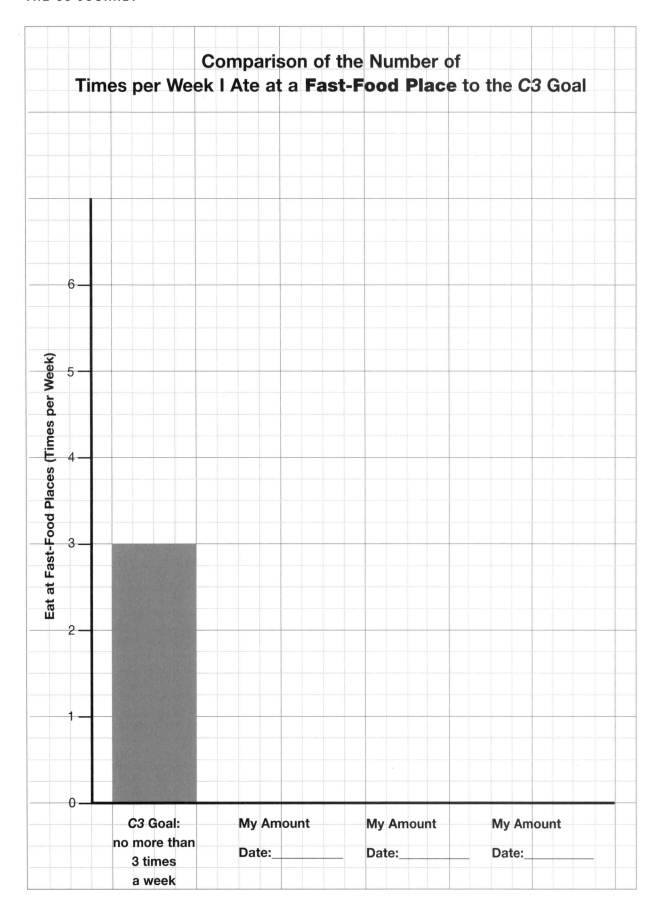

Comparison of the Number of
Times per Week I Ate at a **Fast-Food Place** to the *C3* Goal

Eat at Fast-Food Places (Times per Week)

C3 Goal:
no more than
3 times
a week

My Amount

Date:_____

My Amount

Date:_____

My Amount

Date:_____

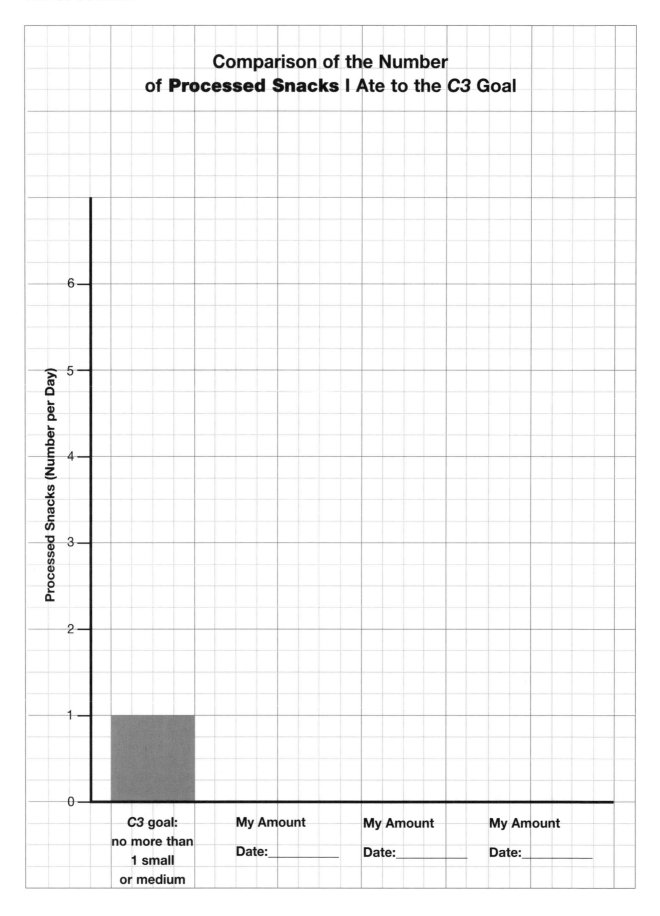

Comparison of the Number of **Processed Snacks** I Ate to the *C3* Goal

Processed Snacks (Number per Day)

6
5
4
3
2
1
0

C3 goal:
no more than
1 small
or medium

My Amount

Date:_____

My Amount

Date:_____

My Amount

Date:_____

Continued from p. 261

Why do you think this goal will improve your health?

Why will meeting this goal help you perform well at all that you want to do?

Develop an Action Plan

STEP 5: Think about exactly what you will do to meet your goal. Add in details such as the time of day and what foods you will or will not eat. Write your notes below. For example, "I will drink water instead of soda each day after school."

STEP 6: Think about any roadblocks you might encounter. Write them below. These are the challenges you will face when making a try at your specific goal. For example, "All my friends drink soda after school. I really like the taste of soda."

STEP 7: Think about strategies you can develop to help you overcome any roadblocks. What things can you do to help yourself be successful at achieving your goal no matter what roadblocks you encounter? Write these strategies below. For example, "I will tell my friends that I think drinking water is very cool. I will make sure I can get really cold water because I think that tastes the best."

The *C3* Tracker

Each time you make a try at your goal, record it on **The *C3* Tracker** table. Write down the date and day of the week in the appropriate columns. In the "How I Did" column, record whether or not you were successful at meeting your specific goal. In the "Triumphs and Challenges" column, record things that helped you to be successful and how it made you feel (triumphs) and things that made it hard when you were not successful (challenges). Your records on this table are important data that will help you become more successful at navigating the food environment so you can take action and make choices that will improve your health and help your body perform better. Read the examples below.

Date	Day	How I Did	Triumphs and Challenges
Mar 1	Tues	I did it! I drank water today after school.	I filled up my water bottle with water from the fountain that has really cold water. It tasted great! I did not even want soda.
Mar 2	Wed	I had a soda today.	Marie and Mike were having soda and that made me want it, too. I had one. But, I did tell them that I am trying to drink water instead of soda after school. When I explained how much healthier water is, they said they would try with me! That made me feel good.
Apr 7	Mon	I did it! I ate corn and salad for dinner.	We had corn tonight for dinner. I love corn! It felt great to eat it. We also had salad and I ate some of that, too.
Apr 8	Tues	I did not have any vegetables at dinner time.	The only vegetable we had at dinner was broccoli. I still really do not like the taste of broccoli. I just ate chicken and rice. I talked to my mom about fixing vegetables that I do like.

Continued

The *C3* Tracker, *Continued*

Date	Day	How I Did	Triumphs and Challenges

Analyze Daily Activities

STEP 1: Review your *Step and Write* activity sheet from Lesson 11. Calculate your average daily steps per day and record the number below.

Average daily steps _____

STEP 2: Look at the bar graph on page 271. Use the graph sheet on the following page to compare your total physical activity to the *C3* physical-activity goal. In the space above "My Amount," draw a bar that represents the amount of your total physical activity. How does your current activity compare to the *C3* goal? Add more bars to track your progress in reaching your goal.

STEP 3: Think about the steps per minute for some of your activities. Compare your physical-activity data to the *C3* physical-activity goal. In the space below, write down the totals you calculated on your *Comparing Activities* activity sheet.

TOTAL NUMBER OF STEPS PER ACTIVITY

Name of Activity	Steps per Minute

My Physical-Activity Goal

STEP 4: Look at the two physical-activity goals below. The goal of walking more, aiming for 10,000 steps per day, requires the use of a pedometer. If you do not have a pedometer, choose the alternative goal. Select one goal. Circle it.

- **Walk more, including stairs** — aim for at least 10,000 steps per day.

- **Alternative goal** — get 60 minutes of moderate or vigorous physical activity each day. For example, participate in active sports, like running, jumping rope, dancing, or biking.

STEP 5: Answer these questions.

Why is it important for you to achieve this goal? ....

....

....

Continued on p. 272

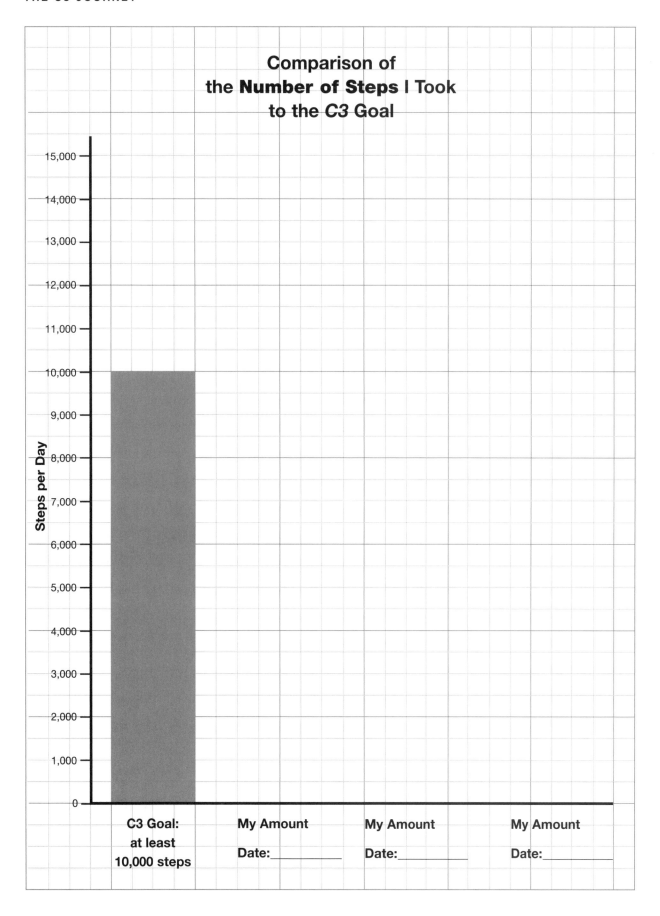

Comparison of the **Number of Steps** I Took to the *C3* Goal

Steps per Day

15,000
14,000
13,000
12,000
11,000
10,000
9,000
8,000
7,000
6,000
5,000
4,000
3,000
2,000
1,000
0

C3 Goal:
at least
10,000 steps

My Amount

Date:_____

My Amount

Date:_____

My Amount

Date:_____

Continued from p. 270

Why do you think this goal will improve your health? _____

_____

_____

Why will meeting this goal help you perform well at all that you want to do? _____

_____

_____

Develop an Activity Action Plan

STEP 6: Think about exactly what you will do to meet your goal. Add in details such as the time of day and what kinds of activities you will add to increase your number of steps. Try to add high-step-count activities, like running or taking a long walk. Be sure to think about activities that you will decrease and record this information. For example, you might decrease the amount of time you watch television or play video games. Write your notes below. For example, "I will walk upstairs instead of taking the elevator; I will walk to the bus stop instead of asking my parents for a ride; I will play sports with my friends; I will watch television for one hour instead of three hours."

_____

_____

_____

STEP 7: Think about any roadblocks you might encounter. Write them below. These are the challenges you will face when making a try at your specific goal. For example, "All my friends play video games after school. I really like playing with them."

_____

_____

_____

STEP 8: Think about strategies you can develop to help you overcome any roadblocks. What things can you do to help yourself be successful at achieving your goal no matter what roadblocks you encounter? Write these strategies below. For example, "I will tell my friends that exercising is very cool. I will make sure I leave the house early enough so that I can walk to school."

_____

_____

_____

_____

Scientific Evidence that Supports My Goals

Before you begin your work in Unit 4, make notes about the scientific evidence you already know that supports your food and activity goals. After you complete each activity in Unit 4, make notes about the additional scientific evidence you have learned that supports your goals.

My Food and Activity Goals Are:

Scientific Evidence I Already Know That Supports My Goals	Additional Scientific Evidence That I Learned

Reflections

Now that you have reached the end of the *C3* journey, it's time to reflect on all that you have learned. Think about the Module Question: *How can we use scientific evidence to help us maintain energy balance?* Write at least one paragraph that answers this question. Be sure to include specific information that you have learned while studying *Choice, Control & Change* to support your answer. If you need more room, write in your LiFE Log.

Next, think about how you can share what you have learned with your family and friends. If you had one important message to share, what would it be? Why do you think this message is important? Explain your answer. If you need more room, write in your LiFE Log.

Name   Date

Homework Notes

Use this page to take notes while you are reading. List the homework questions on the left. Record your notes in the column on the right. Remember, you are taking notes. You do not need to write complete sentences. If you need more space, write in your LiFE Log.

Questions

1. _____

_____

_____

_____

2. _____

_____

_____

_____

3. _____

_____

_____

_____

4. _____

_____

_____

_____

5. _____

_____

_____

_____

What I Have Learned

a. _____

b. _____

c. _____

d. _____

a. _____

b. _____

c. _____

d. _____

a. _____

b. _____

c. _____

d. _____

a. _____

b. _____

c. _____

d. _____

a. _____

b. _____

c. _____

d. _____

Name   Date

Bite and Write Food Log

Use this food log to gather data about your food intake. Record everything you eat and drink. Carry this with you all the time. Fill it in as completely as possible.

Date: _____   **Day of the Week:** _____

Time	Place	What I Ate	How Much?

Name	Date

Step and Write

Use this log to record your daily step counts before you go to bed. After you have recorded the number of steps you took, reset the pedometer. Remember to periodically calibrate your pedometer by doing the 100-step test. It is especially important to calibrate when you wear clothes that have a very high or low waistband. The position of the waistband affects the placement of the pedometer, which can affect how accurately it counts your steps.

You will record the date, the day of the week, the number of steps you took, and notes about anything that might have influenced your step count. Recording the day of the week is very important. You may find that you have higher step counts on some days and lower counts on others. Being able to identify the day will help you identify patterns. For example, you will probably find that on the days you have gym or after-school sports, you have a higher step count. In the column for your notes, record information about what was going on that might have influenced your physical activity. Perhaps it rained and you couldn't go outside, so you sat at home all day. Or perhaps you were in a walk-a-thon and you walked much more than you usually do. Keeping an activity log helps you see patterns.

STEP AND WRITE SAMPLE

Date	Day	Steps	Notes on What Influenced My Step Count
Oct. 21	Thurs	7,780	No gym today; had to study for tests; lots of sitting
Oct. 22	Fri	12,193	Walked to school and had gym; played soccer after school
Oct. 23	Sat	12,347	Walked to soccer field; played soccer with friends; walked home; walked to movies
Oct. 24	Sun	13,532	Went for a short hike with my friends; spent the rest of the afternoon doing homework

Continued

Name   Date

Step and Write, *Continued*

STEP AND WRITE LOG

Date	Day	Steps	Notes on What Influenced My Step Count

Name	Date

24-Hour Activity Log

Use this log to track your activities over a 24-hour period. You can use this data to assess your overall physical activity level and to determine what activities you could change in order to increase your physical activity.

In the "Main Activities" column, record activities you did during that half-hour period. For the "Level" column, use the scale on the following page.

Time	Main Activities	Level
12:00 noon		
12:30 p.m.		
1:00 p.m.		
1:30 p.m.		
2:00 p.m.		
2:30 p.m.		
3:00 p.m.		
3:30 p.m.		
4:00 p.m.		
4:30 p.m.		
5:00 p.m.		
5:30 p.m.		
6:00 p.m.		
6:30 p.m.		
7:00 p.m.		
7:30 p.m.		
8:00 p.m.		
8:30 p.m.		
9:00 p.m.		
9:30 p.m.		
10:00 p.m.		
10:30 p.m.		
11:00 p.m.		
11:30 p.m.		
midnight		

Continued

CALVIN AND CAROL TAKE CHARGE : HOMEWORK QUESTIONS : THE C3 JOURNEY : ACTIVITY SHEETS : RECIPES

Name	Date

24-Hour Activity Log, *Continued*

Time	Main Activities	Level
12:30 a.m.		
1:00 a.m.		
1:30 a.m.		
2:00 a.m.		
2:30 a.m.		
3:00 a.m.		
3:30 a.m.		
4:00 a.m.		
4:30 a.m.		
5:00 a.m.		
5:30 a.m.		
6:00 a.m.		
6:30 a.m.		
7:00 a.m.		
7:30 a.m.		
8:00 a.m.		
8:30 a.m.		
9:00 a.m.		
9:30 a.m.		
10:00 a.m.		
10:30 a.m.		
11:00 a.m.		
11:30 a.m.		

5-Point Scale to Use for "Level" Column

For half-hour periods that included different levels of activity, choose the level that best represents your overall activity level during that time.

1: mostly lying or sitting still
2: some moving but minimal, such as working on a computer, doing homework, or eating
3: a combination of some sitting and some standing or walking
4: walking or light physical activity
5: very active, running or playing sports that make you breathe hard and elevate your heart rate

Play Dough

Several of the lessons in this curriculum use play dough. This dough keeps well in a zippered plastic bag. Use two bags and it will last even longer. One recipe should last the entire module. When making play dough for multiple classes, we have found that it works best to make one batch at a time.

INGREDIENTS

5 cups flour

2 1/2 cups salt

2/3 cup cream of tartar

2/3 cup vegetable oil

5 cups water

Yellow food coloring

SUPPLIES

Hot plate or stove

1 spoon

Measuring cup

Measuring spoons

4- to 6-quart pot

Directions

1. Combine ingredients in pot over medium heat. Use enough yellow food coloring to give the play dough an unappealing color that looks like fat.

2. Stir constantly, frequently scraping the bottom of the pot to make sure it does not stick. When the dough has formed into a sticky, solid mass, remove it from the heat.

3. Set the play dough aside until it is cool enough to be handled.

4. Knead the dough on a smooth, clean surface for several minutes, until it is smooth and elastic.

Adapted from *www.kinderplanet.com/playdo.htm*

Cornstarch "Blood"

INGREDIENTS

(For each cup of blood)

1 cup water
1 tablespoon cornstarch
1/8 cup cold water
Red food coloring

SUPPLIES

Small saucepan
Small bowl
1 spoon
Measuring spoons
Measuring cup
Hot plate or stove
Newspapers or other surface covering
1 covered container, plastic bottle with top, or other nonbreakable container

Directions

1. Put 1 cup of water and a few drops of red food coloring into a pot. Heat the water and the food coloring until it almost reaches a boil.

2. Turn off the heat.

3. In a small bowl, mix cornstarch with 1/8 cup of cold water. Stir until blended well.

4. Add the cornstarch and cold-water mixture to the heated water and red food coloring. Return to medium heat. Stir until it is smooth and has reached the desired thickness. If necessary, turn down the heat so the mixture doesn't burn.

5. Store in a covered container. This prevents a film from forming on the top.

Note: Red food coloring can stain. Be sure to put down newspapers or other surface covering.

Bibliography

References

American Association for the Advancement of Science. (1993). *Benchmarks for science literacy.* New York: Oxford University Press.

Anderson, P. M., & Butcher, K. E. (2006). Childhood obesity: Trends and potential causes. *Future Child,* Spring, 16 (1), 19–45.

Bandura, A. (1989). Human agency in social cognitive theory. *American Psychologist,* 44 (9), 1175–1184.

Bandura, A. (2001). Social cognitive theory: An agentic perspective. *Annual Review of Psychology,* 52, 1–26.

Barlow, S. E., & the Expert Committee. (2007). Expert committee recommendations regarding the prevention, assessment, and treatment of child and adolescent overweight and obesity: Summary report. *Pediatrics,* Dec., 120, Supplement, S164–192.

Brantley, P. J., Myers, V. H., & Roy, H. J. (2005). Environmental and lifestyle influences on obesity. *Journal of the Louisiana State Medical Society,* Jan., 157, Special No 1, S19–27.

Calabrese Barton, A., & Vora, P. (2006). Improving urban science education: New roles for teachers, students and researchers. *Science Education,* 90 (2), 379–381.

Contento, I. R. (2010). *Nutrition education: Linking research, theory, and practice.* 2nd ed. Sudbury, MA: Jones and Bartlett Publishers, Inc.

Katz, D. L. (2005). Competing dietary claims for weight loss: Finding the forest through truculent trees. *Annual Review of Public Health,* 26, 61–88.

Klein, S. (2004). Clinical trial experience with fat-restricted vs. carbohydrate-restricted weight-loss diets. *Obesity Research,* Nov., 12, Supplement 2, 141S–144S.

MedLine Plus. Type 2 Diabetes: Risk factors. (2009). *www.nlm.nih.gov/medlineplus/ency/article/002072.htm,* accessed December 5, 2009.

Miller, T. D., Balady, G. J., & Fletcher, G. F. (1997). Exercise and its role in the prevention and rehabilitation of cardiovascular disease. *Annals of Behavioral Medicine,* Summer, 19 (3), 220–229.

Mirat, J. (2007). Physical activity in the prevention and treatment of cardiovascular diseases. *Acta Medica Croatica,* 61, Supplement 1, 63–67.

National Research Council. (1996). *National science education standards.* Washington, D.C., National Academies Press.

Nemet, D., Barkan, S., Epstein, Y., Friedland, O., Kowen, G., & Eliakim, A. (2005). Short- and long-term beneficial effects of a combined dietary-behavioral-physical activity intervention for the treatment of childhood obesity. *Pediatrics,* Apr., 115 (4), e443–449.

Reinehr, T., Wabitsch, M., Kleber, M., de Sousa, G., Denzer, C., & Toschke, A. M. (2008). Parental diabetes, pubertal stage, and extreme obesity are the main risk factors for prediabetes in children and adolescents: A simple risk score to identify children at risk for prediabetes. *Pediatric Diabetes,* Dec. 18, 395–400.

Publications Related to *C3*

Calabrese Barton, A., & Tan, E. (2008). Funds of knowledge, discourses and hybrid space. *Journal of Research in Science Teaching,* 46 (1), 50–73.

Contento, I. R., Calabrese Barton, A., Koch, P. A., & Dadds, M. (2006). Childhood overweight and science education in teaching and learning science. In K. Tobin, Ed., *Teaching and Learning Science: A handbook.* Westport, CT: Praeger, 515–519.

Contento, I., Koch, P. A., Lee, H. W., Calabrese Barton, A., & Sauberli, W. (submitted). Outcome evaluation of *Choice, Control, and Change (C3),* a middle school curriculum to reduce obesity risk focusing on enhancing personal agency and autonomous motivation. *Journal of the American Dietetic Association.*

Contento, I. R., Koch, P. A., Lee, H. W., Sauberli, W., & Calabrese Barton, A. (2007). Enhancing personal agency and competence in eating and moving: Formative evaluation of a middle school curriculum — Choice, Control, and Change. *Journal of Nutrition Education and Behavior,* 39, Supplement 5, S179–186.

Dadds, M., Contento, I. R., Koch, P. A., & Calabrese Barton, A. (2005). Adolescent perspectives on being overweight. *Journal of Nutrition Education and Behavior,* 37, Supplement 4, S63.

Koch, P. A., Calabrese Barton, A., Whitaker, R. C., & Contento, I. R. (2007). Choice, Control & Change. *Science Scope*, 16–20.

Lee, H. W., Contento, I. R., & Koch, P. (2009). Mediation of behavioral outcomes in a middle school obesity risk-reduction nutrition curriculum intervention: Choice, Control, & Change (C3). *Journal of Nutrition Education and Behavior*, 41, Supplement 4, S15.

Lee, H., Contento, I. R., Koch, P., Calabrese Barton, A. (2009). Factors influencing implementation of nutrition education in the classroom: An analysis of observations in the Choice, Control, and Change (C3) curriculum. *Journal of Nutrition Education and Behavior*, 41, Supplement 4, S37–38.

Lee, H., Contento, I. R., Sauberli, S., Koch, P. A., Calabrese Barton, A. (2007). Using science education to move middle schoolers toward more healthful food and activity choices: An outcome evaluation of Choice, Control, & Change (C3). *Journal of Nutrition Education and Behavior*, 39, Supplement 4, S96.

Petrillo-Meyers, M., Lee, H., Koch, P., & Contento, I. R. (2009). Middle school students' reasons for selecting specific obesity risk reduction goals: Mapping to potential mediators from theory. *Journal of Nutrition Education and Behavior*, 41, Supplement 4, S16.

Sauberli, W., Calabrese Barton, A., Koch, P., Contento, I. R., Lee, H. (2009). A replication of Choice, Control, & Change (C3) obesity prevention curriculum for middle school students using a lead teacher model. *Journal of Nutrition Education and Behavior*, 41, Supplement 4, S31–32.

Sauberli, W., Lee, H., Contento, I. R., Koch, P., Calabrese Barton, A. (2008). Enhancing personal agency and competence in eating and moving: An outcome evaluation of Choice, Control, and Change (C3), an inquiry-based middle school science curriculum to reduce obesity risk. *Journal of Nutrition Education and Behavior*, 40, Supplement 4, S36.

Glossary

Abdominal obesity — The accumulation of fat around the waist. This is associated with obesity, heart disease, and Type 2 diabetes.

Acid — A substance with a sour taste that when combined with a base forms a salt, and has a pH of less than 7.

Aerobic activity — Activity or exercise that increases the body's use of oxygen and has the long-term effect of improving oxygen consumption by the body.

Amylase — A digestive enzyme that helps chemically break down starch.

Antioxidant — A chemical substance that protects the body from damage caused by oxygen reactions, such as aging and heart disease. Examples of antioxidants are vitamin C and vitamin E.

Anus — The opening through which solid waste exits the body.

Artificial — Produced by humans rather than by nature.

Ascorbic acid — The chemical name for vitamin C. An essential nutrient found in fruits and vegetables. It is required for maintenance of bones, blood vessels, and skin.

Bacteria — Certain single-cell organisms. Some are beneficial to humans, some are harmful.

Blood — The red fluid that circulates through the heart, arteries, and veins carrying oxygen and nutrients to the cells of the body and waste products away from the cells.

Blood pressure — The pressure of blood against the walls of blood vessels. Blood pressure varies based on the strength of the heartbeat, the elasticity of blood vessels, the volume and thickness of blood, and other conditions. It is important for the body to maintain a healthy blood pressure. Chronically high blood pressure can increase the risk of heart disease.

Blood sugar — The amount of sugar in the form of glucose in the blood. We use blood sugar as a source of energy for our cells. It is the primary source of energy for the brain. The body has hormonal mechanisms to maintain the level of blood sugar. High levels can be associated with diabetes.

Blood vessels — Channels through which blood normally circulates, such as arteries, veins, and capillaries.

Bloodstream — The flow of blood through the blood vessels and the heart.

Bone health — The general condition and well-being of bones. An important aspect of bone health is that the bones have the proper amount of minerals deposited in them to make them strong.

Caffeine — A compound that stimulates the central nervous system. It can be found naturally in coffee, tea, and chocolate.

Calcium — A mineral that is essential for the normal development of bones and teeth, muscle and nerve activity, and blood clotting. Calcium can be found in food sources such as milk and yogurt.

Calibrate — To make something work correctly by adjusting and comparing it with a standard.

Calorie — Unit used to measure the energy in food.

Cancer — A disease that is characterized by uncontrolled cell growth and spreading.

Carbohydrate — A component of food that is a major source of energy for the body. Carbohydrates can include sugars, starches, cellulose, and dietary fiber.

Carbon dioxide — A gas that is a waste product of cellular metabolism. It is removed from the body through the lungs in exhaled air.

Carcinogens — Substances or chemicals that can cause cancer.

Cardiovascular fitness level — How well the heart, lungs, and blood vessels deliver oxygen and nutrients to cells while exercising.

Cavities — Holes in the two outer protective layers of a tooth caused by the growth of bacteria on the teeth. They can result in pain. Larger cavities can collect food particles and bacteria.

Cell — The basic structural unit of living tissues that functions alone or with other cells to perform all necessary bodily functions.

Cellular respiration — The breakdown of the energy-containing substances in food—carbohydrates, fats, and proteins,—within a cell to release energy.

Chemical energy — When elements are stored together in a compound, energy is stored and can be released by chemical reactions, as seen in cellular respiration.

Chemical reactions — A change in the structure of a substance by which one or more substances undergo a chemical change to become one or more new substances.

Cholesterol — A soft, waxy, fatty substance that is found in the body's cells and in animal food sources. There are several kinds. Two are HDL, or "good," and LDL, or "bad" cholesterol.

Circulatory system — The system of organs and tissues, including the heart, blood, and blood vessels, that circulates blood throughout the body.

Clot — Blood that has been converted from a liquid to a solid state. Clots form at the site of an injury to stop the loss of blood.

Data — Individual facts, statistics, or items of information.

Diastolic — A measurement of the amount of pressure on the walls of blood vessels when the heart is at rest.

Digestion — The process of transforming the food we eat into small units that can be absorbed from the digestive system into the bloodstream to be transported to all parts of the body.

Digestive system — The system that allows eaten food to be acted upon by physical and chemical means to provide the body with nutrients and excrete waste products.

Dynamic equilibrium — The state in which there is balance between energy that is flowing into the body (energy in) and energy that is being used by the body (energy out).

Elimination — The removal of undigested food from the body.

Endurance — The ability to last under stress or sustain an activity for an extended period of time.

Environmental factors — Factors that influence health that one is not born with, such as diet and physical activity. We have more control over our environmental factors than our genetic factors.

Esophagus — The muscular tube that allows food to pass from the pharynx to the stomach.

Fasting blood sugar — The amount of sugar present in blood after an overnight fast. Fasting blood-glucose levels can be used to help detect diabetes.

Fitness — A measure of the body's ability to perform physical activity. Made up of three components: endurance, flexibility, and strength.

Flexibility — A measure of the extent to which we have mobility in our joints.

Food environment — The availability of food within a community and how easily residents have access to food. A neighborhood's food environment helps influence what food people choose to eat.

Genetic factors — Factors that influence one's health that are programmed in the body's DNA. We cannot control our genetics.

Genetics — The scientific study of heredity, or the transmission of inherited characteristics from parents to their offspring.

Glucose — A form of sugar that travels through our bloodstream. The glucose in our blood is also called blood sugar.

HDL cholesterol — Fatty substance that removes fat and cholesterol from the blood so it doesn't build up on blood-vessel walls. It is considered "good" cholesterol because it protects against heart disease.

Heart disease — Any condition that impairs proper functioning of the heart.

Heart rate — The number of times the heart beats during a given period of time.

High blood pressure — The elevation of blood pressure in the arteries. It can also be referred to as hypertension.

High blood sugar — An elevated level of the sugar glucose in the blood resulting from diabetes mellitus or simply eating more sugar than normal. This can result in thirst, fatigue, hunger, and weight loss. It can also be an indicator of heart disease.

Hormone — A chemical substance produced in the body to control or regulate the activity of certain cells or organs.

Immune system — A complex system in the body that is responsible for protection against infection and foreign substances.

Infection — A disease that results from germs or microorganisms entering the body, growing, and increasing in number.

Insulin — A hormone produced by the pancreas that aids in carbohydrate metabolism by stimulating the uptake of sugar from blood into cells.

Large intestine — The tube that extends from the small intestine to the anus, responsible for reabsorbing water and forming solid waste.

LDL cholesterol — Fatty substance that lines cells and circulates in blood. LDL cholesterol is considered "bad" because high levels can clog blood vessels with fat and can lead to high blood pressure, heart attack, and stroke.

Metabolism — All of the chemical processes that happen inside a cell, including breaking down nutrients to release their energy and building the things our bodies need to live.

Minerals — Compounds found in food that are needed for growth and regulation of body processes.

Mitochondria — Organelles within our cells that generate chemical energy.

Molecules — The smallest part of a compound or element that can exist in the free state and still retain the characteristics of that compound or element.

Muscle mass — The amount of muscle (contractile tissue that allows for movement) possessed in the body.

Nutrients — A substance in food that the body can use to obtain energy, create tissues, or regulate function.

Oxygen — A colorless, odorless gas that makes up 20 percent of the air we breathe. It is necessary for humans to inhale it to support life. It is transported through the body via blood.

Pedometer — A measuring instrument used to record the number of steps taken.

Performance — The manner or quality of carrying out an activity or sport.

Peristalsis — Wavelike involuntary muscle contractions that move food matter along part of the digestive tract.

Perspiration — Fluid consisting of water, urea, and salts excreted through the pores of the skin by sweat glands; otherwise known as sweat.

Phytochemicals — Substances in plants that are not essential for human life, but may possess health-protective effects.

QuESTA Learning Cycle — A tool to frame the learning process for inquiry-based science. Includes five phases: Questioning, Experimenting, Searching, Theorizing, and Applying to Life.

Rectum — The muscular final segment of the large intestine. The rectum stores solid waste until it is ready to leave the body through the anus.

Red blood cells — Blood cells that carry oxygen, carbon dioxide, and iron through the bloodstream.

Saliva — The watery fluid that salivary glands secrete into the mouth in order to help taste, chew, and swallow food. It also helps moisten the mouth and begin starch digestion.

Saturated fat — A type of fat that can lead to increased blood cholesterol and clogged arteries, which can cause heart disease. In the diet, this fat comes from animal products. It is solid at room temperature.

Servings — Set amounts of foods and beverages that make up what is considered a usual or customary amount to consume in a single sitting. For example, a typical serving of a beverage is 8 ounces and a serving of cooked vegetables is ½ cup.

Small intestine — The 20-foot-long tube where the digestion of protein, carbohydrates, and fats is completed and nutrients are absorbed.

Sodium — An essential metallic dietary element that plays a major role in water balance. It can most commonly be found in salt.

Soluble fiber — Non-digestible carbohydrate found in plants that dissolves in water, such as pectins and gums.

Starch — The major storage form of carbohydrates in plants, which appears in foods as a white, tasteless, solid substance. It is an important part of rice, corn, wheat, beans, and potatoes.

Stomach — The enlarged muscular, saclike part of the digestive tract located between the esophagus and the small intestine. It plays a role in both storing and digesting food.

Strength — A measure of the body's muscles' physical power or ability to do work.

Systolic — The blood pressure when the heart is contracting.

Toxin — A poisonous substance that can harm your body.

Type 2 diabetes — A disease that occurs when cells lose the ability to respond normally to insulin. It is sometimes referred to as adult-onset diabetes.

Umami — *Umami* is Japanese for *deliciousness* and is the fifth taste. It is associated with the savory taste of protein foods, like meat.

Vitamins — A group of substances found in food that are essential for normal cell function, growth, and development.